Organic Chemistry
3221 / 3222

CENGAGE
Learning·

Australia · Brazil · Japan · Korea · Mexico · Singapore · Spain · United Kingdom · United States

CENGAGE
Learning™

Organic Chemistry 3221 / 3222

Executive Editor:
Michael Stranz

Managing Lab Editor:
Jeff Nunn

Custom Lab Editors:
Cooper Gouge, John Horvath

Custom Production Editor:
Jennifer Flinchpaugh

Project Coordinators:
Lisa Donahue. Peg Hagar

Senior Pre-Press Specialist:
Riley Gibb

Production Supervisor-Labs:
Melanie Evans

Rights and Permissions Specialist:
Kalina Ingham Hintz

Senior Marketing Specialist:
Sara Mercurio

ISBN-13: 978-0-495-83763-3

ISBN-10: 0-495-83763-6

Cengage Learning
5191 Natorp Blvd.
Mason, OH 45040
USA

Cengage Learning is a leading provider of customized learning solutions with office locations around the globe, including Singapore, the United Kingdom, Australia, Mexico, Brazil, and Japan. Locate your local office at:
international.cengage.com/region

Cengage Learning products are represented in Canada by Nelson Education, Ltd.

Visit Signature Labs online at **signaturelabs.com**

Visit our corporate website at **cengage.com**

Printed in the United States of America

Acknowledgements

The content of this text has been adapted from the following product(s):

SYNT0725: Oxidizing Methoxybenzyl Alcohol to Methoxybenzaldehyde Using Phase-Transfer Catalysis
ISBN-10: (0-87540-725-0)
ISBN-13: (978-0-87540-725-8)

SYNT0726: Two Methods for the Synthesis of Phenacetin
ISBN-10: (0-87540-726-9)
ISBN-13: (978-0-87540-726-5)

SYNT0717: The Diels-Alder Reaction of Anthracene with Maleic Anhydride
ISBN-10: (0-87540-717-X)
ISBN-13: (978-0-87540-717-3)

Friedel-Crafts of m-Xylene
ISBN-10: ()
ISBN-13: ()

SYNT0754: A Multistep Synthesis Sequence: An Aldol Condensation, a Michael Addition, and Ethylene Ketal Formation
ISBN-10: (0-534-68141-7)
ISBN-13: (978-0-534-68141-8)

SYNT0713: Preparing Isopentylacetate by the Fischer Esterification
ISBN-10: (0-87540-713-7)
ISBN-13: (978-0-87540-713-5)

M-Aminoacetophenone; Selective Reduction Of Nitro - Landgrebe
ISBN-10: (0-495-25098-8)
ISBN-13: (978-0-495-25098-2)

SYNT0721: Synthesis of trans-9-(2-Phenylethenyl) Anthracene: A Wittig Reaction
ISBN-10: (0-87540-721-8)
ISBN-13: (978-0-87540-721-0)

Qualitative Organic Analysis; Classification Tests - Landgrebe
ISBN-10: (0-495-25267-0)
ISBN-13: (978-0-495-25267-2)

REAC0716: Nitrating Acetanilide or Methyl Benzoate: Electrophilic Aromatic Substitution
ISBN-10: (0-87540-716-1)
ISBN-13: (978-0-87540-716-6)

TECH0700: Practicing Safety in the Organic Chemistry Laboratory
ISBN-10: (0-87540-700-5)

ISBN-13: (978-0-87540-700-5)

Techniques 2: The Laboratory Notebook, Calculations, and Laboratory Records - Microscale - Pavia
ISBN-10: (0-495-30415-8)
ISBN-13: (978-0-495-30415-9)

Technique 3: Laboratory Glassware: Care And Cleaning - A Small-Scale Approach - Pavia
ISBN-10: (0-495-30585-5)
ISBN-13: (978-0-495-30585-9)

TECH0701: Measuring the Melting Points of Compounds and Mixtures
ISBN-10: (0-87540-701-3)
ISBN-13: (978-0-87540-701-2)

TECH0704: Separating Cyclohexane and Toluene by Distillation
ISBN-10: (0-87540-704-8)
ISBN-13: (978-0-87540-704-3)

TECH0703: Purifying Acetanilide by Recrystallization
ISBN-10: (0-87540-703-X)
ISBN-13: (978-0-87540-703-6)

TECH0708: Separating Ferrocene and Acetylferrocene by Adsorption Column Chromatography
ISBN-10: (0-87540-708-0)
ISBN-13: (978-0-87540-708-1)

TECH0707: Separating a Mixture of Biphenyl, Benzhydrol, and Benzophenone by Thin-Layer Chromatography
ISBN-10: (0-87540-707-2)
ISBN-13: (978-0-87540-707-4)

TECH0709: Separating and Identifying Mixtures by Gas Chromatography
ISBN-10: (0-87540-709-9)
ISBN-13: (978-0-87540-709-8)

TECH0705: Separating Acids and Neutral Compounds by Solvent Extraction
ISBN-10: (0-87540-705-6)
ISBN-13: (978-0-87540-705-0)

TECH0722: Isolating Clove Oil from Cloves Using Steam Distillation
ISBN-10: (0-87540-722-6)
ISBN-13: (978-0-87540-722-7)

Organic Chemistry Laboratory: Standard and Microscale Experiments
Bell/Taber/Clark ISBN-10: (0-03-029272-7)
ISBN-13: (978-0-03-029272-9)

Diphenylacetylene From Stilbene - Landgrebe
ISBN-10: (0-495-25083-X)

ISBN-13: (978-0-495-25083-8)

Triphenylcarbinol; Addition Of A Grignard Reagent To A Ketone - Landgrebe
ISBN-10: (0-495-25087-2)
ISBN-13: (978-0-495-25087-6)

ANAL0729: Identifying an Unknown Alcohol
ISBN-10: (0-87540-729-3)
ISBN-13: (978-0-87540-729-6)

Borohydride Reduction Of 9-Fluorenone - Landgrebe
ISBN-10: (0-495-25251-4)
ISBN-13: (978-0-495-25251-1)

Photoreduction Of Aromatic Ketones - Landgrebe
ISBN-10: (0-495-25248-4)
ISBN-13: (978-0-495-25248-1)

Carbocation Rearrangements - Benzopinacolone - Landgrebe
ISBN-10: (0-495-25249-2)
ISBN-13: (978-0-495-25249-8)

Table Of Contents

Practicing Safety in the Organic Chemistry Laboratory

Prepared by Michael W. Rapp, University of Central Arkansas

PURPOSE

Review the basic rules of laboratory safety. Recognize the common hazards in an organic chemistry laboratory. Learn the proper responses to incidents that may occur in the laboratory.

SAFETY RULES FOR THE ORGANIC CHEMISTRY LABORATORY

Follow all rules. A Safety Contract is included within this module. You must hand in a completed contract to indicate your willingness to follow the standard rules of laboratory safety before you will be allowed to work in the laboratory.

1. *Wear safety goggles while in the chemistry laboratory.* Use splash-proof goggles rated as ANSI Z87.1. Goggles are to be worn over prescription glasses. Supply your own goggles because sharing goggles can lead to eye infection from another wearer. Use of contact lenses under the goggles is discouraged because contact lenses may increase the damage done if an irritant gets in your eye. If you must wear contact lenses under your goggles to avoid unreasonably limited vision, indicate that need on your Safety Contract.

2. *Wear proper clothing to provide protection from reagent spills.* Long pants are required and long-sleeved shirts are preferred. A laboratory coat that extends below the knee is recommended. Shoes must be closed-toe and made of nonporous material. Do not wear loose-fitting clothing because it may catch on objects and cause spills. Avoid loosely woven or fuzzy fabrics because they increase the chances of fire hazard to the wearer. Tie back hair that is longer than shoulder length.

3. *Use good housekeeping practices to ensure a safe workplace.* Call to the attention of the laboratory instructor any conditions that seem unsafe. Avoid cluttering the work area, especially the work areas shared by

many students. Place personal items, such as coats and backpacks, in separate storage areas rather than in the laboratory work space. Return items promptly to their proper locations. Disassemble and clean glassware directly after use because residues in glassware may become resistant to cleaning if not washed promptly. Allow hot glassware to cool to room temperature before washing.

4. *Do only authorized experiments, and work only when the laboratory instructor or another qualified person is present.* Do not enter the laboratory until the laboratory instructor is present. Unauthorized experimenting will waste time and may expose you and others to unreasonable risk. Authorized experimental procedures take into account the special hazards of the materials used. Do not treat laboratory reagents and equipment as playthings. Do not remove any reagents from the laboratory. Injuries from laboratory incidents most often occur from violations of the precautions given in this paragraph.

5. *Treat all laboratory reagents as if they are poisonous and corrosive, unless told otherwise. Immediately wash spills off your skin* with plenty of water. Then notify your laboratory instructor. This response is especially important for many organic compounds because their fat solubility enhances their ease of absorption through the skin. Wash your hands thoroughly with soap or detergent before leaving the laboratory. Special hazards of laboratory reagents will be indicated by appropriate labels on the reagent bottles.

   Containers from chemical supply companies may use the National Fire Protection Association's diamond or some similar indicator of potential hazard, as shown in Figure 1. A number from 0 (low) to 4 (high) in each category indicates the degree of hazard.

6. *Dispense reagents carefully and dispose of laboratory reagents as directed.* Do not use reagents from unidentified containers. Double check each label before dispensing a reagent. To prevent contamination, do not return any reagent to its original container. Place any excess reagent in the recovery container provided by your laboratory instructor. Dispose of reagents as directed by the laboratory instructor and the written procedure. Promptly notify the laboratory instructor of any spill. Clean up a spill *only if directed* to do so by your laboratory instructor. Spills should be cleaned up immediately to prevent contact of the chemicals with persons who are not aware of the spill. When

Figure 1
National fire protection association label

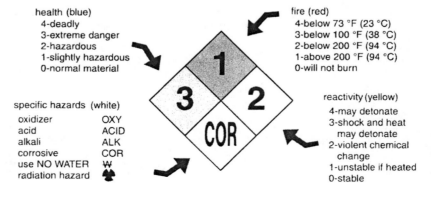

weighing reagents, dispense them into containers so that reagents do not spill onto the balance.

7. *Do not eat, drink, use tobacco, or apply cosmetics in the laboratory.* Violation of this rule can introduce poisons into your system. Especially avoid any contamination to your mouth or eyes. Never bring food or drinks into the laboratory.

8. *Immediately report all incidents to the laboratory instructor.* An **incident** is any situation in the laboratory that might endanger those persons present. Your laboratory instructor must give prompt attention when injuries occur. Even minor incidents may require attention. The laboratory instructor may also be able to use the information you provide to help other students avoid a similar difficulty.

9. *Be familiar with the location and use of all safety equipment in the laboratory.* All laboratories should have an eyewash station, a safety shower, a fume hood, and more than one fire extinguisher. Anticipate the steps to be taken in the event of an incident. Prompt response to an incident can make the difference between a minor event and permanent injury. The laboratory instructor may direct you to assist in responding. However, do not place yourself or others at risk in order to respond to an incident in the laboratory. A subsequent section describes proper responses to incidents in the laboratory.

10. *Become familiar with each laboratory assignment before coming to the laboratory.* Pay particular attention to cautions given in the procedure and by the laboratory instructor. Use of some equipment presents special hazards. For example, vacuum operations include the possibility of implosions, and ultraviolet light is damaging to the eyes if viewed directly. Each laboratory experiment will give special cautions for any hazardous reagents used in that experiment. Your laboratory instructor will provide other information and reminders as needed.

By law, chemical supply companies must provide a **Material Safety Data Sheet (MSDS)** with each reagent they sell. The MSDS is a technical bulletin that gives detailed information on the properties of a laboratory reagent. Some information from an MSDS for 1-propanol is shown in Figure 2 on the next page. Your laboratory instructor may have you consult the reagent MSDS as part of your laboratory work.

COMMON HAZARDS IN THE ORGANIC CHEMISTRY LABORATORY

Anticipate common hazards encountered in the laboratory. Experience has shown that ignoring the following *common concerns* will lead to mishaps.

1. Never pipet by mouth. Many organic chemicals are toxic.

2. Do not use chipped or cracked glassware, which may cause cuts or may crack and spill its contents unexpectedly.

3. Obtain approval from your laboratory instructor before starting a distillation. Make certain the apparatus has an opening. Do not heat a closed apparatus because abrupt release of the increased pressure may propel reagents or pieces of glass at persons nearby. Use a fresh boiling

MATERIAL SAFETY DATA SHEET

ANY SCIENTIFIC COMPANY   EMERGENCY #: (800)-555-XXXX
YOURTOWN, USA

Section 1 (Identity): 1-PROPANOL (and synonyms given) Mol. Formula C_3H_8O Mol. Wt. 60.1
CAS # 71-23-8   NFPA Ratings (scale 0–4):   Health = 1, Fire = 3,   Reactivity = 0

Section 2 (Hazardous Ingredients): 1-PROPANOL (100%)
Exposure Limits: 200 ppm (492 mg/m^3) OSHA TWA
250 ppm (614 mg/m^3) OSHA STEL

Section 3 (Physical & Chemical Characteristics): Description: Colorless liquid with mild alcohol odor
Boiling Point: 207 F (97 C)   Melting Point –195 F (–125 C)   Vapor Pressure (20 C): 15 mm Hg
Odor Threshold: 30 ppm

Section 4 (Physical Hazards): Dangerous fire hazard when exposed to heat or flame. Vapors are heavier
than air and may travel a considerable distance to a source of ignition. Flash Point: 74 F (23 C) (CC)
Upper Explosive Limit 13.7%   Fire Fighting Media: Dry chemical, carbon dioxide, water spray, or alcohol-
resistant foam.   Transportation Data: US DOT Hazard Class 3 — flammable liq.

Section 5 (Reactivity): Stable under normal temperatures and pressures. Incompatibles: alkali & alkaline
earth metals. Attacks coatings, plastics, and rubber.

Section 6 (Health Hazards — Inhalation, Skin Contact, Eye Contact, and Ingestion):
INHALATION: Irritant/Narcotic. 4000 ppm is immediately dangerous to life or health.
Acute Exposure: Inhalation of vapors may cause moderate irritation of the upper respiratory tract with
coughing and shortness of breath. High concentrations may cause CNS depression, with dizziness,
headache, and vomiting.
Chronic Exposure: Reproductive effects have been reported.
First Aid: Remove from exposure area. Perform artificial respiration if necessary. Get medical attention immed.

Section 7 (Precautions for Safe Handling and Use — Storage, Disposal, Spill & Leak Procedures):
May be ignited by electrostatic sparks, so should be stored in grounded container, as specified in NFPA
77-1983. Disposal must be in accordance with 40 CFR 262 (EPA Hazardous Waste Number D001). For small
spills, take up with sand or other noncombustible absorbent and place into containers for later disposal.

Section 8 (Control Measures — Ventilation, Firefighting, Clothing, Gloves, Eye Protection): Wear
appropriate protective clothing and equipment to prevent prolonged skin contact.

Figure 2
Selected information from MSDS for 1-propanol

chip each time a liquid is boiled to avoid **bumping**, the sudden eruptive release of vapor. Such a release can burn persons nearby. Do not heat any distillation pot to dryness because the residue that remains may be heat sensitive, and overheating could cause it to detonate. Also, glassware that is superheated could crack. Before heating a flask, clamp the neck of the flask to support it in an elevated position to allow withdrawal of the heat source and rapid cooling, if needed.

4. Lubricate and clamp ground glass joints so they will not freeze or spring open in use. Use lubricant sparingly.

5. Do not point the open end of a container at anyone. Abrupt formation of bubbles, such as from boiling, could propel the contents into a person's face.

6. Place heated glass and other hot objects on an appropriate surface, such as a wire gauze or ceramic pad, until they have cooled. Hot glass

or metal may look like cool glass or metal, so cautiously touch objects that have been heated before handling them. Place a note nearby any hot objects remaining at the end of a laboratory period, so students in a subsequent laboratory period will not be endangered.

7. Use a fume hood when working with reagents whose vapors are harmful. Except for small quantities heated by steam or a hot-water bath, heating of highly flammable organic substances in open containers must be done in a hood. In using a fume hood, position any apparatus well within the hood space, keeping your head outside the hood. The flow of air through the hood must be adequate and unobstructed. The hood sash should be lowered, except when making manipulations within the hood. Place within the hood only those items necessary for the operation being performed. Keep the exhaust fan on as long as any reagents remain within the hood.

8. When testing odors of reagents, gently waft vapors from the container toward your nose. Do not directly sniff the contents of a container.

9. Do not use open flames (Bunsen burners) in the presence of flammable materials, especially organic solvents such as acetone, diethyl ether, or petroleum ether. Use of a flameless heat source diminishes the danger of a fire, but such heat sources remain hot for quite some time after they are turned off. Overheated sand baths, hot plates, or heating wells can ignite fumes from volatile organic solvents.

10. Wear gloves when dispensing irritating reagents. This precaution is especially important for organic reagents, which can penetrate the skin readily. Your laboratory instructor will designate gloves that are appropriate for the reagents to be used. Latex surgical gloves are not appropriate because they allow passage of many organic reagents. Gloves should be inflated to check for breaks by whipping them through the air. Do not check gloves by inflating them by mouth.

11. Take special care when working with strong acids or strong bases. Contact with these materials can cause severe chemical burns. Prepare dilute acids by slowly adding the concentrated acid to a larger volume of water, with stirring. The water dissipates the evolved heat and prevents localized boiling that could spew the contents from the container.

12. If you must insert glass tubing into stoppers, follow the directions given by your laboratory instructor.

RESPONSES TO INCIDENTS IN THE ORGANIC CHEMISTRY LABORATORY

Become familiar with actions to be taken in the event of incidents in the laboratory. Provide appropriate assistance to others in emergencies. The items that follow describe the actions that should be taken in certain situations.

1. Report all incidents to the laboratory instructor, who is responsible for actions to be taken in response to incidents and for reports to be made to other authorities. As defined in Safety Rule 8, an incident is any

situation in the laboratory that might endanger those persons present. An improper response may change a trivial difficulty into a much more hazardous situation. Sometimes an irritation or personal injury is not manifested immediately. A student who experiences an irritation later in the day, and who has a reasonable suspicion that contact with laboratory reagents could have caused the problem, should contact the laboratory instructor or a health care professional for advice.

The safety of persons in the laboratory has absolute priority over all other considerations. While you will not have the responsibility for directing others in the laboratory, you should be aware that the typical sequence of actions to take in the event of an incident in the laboratory is *ALERT, CONFINE*, and *EVACUATE*. If you are the first to notice a hazard in the laboratory, you should *alert* your laboratory instructor and others nearby. After you and others are clear of danger, your laboratory instructor will *confine* the hazard. If the hazard persists, the laboratory instructor may give instructions to *evacuate* the area.

Severe injuries may result from unreasonable responses to unexpected situations. For example, a person who spills a corrosive reagent on himself or herself might hope no one else notices, waiting until leaving the laboratory to wash off the spill. In the meantime, the burn from the reagent may have progressed from a superficial irritation to one that requires medical attention. Or a person who has lifted a test tube at the time the contents ignite might throw the tube through the air onto another person, catching that person's clothes on fire. Consider the consequences of your actions.

2. Dispose of broken glass as directed by the laboratory instructor. Use a hand brush and dust pan to collect the pieces. Do not attempt to gather sharp glass by hand. Place broken glass in specially designated receptacles in order to avoid placing other persons at risk. Place very small, sharp objects—for example, syringe needles and pieces of capillary tube—in specially designated receptacles.

   If a mercury thermometer is broken, step back from the work area and notify the laboratory instructor, who will use special techniques to collect the spilled mercury. The special hazard with mercury is not from contact with the skin, but from prolonged exposure to the vapor. A cut by a broken thermometer should get the same attention as other cuts.

3. For either minor cuts or burns, wash the affected area using soap or detergent. Tissue damage from a superficial burn will be minimal if the affected area is cooled quickly, so you should flush the affected area with cold water. Then notify the laboratory instructor. When work is resumed, protect any break in the skin by wearing a glove, in order to prevent introduction of laboratory reagents.

4. In the event of a reagent spill, notify the laboratory instructor. Appropriate steps to be taken in response to a reagent spill will vary, depending on the amount and identity of the reagent. Concerns for hazards other than the reagent itself, such as danger of shorting electrical equipment, may even take precedence. Spills of organic solvents may be a fire hazard. In such an event, remove all ignition sources, including any equipment that could produce a spark—for example, switches being turned on and off. Hot plates and sand baths at a high

temperature do not cool rapidly on turning off, so move these heat sources away from the spill. If a spill creates a large amount of fumes, evacuate the laboratory. Stop any experiments, if doing so doesn't place anyone at risk.

Deal promptly with reagent spills on a person. Wash the affected area with large volumes of water. Rapid response is necessary because many organic solvents are fat soluble and can be absorbed through the skin. Use the sink or safety shower as needed, depending on the size of the spill. Remove clothing and wash skin with soap or detergent to complete the removal of the reagent. Do not remove goggles before washing any reagent spill from the face, to lessen the likelihood of getting the reagent in the eyes.

A person whose eyes have had reagents splashed into them requires assistance from others. A person's automatic response to an irritation to the eyes is closing of the lids and rubbing, actions that will only increase the irritation. Other persons should assist the person to the eyewash fountain and operate the water flow, while the person holds open his/her eyelids. The flow of water must get to the entire eye surface, continuing for twenty minutes. Cold water may be intolerable for such an uninterrupted period, so periodic washing may have to be done. Irrigation of the eye will not be adequate if contact lenses that are present are not removed. Further treatment of irritation to the eye from a reagent spill must be done only by a health care professional.

5. Many common solvents used in the organic chemistry laboratory are highly flammable, and a small fire may occur in the laboratory. Do not react without thinking. The immediate response to a fire in the laboratory is to take those actions that remove individuals from the hazard. For example, stepping back from a small fire and cautioning neighbors of the hazard would be a reasonable response. Move flammable materials away, and turn equipment off or remove equipment from the vicinity of the fire. Shut off the gas spigot or heating element. Place a watch glass or beaker over a small container to smother the burning material. Some *small* fires, such as alcohol fires, may be allowed to burn out.

If a fire spreads to a larger area of the bench, the laboratory instructor or other authorized persons should operate the fire extinguisher. Should a fire reach a stage where it cannot be easily controlled, the laboratory instructor will direct you to evacuate the laboratory and the building.

The most distressing incidents in laboratories are those where an individual is on fire. Using small quantities of flammable substances and following safe practices in the laboratory ensure that such an event is unlikely to happen. Proper response can make the difference between loss of some clothing or, in the extreme case, loss of life. If a person's lungs are seared from inhaling flames, there will be little chance of recovery.

The safety shower or water from the sink may be sufficient to extinguish a fire on a person. In a severe situation, the proper response to fire on an individual's clothing is to STOP, DROP, and ROLL. That is, if you have fire on your body, *stop* where you are, *drop* to the floor, and *roll* to smother the flames. Staying upright will allow the flames to rise to the face. Nearby persons can use a laboratory coat to beat out the flames. When the flames are extinguished, remove any smoldering fabric. If the person has been burned, place the person under the safety shower. Other persons nearby can assist as needed, such as extinguishing fire on the bench, shutting off equipment, and cleaning up. Most other persons in the laboratory should simply move away.

6. Ingestion or inhalation of a reagent will likely require the assistance of a health care professional. In such an event, immediately notify the laboratory instructor, who will gather the information needed to report the incident to the poison control center. Space is provided at the end of this module for you to record the phone number of the poison control center in your area.

   Avoid the inhalation of unsafe levels of irritating or toxic vapors by following the directions for using laboratory reagents and by using the reagents in a fume hood. While you must not depend upon your senses to alert you to inadvisable conditions, notify your laboratory instructor promptly if your eyes begin to sting or if you develop a headache that may be caused by fumes in the laboratory. Especially avoid breathing the vapors from chlorinated solvents and aromatic compounds.

7. Immediately notify the laboratory instructor if you or a neighbor feels faint. A person who has become unconscious from inhalation of fumes must be removed from the source of the fumes. Other than checking the person's airway and treatment for shock (elevating limbs, keeping warm), further treatment should only be made by a health care professional.

Safety Information

Complete this form and keep it for possible use.

1. **Emergency health providers** (telephone numbers to call)
   Campus Health Services:

   on campus _____   off campus _____

   Emergency Medical Assistance:

   on campus _____   off campus _____

   State Poison Control Center: _____
   Campus Police:

   on campus _____   off campus _____

   City Police or Fire Department:

   on campus _____   off campus _____

2. **Contacting the laboratory instructor**

   Name: _____   Office: _____

   Office phone: on campus _____   off campus _____

   Home phone: _____   E-mail address: _____

3. **Reporting incidents** (for reference)

   The following information will be needed when communicating with health professionals and/or recording incidents.

   Nature of the incident (description – including fire, substances involved, number of individuals involved and their physical conditions):

   Individuals involved (identification – name, gender, age):

   Location of the incident, including who will meet any emergency vehicle, and where:

   Person reporting the incident (name, phone number being used to report the incident. *Note*: Do not allow this phone to be tied up for calls unrelated to control of the incident.):

Safety Contract

Complete this form and give to your laboratory instructor.

I have carefully read the organic chemical laboratory safety module. I have given my answers to the accompanying safety quiz and given that completed quiz to the laboratory instructor as an indication of my familiarity with the module. Whenever I am in an area where laboratory reagents are being used, I agree to abide by the following rules:

1. Wear safety goggles.
2. Wear proper clothing.
3. Use good housekeeping practices.
4. Do only authorized experiments, and work only when the laboratory instructor or another qualified person is present.
5. Treat laboratory reagents as if they are poisonous and corrosive.
6. Dispense reagents carefully. Dispose of laboratory reagents as directed.
7. Do not eat, drink, use tobacco, or apply cosmetics in the laboratory.
8. Report all incidents to the laboratory instructor.
9. Be familiar with the location and use of all safety equipment.
10. Become familiar with each laboratory assignment before coming to the laboratory.
11. Anticipate the common hazards that may be encountered in laboratory.
12. Become familiar with actions to be taken in the event of incidents in the laboratory.

_____   _____
student signature   date

_____   _____
laboratory instructor   date

In the space below, give any health information, such as pregnancy or other circumstance, that might help the laboratory instructor provide a safer environment for you, or that could aid the laboratory instructor in responding to an incident involving you in the laboratory.

1. I do/do not (circle one) expect to wear contact lenses during laboratory work. [*Note*: Goggles must still be worn when contact lenses are worn.]

2. List any known allergies to medication or other chemicals.

_____   _____   _____
name   *section*   *date*

Safety Quiz

1. On a separate sheet of paper, sketch the layout of the laboratory. (a) Note the location of each important safety feature (fire extinguisher, fume hood, eye wash, safety shower, and exits). (b) Draw a line from your work location, showing the path you would take to evacuate the laboratory. (c) Indicate the nearest location where you can activate the fire alarm.

2. Describe the steps to be taken in the event 10 mL of ethanol in a 50-mL beaker ignites in the laboratory.

3. Identify two important reasons for notifying the laboratory instructor of any incidents that occur in laboratory.

4. Why is unauthorized experimenting by a student in the laboratory not allowed?

5. Describe the steps to be taken in the laboratory if a large bottle of acetone (noncorrosive, nontoxic, highly volatile, water-soluble, flammable solvent) is broken and spilled.

6. According to the information in the MSDS (Figure 2), which hazardous category (health, fire, or reactivity) is of greatest concern for 1-propanol?

7. What is the first action to be taken in the event a person spills some reagent on himself or herself? What is the second action to be taken?

8. Identify three precautions to be taken before beginning the distillation of an organic liquid.

2

TECHNIQUE 2

The Laboratory Notebook, Calculations, and Laboratory Records

It is important that you do some advance preparation for all laboratory work. Presented here are some suggestions about what specific information you should try to obtain in your advance studying. Because much of this information must be obtained while preparing your laboratory notebook, the two subjects, advance study and notebook preparation, are developed simultaneously.

An important part of any laboratory experience is learning to maintain complete records of every experiment undertaken and every item of data obtained. Far too often, careless recording of data and observations has resulted in mistakes, frustration, and lost time due to needless repetition of experiments. If reports are required, you will find that proper collection and recording of data can make your report writing much easier.

Because organic reactions are seldom quantitative, special problems result. Frequently, reagents must be used in large excess to increase the amount of product. Some reagents are expensive, and, therefore, care must be used in measuring the amounts of these substances. Often, many more reactions take place than you desire. These extra reactions, or **side reactions,** may form products other than the desired product. These are called **side products.** For all these reasons, you must plan your experimental procedure carefully before undertaking the actual experiment.

2.1 The Notebook

For recording data and observations during experiments, use a *bound notebook.* The notebook should have consecutively numbered pages. If it does not, number the pages immediately. A spiral-bound notebook or any other notebook from which the pages can be removed easily is not acceptable, because the possibility of losing the pages is great.

All data and observations must be recorded in the notebook. Paper towels, napkins, toilet tissue, or scratch paper tend to become lost or destroyed. It is bad laboratory practice to record information on such random and perishable pieces of paper. All entries must be recorded in *permanent ink.* It can be frustrating to have important information disappear from the notebook because it was recorded in washable ink or pencil and could not survive a flood caused by the student at the next position on the bench. Because you will be using your notebook in the laboratory, the book will probably become soiled or stained by chemicals, filled with scratched-out entries, or even slightly burned. That is expected and is a normal part of laboratory work.

Your instructor may check your notebook at any time, so you should always have it up to date. If your instructor requires reports, you can prepare them quickly from the material recorded in the laboratory notebook.

2.2 Notebook Format

A. Advance Preparation

Individual instructors vary greatly in the type of notebook format they prefer; such variation stems from differences in philosophies and experience.

You must obtain specific directions from your own instructor for preparing a notebook. Certain features, however, are common to most notebook formats. The following discussion indicates what might be included in a typical notebook.

It will be helpful and you can save much time in the laboratory if for each experiment you know the main reactions, the potential side reactions, the mechanism, and the stoichiometry and you understand fully the procedure and the theory underlying it before you come to the laboratory. Understanding the procedure by which the desired product is to be separated from undesired materials is also important. If you examine each of these topics before coming to class, you will be prepared to do the experiment efficiently. You will have your equipment and reagents already prepared when they are to be used. Your reference material will be at hand when you need it. Finally, with your time efficiently organized, you will be able to take advantage of long reaction or reflux periods to perform other tasks, such as doing shorter experiments or finishing previous ones.

For experiments in which a compound is synthesized from other reagents, that is, **preparative experiments,** it is essential to know the main reaction. To perform stoichiometric calculations, you should balance the equation for the main reaction. Therefore, before you begin the experiment, your notebook should contain the balanced equation for the pertinent reaction. Using the preparation of isopentyl acetate, or banana oil, as an example, you should write the following:

$$CH_3-\overset{\overset{\text{O}}{\|}}{C}-OH \ + \ CH_3-\overset{\overset{\text{CH}_3}{|}}{CH}-CH_2-CH_2-OH \ \xrightarrow{H^+}$$

Acetic acid   Isopentyl alcohol

$$CH_3-\overset{\overset{\text{O}}{\|}}{C}-O-CH_2-CH_2-\overset{\overset{\text{CH}_3}{|}}{CH}-CH_3 \ + \ H_2O$$

Isopentyl acetate

Also enter in the notebook the possible side reactions that divert reagents into contaminants (side products), before beginning the experiment. You will have to separate these side products from the major product during purification.

You should list physical constants such as melting points, boiling points, densities, and molecular weights in the notebook when this information is needed to perform an experiment or to do calculations. These data are located in sources such as the *CRC Handbook of Chemistry and Physics, The Merck Index, Lange's Handbook of Chemistry,* or *Aldrich Handbook of Fine Chemicals.* Write physical constants required for an experiment in your notebook before you come to class.

Advance preparation may also include examining some subjects, information not necessarily recorded in the notebook, that should prove useful in understanding the experiment. Included among these subjects are an understanding of the mechanism of the reaction, an examination of other methods by which the same compound might be prepared, and a detailed study of the experimental procedure. Many students find that an outline of the procedure, prepared *before* they come to class, helps them use their time more efficiently once they begin the experiment. Such an outline could well be prepared on some loose sheet of paper rather than in the notebook itself.

Once the reaction has been completed, the desired product does not magically appear as purified material; it must be isolated from a frequently complex mixture of side products, unreacted starting materials, solvents, and catalysts. You should try to outline a **separation scheme** in your notebook for isolating the product from its contaminants. At each stage, you should try to understand the reason for the particular instruction given in the experimental procedure. This not only will familiarize you with the basic separation and purification techniques used in organic chemistry but also will help you understand when to use these techniques. Such an outline might take the form of a flowchart. For example, see the separation scheme for isopentyl acetate (Figure 2.1). Careful attention to understanding the separation,

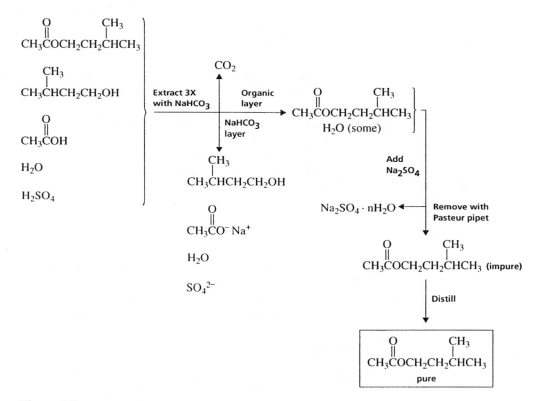

Figure 2.1
Separation scheme for isopentyl acetate.

besides familiarizing you with the procedure by which the desired product is separated from impurities in your particular experiments, may prepare you for original research in which no experimental procedure exists.

In designing a separation scheme, note that the scheme outlines those steps undertaken once the reaction period has been concluded. For this reason, the represented scheme does not include steps such as the addition of the reactants (isopentyl alcohol and acetic acid) and the catalyst (sulfuric acid) or the heating of the reaction mixture.

For experiments in which a compound is isolated from a particular source and is not prepared from other reagents, some information described in this section will not be applicable. Such experiments are called **isolation experiments.** A typical isolation experiment involves isolating a pure compound from a natural source. Examples include isolating caffeine from tea or isolating cinnamaldehyde from cinnamon. Although isolation experiments require somewhat different advance preparation, this advance study may include looking up physical constants for the compound isolated and outlining the isolation procedure. A detailed examination of the separation scheme is important here because it is the heart of such an experiment.

B. Laboratory Records

When you begin the actual experiment, keep your notebook nearby so you will be able to record those operations you perform. When working in the laboratory, the notebook serves as a place in which to record a rough transcript of your experimental method. Data from actual weighings, volume measurements, and determinations of physical constants are also noted. This section of your notebook should *not* be prepared in advance. The purpose is not to write a recipe but rather to record what you *did* and what you *observed*. These observations will help you write reports without resorting to memory. They will also help you or other workers repeat the experiment in as nearly as possible the same way. The sample notebook pages found in Figures 2.2 and 2.3 illustrate the type of data and observations that should be written in your notebook.

When your product has been prepared and purified, or isolated if it is an isolation experiment, record pertinent data such as the melting point or boiling point of the substance, its density, its index of refraction, and the conditions under which spectra were determined.

C. Calculations

A chemical equation for the overall conversion of the starting materials to products is written on the assumption of simple ideal stoichiometry. Actually, this assumption is seldom realized. Side reactions or competing reactions will also occur, giving other products. For some synthetic reactions, an equilibrium state will be reached in which an appreciable amount of starting material is still present and can be recovered. Some of the reactant may also remain if it is present in excess or if the reaction was incomplete. A reaction involving an expensive reagent illustrates another reason for needing to know how far a particular type of reaction converts reactants to products. In such a case, it is preferable to use the most efficient method for this conversion. Thus, information about the efficiency of conversion for various reactions is of interest to the person contemplating the use of these reactions.

The quantitative expression for the efficiency of a reaction is found by calculating the **yield** for the reaction. The **theoretical yield** is the number of grams of the product expected from the reaction on the basis of ideal stoichiometry, with side reactions, reversibility, and losses ignored. To calculate the theoretical yield, it is first necessary to determine the **limiting reagent.** The limiting reagent is the reagent that is not present in excess and on which the overall yield of product depends. The method for determining the limiting reagent in the isopentyl acetate experiment is illustrated in the sample notebook pages shown in Figures 2.2 and 2.3. You should consult your general chemistry textbook for more complicated examples. The theoretical yield is then calculated from the expression

Theoretical yield = (moles of limiting reagent)(ratio)(molecular weight of product)

The ratio here is the stoichiometric ratio of product to limiting reagent. In preparing isopentyl acetate, that ratio is 1:1. One mole of isopentyl alcohol, under ideal circumstances, should yield 1 mole of isopentyl acetate.

The **actual yield** is simply the number of grams of desired product obtained. The **percentage yield** describes the efficiency of the reaction and is determined by

$$\textbf{Percentage yield } = \frac{\textbf{Actual yield}}{\textbf{Theoretical yield}} \times \textbf{100}$$

THE PREPARATION OF ISOPENTYL ACETATE (BANANA OIL)

MAIN REACTION

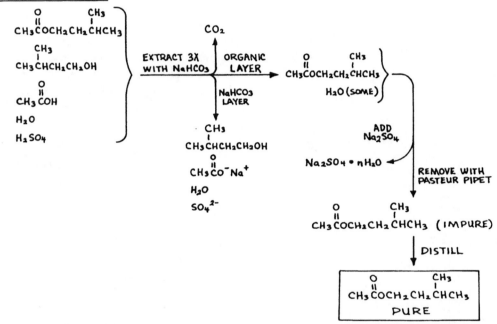

TABLE OF PHYSICAL CONSTANTS

	MW	BP	DENSITY
ISOPENTYL ALCOHOL	88.2	132°C	0.813 g/mL
ACETIC ACID	60.1	118	1.06
ISOPENTYL ACETATE	130.2	142	0.876

SEPARATION SCHEME

DATA AND OBSERVATIONS

0.70 mL OF ISOPENTYL ACETATE WAS ADDED TO A PREWEIGHED
5-mL CONICAL VIAL:

VIAL + ALCOHOL   25.524 g

VIAL   24.955 g

0.569 g ISOPENTYL ALCOHOL

ACETIC ACID (1.4 mL) AND 3 DROPS OF CONCENTRATED H_2SO_4 (USING A PASTEUR
PIPET) WERE ALSO ADDED TO THE CONICAL VIAL ALONG WITH A SMALL BOILING STONE.
A WATER-COOLED CONDENSER TOPPED WITH A DRYING TUBE CONTAINING A LOOSE
PLUG OF GLASS WOOL WAS ATTACHED TO THE VIAL. THE REACTION MIXTURE WAS
REFLUXED IN AN ALUMINUM BLOCK (ABOUT 155°) FOR 75 MIN. AND THEN COOLED TO
ROOM TEMPERATURE. THE COLOR OF THE REACTION MIXTURE WAS BROWNISH-YELLOW.

Figure 2.2

A sample notebook, page 1.

THE BOILING STONE WAS REMOVED AND THE REACTION MIXTURE WAS EXTRACTED THREE TIMES WITH 1.0 mL OF 5% $NaHCO_3$. THE BOTTOM AQUEOUS LAYER WAS REMOVED AND DISCARDED AFTER EACH EXTRACTION. DURING THE FIRST TWO EXTRACTIONS, MUCH CO_2 GAS WAS GIVEN OFF. THE ORGANIC LAYER WAS A LIGHT YELLOW COLOR. IT WAS TRANSFERRED TO A DRY CONICAL VIAL, AND 2 FULL MICROSPATULAS OF ANHYDROUS Na_2SO_4 WERE ADDED TO DRY THE CRUDE PRODUCT. IT WAS ALLOWED TO SET WITH OCCASIONAL STIRRING FOR 10 MINS.

THE DRY PRODUCT WAS TRANSFERRED TO A 3-mL CONICAL VIAL, AND A BOILING STONE WAS ADDED. A DISTILLATION APPARATUS USING A HICKMAN STILL, A WATER-COOLED CONDENSER, AND A DRYING TUBE PACKED WITH $CaCl_2$ WAS ASSEMBLED. THE SAMPLE WAS HEATED IN AN ALUMINUM BLOCK AT ABOUT 180°C. THE LIQUID BEGAN BOILING AFTER ABOUT FIVE MINS, BUT NO DISTILLATE APPEARED IN THE HICKMAN STILL UNTIL ABOUT 20 MINS. LATER. ONCE THE PRODUCT BEGAN COLLECTING IN THE HICKMAN STILL, THE DISTILLATION REQUIRED ONLY ABOUT TWO MINS. TO COMPLETE. ABOUT 1-2 DROPS REMAINED IN THE DISTILLING VIAL. THE ISOPENTYL ACETATE WAS TRANSFERRED TO A PREWEIGHED 3-mL CONICAL VIAL.

$$\begin{array}{rl} \text{VIAL + PRODUCT} & 20.428g \\ \text{VIAL} & 20.074g \\ \hline & 0.354g \quad \text{ISOPENTYL ACETATE} \end{array}$$

THE PRODUCT WAS COLORLESS AND CLEAR. BP (MICRO TECHNIQUE): 140°C. THE IR SPECTRUM WAS OBTAINED.

CALCULATIONS

DETERMINE LIMITING REAGENT:

ISOPENTYL ALCOHOL $0.569g \left(\dfrac{1 \text{ MOL ISOPENTYL ALCOHOL}}{88.2g} \right) = 6.45 \times 10^{-3}$ MOL

ACETIC ACID $1.40 \text{ mL} \left(\dfrac{1.06g}{\text{mL}} \right) \left(\dfrac{1 \text{ MOL ACETIC ACID}}{60.1g} \right) = 2.47 \times 10^{-2}$ MOL

SINCE THEY REACT IN A 1:1 RATIO, ISOPENTYL ALCOHOL IS THE LIMITING REAGENT.

THEORETICAL YIELD =

6.45×10^{-3} MOL ISOPENTYL ALCOHOL $\left(\dfrac{1 \text{ MOL ISOPENTYL ACETATE}}{1 \text{ MOL ISOPENTYL ALCOHOL}} \right) \left(\dfrac{130.2g \text{ ISOPENTYL ACETATE}}{1 \text{ MOL ISOPENTYL ACETATE}} \right)$

$= 0.840g$ ISOPENTYL ACETATE

PERCENTAGE YIELD $= \dfrac{0.354g}{0.840g} \times 100 = 42.1\%$

Figure 2.3
A sample notebook, page 2.

Calculation of the theoretical yield and percentage yield can be illustrated using hypothetical data for the isopentyl acetate preparation:

$$\text{Theoretical yield} = (6.45 \times 10^{-3} \text{ mol isopentyl alcohol}) \left(\frac{1 \text{ mol isopentyl acetate}}{1 \text{ mol isopentyl alcohol}} \right)$$

$$\times \left(\frac{(130.2 \text{ g isopentyl acetate})}{1 \text{ mol isopentyl acetate}} \right) = 0.840 \text{ g isopentyl acetate}$$

$$\text{Actual yield} = 0.354 \text{ g isopentyl acetate}$$

$$\text{Percentage yield} = \frac{0.354 \text{ g}}{0.840 \text{ g}} \times 100 = 42.1\%$$

For experiments that have the principal objective of isolating a substance such as a natural product rather than preparing and purifying some reaction product, the **weight percentage recovery** and not the percentage yield is calculated. This value is determined by

$$\text{Weight percentage recovery } = \frac{\textbf{Weight of substance isolated}}{\textbf{Weight of original material}} \times 100$$

Thus, for instance, if 0.014 g of caffeine was obtained from 2.3 g of tea, the weight percentage recovery of caffeine would be

$$\text{Weight percentage recovery } = \frac{\textbf{0.014 g Caffeine}}{\textbf{2.3 g Tea}} \times 100 = 0.61\%$$

2.3 Laboratory Reports

Various formats for reporting the results of the laboratory experiments may be used. You may write the report directly in your notebook in a format similar to the sample notebook pages included in this section. Alternatively, your instructor may require a more formal report that is not written in your notebook. When you do original research, these reports should include a detailed description of all the experimental steps undertaken. Frequently, the style used in scientific periodicals such as *Journal of the American Chemical Society* is applied to writing laboratory reports. Your instructor is likely to have his or her own requirements for laboratory reports and should describe the requirements to you.

2.4 Submission of Samples

In all preparative experiments and in some isolation experiments, you will be required to submit to your instructor the sample of the substance you prepared or isolated. How this sample is labeled is important. Again, learning a correct method of labeling bottles and vials can save time in the laboratory because fewer mistakes will be made. More important, learning to label properly can decrease the danger inherent in having samples of material that cannot be identified correctly at a later date.

Solid materials should be stored and submitted in containers that permit the substance to be removed easily. For this reason, narrow-mouthed bottles or vials are not used for solid substances. Liquids should be stored in containers that will not let them escape through leakage. Be careful not to store volatile liquids in containers that have plastic caps, unless the cap is lined with an inert material such as Teflon. Otherwise, the vapors from the liquid are likely to contact the plastic and dissolve some of it, thus contaminating the substance being stored.

On the label, print the name of the substance, its melting or boiling point, the actual and percentage yields, and your name. An illustration of a properly prepared label follows:

```
+----------------------------------------+
|                                        |
|          Isopentyl Acetate             |
|              BP 140°C                   |
|          Yield 3.81 g (42.1%)          |
|            Joe Schmedlock              |
|                                        |
+----------------------------------------+
```

3

TECHNIQUE 3

Laboratory Glassware: Care and Cleaning

Because your glassware is expensive and you are responsible for it, you will want to give it proper care and respect. If you read this section carefully and follow the procedures presented here, you may be able to avoid some unnecessary expense. You may also save time, because cleaning problems and replacing broken glassware are time consuming.

If you are unfamiliar with the equipment found in an organic chemistry laboratory or are uncertain about how such equipment should be treated, this section provides some useful information, such as cleaning glassware and caring for glassware when using corrosive or caustic reagents. At the end of this section are illustrations that show and name most of the equipment you are likely to find in your drawer or locker.

3.1 CLEANING GLASSWARE

Glassware can be cleaned easily if you clean it immediately after use. It is good practice to do your "dish washing" right away. With time, organic tarry materials left in a container begin to attack the surface of the glass. The longer you wait to clean glassware, the more extensively this interaction will have progressed. If you wait, cleaning is more difficult, because water will no longer wet the surface of the glass as effectively. If you cannot wash your glassware immediately after use, soak the dirty pieces of glassware in soapy water. A half-gallon plastic container is convenient for soaking and washing glassware. Using a plastic container also helps prevent the loss of small pieces of equipment.

Various soaps and detergents are available for washing glassware. They should be tried first when washing dirty glassware. Organic solvents can also be used, because the residue remaining in dirty glassware is likely to be soluble. After the solvent has been used, the glass item probably will have to be washed with soap and water to remove the residual solvent. When you use solvents to clean glassware, use caution, because the solvents are hazardous (see Technique 1). Use fairly small amounts of a solvent for cleaning purposes. Usually less than 5 mL (or 1–2 mL for microscale glassware) will be sufficient. Acetone is commonly used, but it is expensive. Your **wash acetone** can be used effectively several times before it is "spent." Once your acetone is spent, dispose of it as your instructor directs. If acetone does not work, other organic solvents such as methylene chloride or toluene can be used.

Caution: Acetone is very flammable. Do not use it around flames.

For troublesome stains and residues that adhere to the glass despite your best efforts, use a mixture of sulfuric acid and nitric acid. Cautiously add about 20 drops of concentrated sulfuric acid and 5 drops of concentrated nitric acid to the flask or vial.

> **Caution:** You must wear safety glasses when you are using a cleaning solution made from sulfuric acid and nitric acid. Do not allow the solution to come into contact with your skin or clothing. It will cause severe burns on your skin and create holes in your clothing. The acids may also react with the residue in the container.

Swirl the acid mixture in the container for a few minutes. If necessary, place the glassware in a warm water bath and heat it cautiously to accelerate the cleaning process. Continue heating the glassware until any sign of a reaction ceases. When the cleaning procedure is completed, decant the mixture into an appropriate waste container.

> **Caution:** Do not pour the acid solution into a waste container that is intended for organic wastes.

Rinse the piece of glassware thoroughly with water and then wash it with soap and water. For most common organic chemistry applications, any stains that survive this treatment are not likely to cause difficulty in subsequent laboratory procedures.

If the glassware is contaminated with stopcock grease, rinse the glassware with a small amount (1–2 mL) of methylene chloride. Discard the rinse solution into an appropriate waste container. Once the grease is removed, wash the glassware with soap or detergent and water.

3.2 DRYING GLASSWARE

The easiest way to dry glassware is to let it stand overnight. Store vials, flasks, and beakers upside down on a piece of paper towel to permit the water to drain from them. Drying ovens can be used to dry glassware if they are available and if they are not being used for other purposes. Rapid drying can be achieved by rinsing the glassware with acetone and air drying it or placing it in an oven. First, thoroughly drain the glassware of water. Then rinse it with one or two *small* portions (1–2 mL) of acetone. Do not use any more acetone than is suggested here. Return the used acetone to an acetone waste container for recycling. After you rinse the glassware with acetone, dry it by placing it in a drying oven for a few minutes or allow it to air dry at room temperature. The acetone can also be removed by aspirator suction. In some laboratories, it may be possible to dry the glassware by blowing a *gentle* stream of dry air into the container. (Your laboratory instructor will indicate if you should do this.) Before drying the glassware with air, make sure that the air line is not filled with oil. Otherwise, the oil will be blown into the container, and you will have to clean it again. It is not necessary to blast the acetone out of the glassware with a wide-open stream of air; a gentle stream of air is just as effective and will not startle other people in the room.

Do not dry your glassware with a paper towel unless the towel is lint free. Most paper will leave lint on the glass that can interfere with subsequent procedures. Sometimes it is not necessary to dry a piece of equipment thoroughly. For example, if you are going to place water or an aqueous solution in a container, it does not need to be completely dry.

3.3 GROUND-GLASS JOINTS

It is likely that the glassware in your organic kit has **standard-taper ground-glass joints.** For example, the Claisen head in Figure 3.1 consists of an inner (male) ground-glass joint at the bottom and two outer (female) joints at the top. Each end is ground to a precise size, which is designated by the symbol ꙟ followed by two numbers. A common joint size in many macroscale organic glassware kits is ꙟ 19/22. The first number indicates the diameter (in millimeters) of the joint at its widest point, and the second number refers to its length (see Figure 3.1). One advantage of standard-taper joints is that the pieces fit together snugly and form a good seal. In addition, standard-taper joints allow all glassware components with the same joint size to be connected, thus permitting the assembly of a wide variety of apparatuses. One disadvantage of glassware with ground-glass joints, however, is that it is expensive.

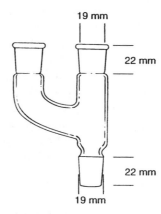

Figure 3.1   Illustration of inner and outer joints, showing dimensions. A Claisen head with ꙟ 19/22 joints.

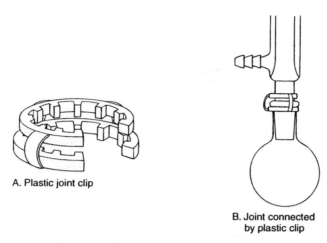

A. Plastic joint clip

B. Joint connected
by plastic clip

Figure 3.2   Connection of ground-glass joints. The use of a plastic clip (A) is also shown (B).

3.4 CONNECTING GROUND-GLASS JOINTS

It is a simple matter to connect pieces of macroscale glassware using standard-taper ground-glass joints. Figure 3.2B illustrates the connection of a condenser to a round-bottom flask. At times, however, it may be difficult to secure the connection so that it does not come apart unexpectedly. Figure 3.2A shows a plastic clip that serves to secure the connection. Methods to secure ground-glass connections with macroscale apparatus, including the use of plastic clips, are covered in Technique 7.

It is important to make sure no solid or liquid is on the joint surfaces. Either of these will decrease the efficiency of the seal, and the joints may leak. With microscale glassware, the presence of solid particles could cause the ground-glass joints to break when the plastic cap is tightened. Also, if the apparatus is to be heated, material caught between the joint surfaces will increase the tendency for the joints to stick. If the joint surfaces are coated with liquid or adhering solid, you should wipe the surfaces with a cloth or a lint-free paper towel before assembling.

3.5 CAPPING FLASKS, CONICAL VIALS, AND OPENINGS

The sidearms in two-necked or three-necked round-bottom flasks can be capped using the ℣ 19/22 ground-glass stoppers that are part of a normal macroscale organic kit. Figure 3.3 shows such a stopper being used to cap the sidearm of a three-necked flask.

3.6 SEPARATING GROUND-GLASS JOINTS

When ground-glass joints become "frozen" or stuck together, you are faced with the often vexing problem of separating them. The techniques for separating ground-glass

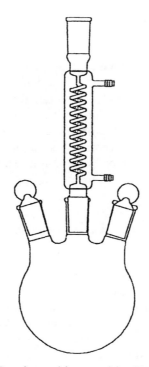

Figure 3.3 Capping a sidearm with a ᵀ 19/22 stopper.

joints, or for removing stoppers that are stuck in the openings of flasks and vials, are the same for both macroscale and microscale glassware.

The most important thing you can do to prevent ground-glass joints from becoming frozen is to disassemble the glassware as soon as possible after a procedure is completed. Even when this precaution is followed, ground-glass joints may become stuck tightly together. The same is true of glass stoppers in bottles or conical vials. Because certain items of microscale glassware may be small and very fragile, it is relatively easy to break a piece of glassware when trying to pull two pieces apart. If the pieces do not separate easily, you must be careful when you try to pull them apart. The best way is to hold the two pieces, with both hands touching, as close as possible to the joint. With a firm grasp, try to loosen the joint with a slight twisting motion (do not twist very hard). If this does not work, try to pull your hands apart without pushing sideways on the glassware.

If it is not possible to pull the pieces apart, the following methods may help. A frozen joint can sometimes be loosened if you tap it *gently* with the wooden handle of a spatula. Then try to pull it apart as already described. If this procedure fails, you may try heating the joint in hot water or a steam bath. If heating fails, the instructor may be able to advise you. As a last resort, you may try heating the joint in a flame. You should not try this unless the apparatus is hopelessly stuck, because heating by flame often causes the joint to expand rapidly and crack or break. If you use a flame, make sure the joint is clean and dry. Heat the outer part of the joint slowly, in the yellow portion of a low flame, until it expands and separates from the inner section. Heat the joint very slowly and carefully, or it may break.

3.7 ETCHING GLASSWARE

Glassware that has been used for reactions involving strong bases such as sodium hydroxide or sodium alkoxides must be cleaned thoroughly *immediately* after use. If these caustic materials are allowed to remain in contact with the glass, they will etch the glass permanently. The etching makes later cleaning more difficult, because dirt particles may become trapped within the microscopic surface irregularities of the etched glass. Furthermore, the glass is weakened, so the lifetime of the glassware is shortened. If caustic materials are allowed to come into contact with ground-glass joints without being removed promptly, the joints will become fused or "frozen." It is extremely difficult to separate fused joints without breaking them.

3.8 ATTACHING RUBBER TUBING TO EQUIPMENT

When you attach rubber tubing to the glass apparatus or when you insert glass tubing into rubber stoppers, first lubricate the rubber tubing or the rubber stopper with either water or glycerin. Without such lubrication, it can be difficult to attach rubber tubing to the sidearms of items of glassware such as condensers and filter flasks. Furthermore, glass tubing may break when it is inserted into rubber stoppers. Water is a good lubricant for most purposes. Do not use water as a lubricant when it might contaminate the reaction. Glycerin is a better lubricant than water and should be used when there is considerable friction between the glass and rubber. If glycerin is the lubricant, be careful not to use too much.

3.9 DESCRIPTION OF EQUIPMENT

Figures 3.4 and 3.5 include examples of glassware and equipment that are commonly used in the organic laboratory. Your glassware and equipment may vary slightly from the pieces shown on pages 589–591.

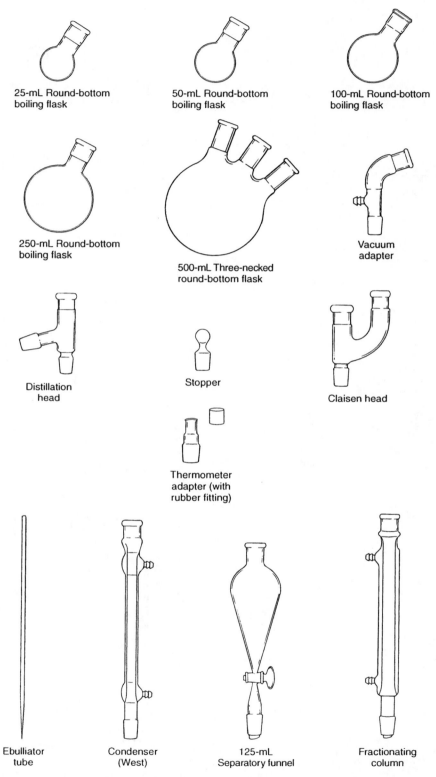

25-mL Round-bottom
boiling flask

50-mL Round-bottom
boiling flask

100-mL Round-bottom
boiling flask

250-mL Round-bottom
boiling flask

500-mL Three-necked
round-bottom flask

Vacuum
adapter

Distillation
head

Stopper

Claisen head

Thermometer
adapter (with
rubber fitting)

Ebulliator
tube

Condenser
(West)

125-mL
Separatory funnel

Fractionating
column

Figure 3.4 Components of the macroscale organic laboratory kit.

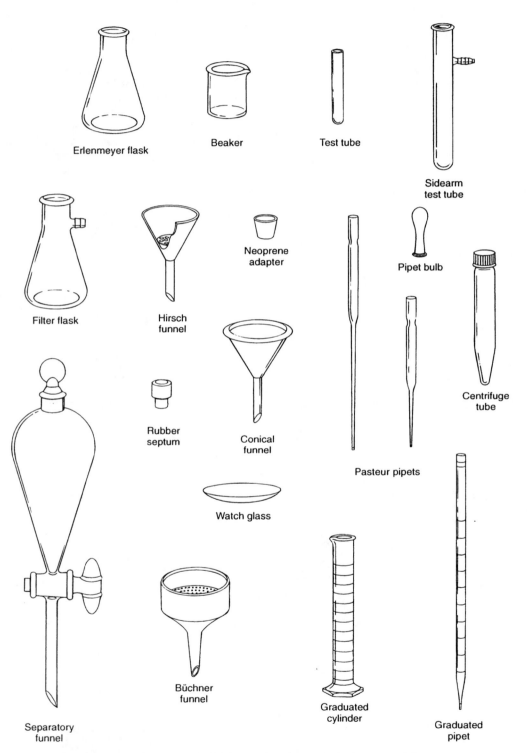

Figure 3.5 Equipment commonly used in the organic chemistry laboratory.

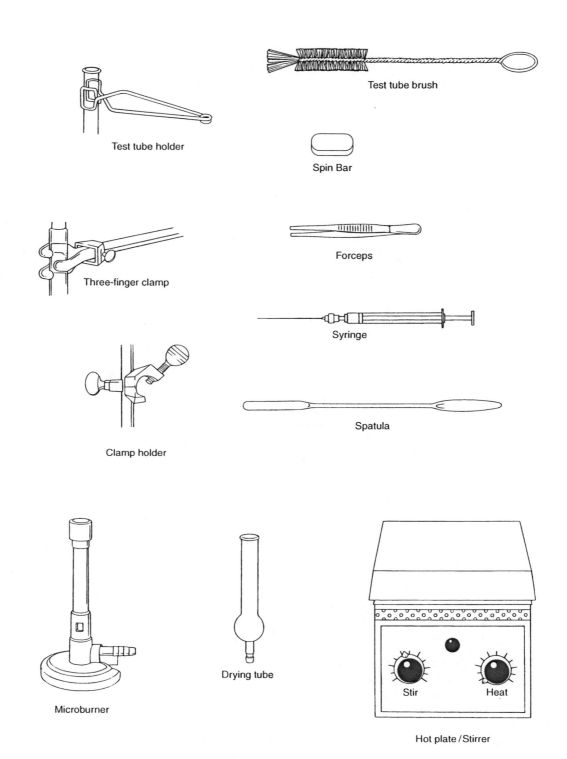

Test tube brush

Test tube holder

Spin Bar

Three-finger clamp

Forceps

Syringe

Clamp holder

Spatula

Microburner

Drying tube

Hot plate / Stirrer

Stir   Heat

Measuring the Melting Points of Compounds and Mixtures

Prepared by Joseph W. LeFevre, SUNY Oswego

PURPOSE OF THE EXPERIMENT

Measure the melting points of pure benzoic acid and pure mandelic acid. Determine the eutectic composition and the eutectic temperature of benzoic acid–mandelic acid mixtures. Identify an unknown compound using mixture melting points.

BACKGROUND REQUIRED

None

BACKGROUND INFORMATION

The **melting point** of a compound is the temperature at which the solid is in equilibrium with its liquid. A solid compound changes to a liquid when the molecules acquire enough energy to overcome the forces holding them together in an orderly crystalline lattice. For most organic compounds, these intermolecular forces are relatively weak.

The **melting point range** is defined as the span of temperature from the point at which the crystals first begin to liquefy to the point at which the entire sample is liquid. Most pure organic compounds melt over a narrow temperature range of 1–2 °C.

The presence of a soluble impurity almost always causes a decrease in the melting point expected for the pure compound and a broadening of the melting point range. In order to understand the effects of impurities on melting point behavior, consider the melting point–mass percent composition diagram for two different fictitious organic compounds, *X* and *Y*, shown in Figure 1. The vertical axis represents temperature and the horizontal axis represents varying mass percent compositions of *X* and *Y*.

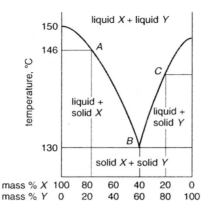

Figure 1
Melting point–mass percent composition diagram for a two-component mixture

Both compounds have sharp melting points. Compound X melts at 150 °C, as shown on the left vertical axis, and Y melts at 148 °C, as shown on the right vertical axis. As compound X is added to pure Y, the melting point of the mixture decreases along curve CB until a minimum temperature of 130 °C is reached. Point B corresponds to 40 mass percent X and 60 mass percent Y and is called the **eutectic composition** for compounds X and Y. Here, both solid X and solid Y are in equilibrium with the liquid. The **eutectic temperature** of 130 °C is the lowest possible melting point for a mixture of X and Y. At temperatures below 130 °C, mixtures of X and Y exist together only in solid form.

Consider a 100-microgram (μg) mixture composed of 20 μg of X and 80 μg of Y. In this mixture, X acts as an impurity in Y. As the mixture is heated, the temperature rises to the eutectic temperature of 130 °C. At this temperature, X and Y begin to melt together at point B, the eutectic composition of 40 mass percent X and 60 mass percent Y. The temperature remains constant at 130 °C until all 20 μg of X melts. At the eutectic temperature, X and Y will melt in the ratio of 40 parts X to 60 parts Y. If 20 μg of X melts, then 30 μg of Y (20 μg X × 60/40 ratio = 30 μg Y) also melts. At this point, the remaining 50 μg of solid Y (80 μg – 30 μg = 50 μg) is in equilibrium with a molten mixture of the eutectic composition.

As more heat is applied to the mixture, the temperature begins to rise, and the remaining Y begins to melt. Y continues to melt as the temperature increases, shown by curve BC.

Finally, at 142 °C, point C, where the liquid composition is 20 mass percent X and 80 mass percent Y, all of Y is melted. At temperatures higher than 142 °C, liquid X and liquid Y exist together with a composition of 20 mass percent X and 80 mass percent Y. Thus, the melting point at which the entire mixture liquefies is 142 °C, six degrees lower than the melting point of pure Y. Also, the melting point range 130–142 °C is quite broad.

In the previous example, X acts as an impurity in Y. Compound Y can also act as an impurity in X, as indicated in Figure 1 earlier in this experiment. For example, in a mixture composed of 80 μg of X and 20 μg of Y, the mixture begins to melt at the eutectic temperature of 130 °C. As before, at this temperature, the eutectic composition is 40 mass percent X and 60 mass percent Y. The temperature remains at 130 °C until all 20 μg of Y melts. At the eutectic temperature, X and Y will melt in the ratio of 40 parts X to 60 parts Y. Thus, if 20 μg of Y melts, 13 μg of X (20 μg $Y \times 40/60$ ratio = 13 μg X) also melts.

The remaining 67 μg of X (80 μg – 13 μg = 67 μg) melts over the range of 130 –146 °C, shown by curve BA. At 146 °C, the last traces of X melt. This melting range is larger than the range over which 20 mass percent X and 80 mass percent Y melts.

If a mixture has exactly the eutectic composition of 40 mass percent X and 60 mass percent Y, the mixture shows a sharp melting point at 130 °C. Observing this melting point could lead to the false conclusion that the mixture is a pure compound. Addition of either pure X or pure Y to the mixture causes an increase in the melting point, as indicated by curve BA or BC, respectively. Observing this melting point increase indicates that the original sample is not pure.

The initial melting that occurs at the eutectic temperature is sometimes very difficult to observe. This difficulty is especially true if only a small amount of an impurity is present, because the quantity of liquid produced at the eutectic temperature is very small. However, the temperature at which the last trace of solid melts can be accurately measured. Hence, a sample with a small amount of impurity will have an observed melting point much higher than the eutectic temperature, but lower than that of the pure compound.

Because the melting point of a compound is a physical constant, the melting point can be helpful in determining the identity of an unknown compound. A good correlation between the experimentally measured melting point of an unknown compound and the accepted melting point of a known compound suggests that the compounds may be the same. However, many different compounds have the same melting point.

A **mixture melting point** is useful in confirming the identity of an unknown compound. A small portion of a known compound, whose melting point is known from the chemical literature, is mixed with the unknown compound. If the melting point of the mixture is the same as that of the known compound, then the known and the unknown compounds are most likely identical. A decrease in the melting point of the mixture and a broadening of the melting point range indicates that the compounds are different. A flowchart for using a mixture melting point to identify an unknown compound is shown in Figure 2.

Melting points can also be used to assess compound purity. A melting point range of 5 °C or more indicates that a compound is impure. Purification of the compound causes the melting point range to narrow and the melting point to increase. Repeated purification may be necessary before the melting point range narrows to 1–2 °C and reaches its maximum value, indicating that the compound is pure.

Measuring Melting Points

In practice, measuring the melting point of a crystalline compound involves several steps. First, a finely powdered compound is packed into a melting point capillary tube to a depth of 1–2 mm. Then the capillary tube containing the sample compound is inserted into one of several devices used to measure melting points.

Figure 3(a) shows the Thiele tube apparatus, filled to the base of the neck with silicone oil or mineral oil. The capillary tube is attached to a thermometer so that the sample is located next to the middle of the

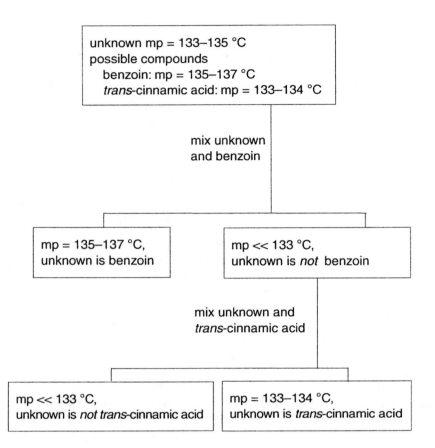

Figure 2

Flowchart for mixture melting point determination of an unknown

thermometer bulb. The thermometer is inserted into the oil and then the side arm of the Thiele tube is heated with a Bunsen burner flame.

The Thomas–Hoover Uni-Melt device, shown in Figure 3(b), contains silicone oil that is stirred and heated electrically. Silicone oil can be heated to temperatures up to 250 °C. With this device, up to seven samples can be analyzed at one time.

The Mel-Temp apparatus, shown in Figure 3(c) consists of an aluminum block that is heated electrically. The aluminum block can be heated easily to temperatures up to 400 °C, and can tolerate temperatures up to 500 °C for brief time periods. A thermometer and up to three samples can be inserted into the block at one time. A light and magnifier permit easy viewing of the sample(s).

If the melting point of the compound is unknown, it is convenient to first measure the approximate melting point of the compound, called the **orientation melting point.** The sample is heated at a rate of 10–15 °C per minute until it melts. Then the melting point apparatus is cooled to approximately 15 °C below the orientation melting point. A new sample is heated, increasing the temperature at a much slower rate of 1–2 °C per minute, to accurately measure the melting point. A slow heating rate is necessary because heating a sample too rapidly may cause the thermometer reading to differ from the actual temperature of the heat source. The

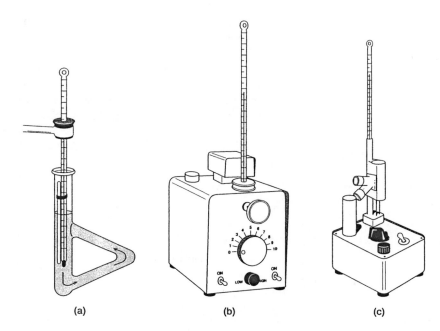

Figure 3
Different types of melting point apparatus: (a) Thiele tube; (b) Thomas–Hoover; (c) Mel-Temp

(a)   (b)   (c)

result would be an observed temperature reading that differs from the actual melting point temperature.

If the melting point of the sample is known, the sample can be quickly heated to within 10–15 °C of its melting point. Then the heating rate can be slowed to increase 1–2 °C per minute until the sample melts.

Errors in observed melting points often occur due to a poor heat transfer rate from the heat source to the compound. One cause of a poor heat transfer rate is the placement of too much sample into the capillary tube. Finely ground particles of the compound are also necessary for good heat transfer. If the particles are too coarse, they do not pack well, causing air pockets that slow heat transfer.

Sometimes slight changes, such as shrinking and sagging, occur in the crystalline structure of the sample before melting occurs. Also, traces of solvent may be present due to insufficient drying and may appear as droplets on the outside surface of the sample. This phenomenon is called **sweating** and should not be mistaken for melting. The initial melting point temperature always corresponds to the first appearance of liquid within the bulk of the sample itself.

Some compounds decompose at or near their melting points. This decomposition is usually characterized by a darkening in the color of the compound as it melts. If the decomposition and melting occur over a narrow temperature range of 1–2 °C, the melting point is used for identification and as an indication of sample purity. The melting point of such a compound is listed in the literature accompanied by *d* or *decomp.* If the sample melts over a large temperature range with decomposition, the data cannot be used for identification purposes.

Some compounds pass directly from solid to vapor without going through the liquid phase, a behavior called **sublimation.** When sublimation occurs, the sample at the bottom of the capillary tube vaporizes and recrystallizes higher up in the capillary tube. A sealed capillary tube is used to take the melting point of a compound that sublimes at or below its melting point. The literature reports the melting point for these compounds accompanied by *s, sub,* or *subl.*

In this experiment you will measure the melting points of benzoic acid, mandelic acid, and mixtures of these two compounds. Both compounds melt near 122 °C. You will use these data to construct a melting point–mass percent composition diagram. From this diagram, you will estimate the eutectic temperature and eutectic composition for benzoic acid and mandelic acid. Finally, using the mixture melting point method, you will identify an unknown compound.

Measuring the Melting Points of Compounds and Mixtures

Equipment

graph paper	metric ruler (mm)
marking pen	microspatula
melting point capillary tubes	2 watch glasses

Reagents and Properties

Substance	Quantity	Molar mass (g/mol)	mp (°C)	bp(°C)
benzoic acid	10 mg	122.12	122–123	249
mandelic acid	10 mg	152.15	120–122	

Preview

- Measure the melting point of benzoic acid
- Measure the melting point of mandelic acid
- Measure the melting point range of four mixtures containing various amounts of benzoic acid and mandelic acid
- Obtain a sample of an unknown compound
- Measure an orientation melting point and an accurate melting point of your unknown compound
- Obtain a sample of each of two substances appearing in Table 1 that have melting points similar to your unknown
- Prepare a mixture of your unknown compound and each of your selected compounds
- Measure the melting point of each mixture
- Identify your unknown compound

PROCEDURE

Wear departmentally approved safety goggles at all times while in the chemistry laboratory.

Always use caution in the laboratory. Many chemicals are potentially harmful. Prevent contact with your eyes, skin, and clothing. Avoid ingesting any of the reagents.

1. Measuring Melting Points of Benzoic Acid and Mandelic Acid

CAUTION

Benzoic acid is an irritant.

Place 2–3 mg of benzoic acid on a clean, dry watch glass. If the compound is not a fine powder, pulverize it using a microspatula.

CAUTION

Capillary tubes are fragile and easily broken.

Load a melting point capillary tube by pressing the open end of the tube into the powder. Pack the powder into the closed end of the tube by tapping the closed end against the bench top. Repeat the cycle of loading and packing until you can see 1–2 mm of benzoic acid through the tube.

NOTE: Make certain that no more than 1–2 mm of compound is placed in the capillary tube. A larger amount will give a melting point range that is too large.

To ensure good packing, drop the capillary tube with the open end up through a 1-m-long piece of glass tubing onto the bench top. Repeat several times. Place the capillary tube in the melting point apparatus provided by your laboratory instructor.

Because pure benzoic acid melts at 122–123 °C, heat the capillary tube rapidly to 110 °C. Then slow the heating rate to 1–2 °C per min. Record the temperature at which liquid first appears in the bulk of the sample and the temperature at which the entire sample becomes liquid.

NOTE: Heating the capillary tube too quickly near the melting point will result in an inaccurate melting point measurement.

CAUTION

The capillary tubes are hot. Allow them to cool enough to avoid burning your fingers.

When finished, remove the capillary tube. Place all used capillary tubes in the container labeled "Discarded Capillary Tubes", provided by your laboratory instructor.

Obtain 2–3 mg of mandelic acid and measure the melting point following the procedure described for benzoic acid. Pure mandelic acid melts at 120–122 °C.

2. Determining the Eutectic Temperature and Composition of a Benzoic Acid–Mandelic Acid Mixture

From your laboratory instructor, obtain four benzoic acid–mandelic acid mixtures of the following compositions:

	Percent benzoic acid	Percent mandelic acid
mixture 1	80	20
mixture 2	60	40
mixture 3	40	60
mixture 4	20	80

Using a marking pen, carefully label a capillary tube for each mixture. For example, near the top of the tube, mark the tube that will contain mixture 1 with one horizontal line. Similarly, mark the tubes for mixtures 2–4 with two, three, and four lines, respectively. Load each mixture into its capillary tube as previously described.

Place the capillaries containing mixtures 1 and 2 into the melting point apparatus. Heat the samples rapidly to 80 °C. Then slow the rate of increase to 1–2 °C per min. *Carefully* observe and record the temperature at which the crystals first begin to melt and the temperature at which the last trace of crystals melts.

NOTE: If you are using a Thiele tube, place the samples to the left and right of the thermometer bulb. Secure them in place with a small ring of rubber tubing, as shown in Figure 4. Make certain the bottom of the capillary tube is positioned vertically near the midpoint of the thermometer bulb. Also, be certain the rubber tubing and pen marks are 2–3 cm above the oil surface because the oil expands when heated.

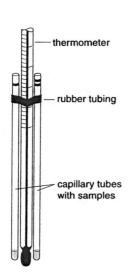

Figure 4
Attachment of two capillary tubes to a thermometer

NOTE: If you are using a Mel-Temp apparatus, you will need to lift the samples a few millimeters above the base and slowly rotate the samples to see the last trace of crystals melt. Be careful not to break the capillary tubes.

Allow the apparatus to cool to 80 °C and repeat the melting point measurements, using the capillaries containing mixtures 3 and 4.

3. Identifying an Unknown Compound by Mixture Melting Point

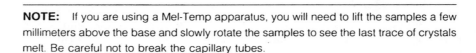

Unknowns may be flammable, toxic, and irritating.

Obtain 10 mg of an unknown compound from your laboratory instructor and record its identification code. Pulverize the sample, label and load a capillary tube, and take an orientation melting point. Cool the apparatus to 15 °C below its orientation melting point. Prepare a new sample, and accurately measure the melting point.

From Table 1 (on the next page), identify the two compounds that have melting points closest to the melting point of your unknown compound. Obtain a few milligrams of each of these compounds. Place one known compound on a clean, dry, labeled watch glass. Add an approximately equal amount of your unknown compound.

Table 1 *Melting points of compounds used as unknowns*

Compound	mp (°C)	Compound	mp(°C)
benzhydrol	65–67	*trans*-cinnamic acid	133–134
biphenyl	69–72	benzoin	135–137
phenanthrene	99–101	benzilic acid	150–153
o-toluic acid	103–105	adipic acid	152–154
acetanilide	113–115	benzanilide	164–166
fluorene	114–116	4-bromoacetanilide	167–169
(*R,S*)-mandelic acid	120–122	4-hydroxybenzoic acid	215–217
benzoic acid	122–123	anthracene	216–218

Similarly, place the other known compound on a second watch glass and add an approximately equal amount of your unknown. Pulverize and mix each sample thoroughly, using a clean microspatula each time. Load the samples into separate, labeled capillary tubes. Also, load two capillary tubes with pure unknown.

Take the melting point of one of the mixtures and the pure unknown *simultaneously*. Quickly heat the samples to within 30 °C of the pure compound's melting point. Then slow the heating rate increase to 1–2 °C per min.

Repeat the procedure using the other mixture. Compare your data and identify your unknown.

4. Cleaning Up

Use the labeled collection containers provided by your laboratory instructor. Wash your glassware with soap or detergent.

CAUTION

Wash your hands thoroughly with soap or detergent before leaving the laboratory.

name   _section_   _date_

Post-Laboratory Questions

1. Using the data from Parts 1 and 2 of the Procedure, plot on graph paper the _upper temperatures_ of the melting point ranges for benzoic acid and mandelic acid on the left and right vertical axes, respectively, as was done in Figure 1 for compounds _X_ and _Y_. Plot the _upper temperatures_ of the melting point ranges of the four mixtures on the same graph, using the proper mass percent of each compound on the horizontal axis. Use a temperature range of 80–130 °C on the vertical axis. From the graph, determine the approximate eutectic temperature and eutectic composition of a benzoic acid–mandelic acid mixture.

NOTE: Draw straight lines through the points, one straight line through the points for benzoic acid, mixture 1, and mixture 2; another straight line through the points for mandelic acid, mixture 3, and mixture 4. Do not attempt to curve lines as shown in Figure 1.

---

2. Using the melting point–mass percent composition diagram you drew for Question 1, identify the approximate melting point ranges for benzoic acid–mandelic acid mixtures of the following compositions.

   (a) 90:10

   (b) 70:30

   (c) 30:70

   (d) 10:90

3. Describe in detail the melting point behavior of the 80:20 benzoic acid–mandelic acid mixture.

4. Devise a flowchart similar to the one in Figure 2 to show how you identified your unknown.

5. Using your textbook or another appropriate resource, find the structural formula for your unknown. Make a drawing of the formula.

6. Briefly explain why you were told to simultaneously measure the melting points of the mixtures and of the pure unknown in Part 3 of the Procedure.

_____   _____   _____

Pre-Laboratory Assignment

1. Briefly identify or explain

(a) two useful functions served by knowing the melting point of an organic compound.

(b) why a finely powdered sample should be used in a melting point measurement.

(c) why it is important to heat a sample slowly to obtain an accurate melting point.

(d) two reasons why it is sometimes difficult to measure the temperature at which the crystals first begin to liquefy.

(e) what two effects a soluble impurity usually has on the melting point of a compound.

(f) what occurred when crystals began to disappear from the bottom of the capillary tube rather than turning to a liquid.

2. A sample has an experimental melting point of 100–101 °C. Can you conclude that the sample is pure? Briefly explain your reasoning.

3. Using Figure 1, explain in detail the melting point behavior of a mixture composed of 60 mass percent X and 40 mass percent Y.

4. An unknown compound melted at 131–133 °C. It is thought to be one of the following compounds (mp, °C): *trans*-cinnamic acid (133–134); benzamide (128–130); DL-malic acid (131–133); or benzoin (135–137). The mixture melting points of the unknown compound with each of the test compounds are listed below. What is the unknown compound? Briefly explain your reasoning.

Unknown plus	mp range (°C)
trans-cinnamic acid	110–120
benzamide	130–132
DL-malic acid	114–124
benzoin	108–116

5. Using your textbook or another appropriate resource, find the structural formula for benzoic acid and mandelic acid. Draw the structural formulas of these compounds.

Separating Cyclohexane and Toluene by Distillation

Prepared by Jerry Manion, University of Central Arkansas

PURPOSE OF THE EXPERIMENT

Separate two miscible liquids, either by macroscale or microscale process, using simple and fractional distillation. Compare the efficiencies of simple and fractional distillation.

EXPERIMENTAL OPTIONS

Macroscale Distillation
Microscale Distillations

A. Using Glassware with Elastomeric Connectors

B. Using the Hickman Still

C. Using Test Tube Reflux

BACKGROUND REQUIRED

You should be familiar with basic laboratory techniques for measuring volumes of chemical compounds. You should know how to prepare a bent-tip Pasteur pipet for microscale distillations. You should know how to use a refractometer to measure refractive index.

BACKGROUND INFORMATION

Distillation is a technique widely used in organic chemistry for separating compounds based on differences in their boiling points. Many organic compounds are **volatile**; that is, they have relatively high vapor pressures and low boiling points. During distillation, such volatile compounds are heated to boiling in one container, called the **pot**. The vapors produced are then cooled and reliquefied by passing them through a water-cooled **condenser**, and collected in a separate container, called the **receiver**. This

CENGAGE Learning

technique can be used to remove a volatile solvent from a nonvolatile product; to separate a volatile product from nonvolatile impurities; or to separate two or more volatile products that have sufficiently different boiling points.

When a liquid is placed in a closed container, some of the molecules evaporate into any unoccupied space in the container. **Evaporation**, which occurs at temperatures below the boiling point of a compound, involves the transition from liquid to vapor of *only* those molecules at the liquid surface. Evaporation continues until an equilibrium is reached between molecules entering and leaving the liquid and vapor states. The pressure exerted by these gaseous molecules on the walls of the container is the **equilibrium vapor pressure**. The magnitude of this vapor pressure depends on the physical characteristics of the compound and increases as temperature increases.

If the liquid is heated to its boiling point, quite a different phenomenon occurs. The **boiling point** is the temperature at which the vapor pressure of the liquid is equal to the external pressure applied to the surface of the liquid. This external pressure is commonly atmospheric pressure. At the boiling point, bubbles of vapor are produced throughout the liquid, and the vapor pressure inside the bubbles is sufficiently high to allow them to grow in size. The escape of these bubbles results in the characteristic chaotic motion of the liquid identified as **boiling**.

Liquid is converted to vapor more rapidly by boiling than by evaporation. If the heating rate is increased, the temperature of the boiling liquid does not change, but the rate at which vapor is produced from the liquid increases. This increase occurs because the energy that is supplied by the increased heating rate is absorbed as more liquid molecules overcome intermolecular interactions and enter the vapor phase.

When a mixture of two or more volatile compounds is heated, the vapor pressure of the mixture equals the sum of the vapor pressures of each compound in the mixture. The magnitude of the vapor pressure exerted by each compound is determined by the vapor pressure of that compound (P^0) and the mole fraction of that compound present in the mixture (X). For an ideal two-compound solution, the solution vapor pressure is expressed by Raoul's law, shown in Equation 1.

$$P_T = X_1 P_1^{\,0} + X_2 P_2^{\,0} \qquad\qquad \text{(Eq. 1)}$$

In this equation, P_T is the total vapor pressure of the solution, $P_1^{\,0}$ is the vapor pressure of pure compound 1, X_1 is the mole fraction of compound 1, $P_2^{\,0}$ is the vapor pressure of pure compound 2, and X_2 is the mole fraction of compound 2.

When two liquids form a homogeneous solution, they are said to be **miscible**. Such a homogeneous mixture will boil at a temperature between the boiling points of the pure compounds. The exact boiling point of the mixture depends upon the relative amounts of the compounds present. Figure 1 shows the relationship between boiling point and composition for a two-compound mixture of cyclohexane and toluene.

When vapor is produced from such a liquid mixture, the composition of the vapor mixture is different from the composition of the liquid mixture from which it forms, as shown in Figure 2. The vapor contains a larger percent of the more volatile compound of the mixture, in this case cyclohexane. For example, a liquid composed of 50 percent cyclohexane

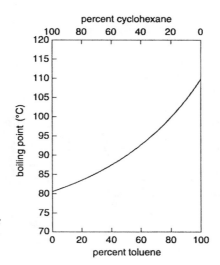

Figure 1
The boiling point of a miscible mixture is between the boiling points of the pure compounds

and 50 percent toluene would boil at 90 °C and yield a vapor composed of 70 percent cyclohexane and 30 percent toluene.

This composition change that accompanies the vaporization process is the basis for the separation of mixtures by distillation. As the vapors produced by the distillation move into the water-cooled condenser, these vapors condense to a liquid, the **distillate**, which has the same composition as the vapor from which it is formed. The distillate collected in the receiver will contain more of the more volatile compound than was present in the original mixture.

If one compound is much more volatile than the other, the compounds can be separated in one vaporization step. Such a step is called **simple distillation** and uses an apparatus that consists of only a pot, a distilling head, a condenser, an adapter, and a receiver, as shown in Figure 3.

When the boiling points of two compounds differ by less than 40 °C, they cannot be separated by simple distillation. **Fractional distillation**, a process that has the effect of many simple distillations, must be used. A fractional distillation apparatus includes a fractionating column placed

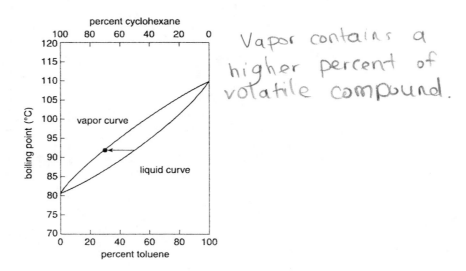

Vapor contains a higher percent of volatile compound.

Figure 2
Vaporizing a mixture of cyclohexane and toluene produces a vapor that is enriched in cyclohexane

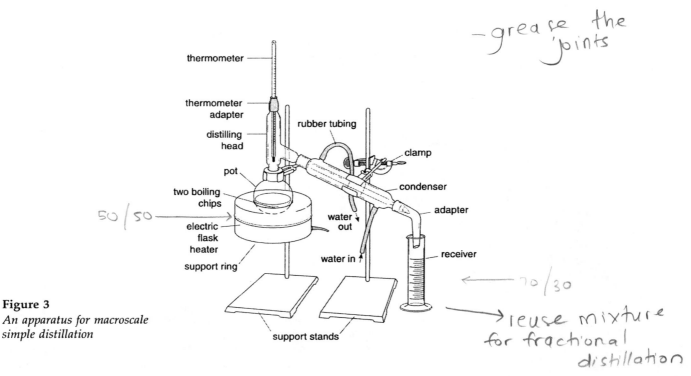

-grease the joints

50/50

70/30

→ reuse mixture for fractional distillation

Figure 3

An apparatus for macroscale simple distillation

25ml water and ethanol each

between the pot and the distilling head, as shown in Figure 4. Typically, any one of a variety of materials, including glass beads and metal sponge, fill the fractionating column.

The vapors generated in the pot rise up the fractionating column and encounter cooler surfaces, upon which they condense. The condensed liquid is then reheated by rising hot vapors and revaporizes. This process

-record every 2mL
- distill at 1drop/2-3 seconds

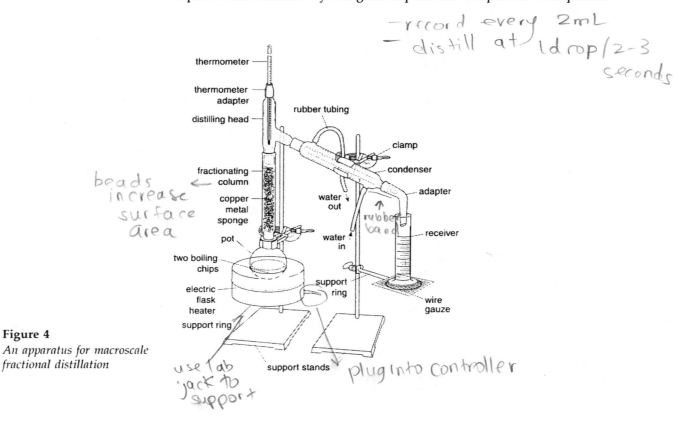

beads increase surface area

rubber band

Figure 4

An apparatus for macroscale fractional distillation

use lab jack to support

plug into controller

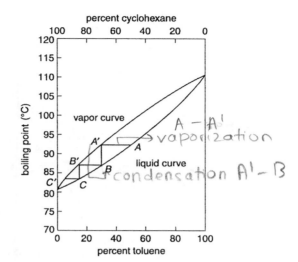

Figure 5

Each condensation and revaporization increases the concentration of the more volatile compound

of condensation and revaporization, shown graphically in Figure 5, may occur again and again as the vapors rise up the column.

Each vaporization is represented by a horizontal line connecting the liquid composition curve to the vapor composition curve. Each condensation is represented by a vertical line connecting the vapor curve to the liquid curve. For example, the 50:50 liquid mixture (*A*) vaporizes to produce a 30:70 vapor mixture (*A'*). The 30:70 vapor mixture condenses to a 30:70 liquid mixture (*B*). The 30:70 liquid mixture, in turn, vaporizes to produce a 15™:85 vapor mixture (*B'*), and so on. Each condensation–revaporization results in an increase in the concentration of the more volatile compound. These composition changes are reflected by a *decrease* in boiling temperature as the mixture moves up the fractionating column. If the condensation–revaporization is repeated a sufficient number of times, the vapors of the more volatile compound reach the top of the fractionating column in a pure form. As these vapors move into the condenser, the compound condenses and is collected as a liquid.

At the same time, the less volatile compound is enriched in the opposite direction. As the condensed liquid falls toward the pot, the pot gradually contains a higher and higher percent of the less volatile compound. Thus, a separation of the two compounds is achieved.

Each condensation and revaporization that occurs on a fractionating column is called a **theoretical plate**. A fractionating column with a large number of theoretical plates accomplishes many condensation–revaporization steps and very efficiently separates the compounds in a mixture.

The fractionating column must be positioned vertically so that condensed liquid can percolate down through the rising hot vapors. This percolation promotes equilibrium between the liquid and vapor phases, a condition that allows the column to operate at maximum efficiency and provide an optimum separation.

An equally important factor affecting separation of the compounds is the distillation rate. If the distillation is conducted too rapidly, liquid–vapor equilibria will not be established in the fractionating column, and poor separation of the compounds will result.

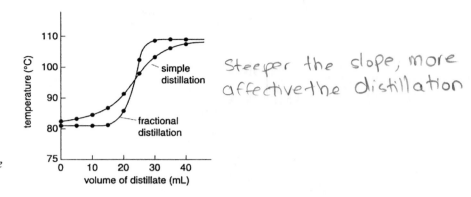

Steeper the slope, more affective the distillation

Figure 6
Distillation curves for simple and fractional distillation

simple: more than 40°C apart
fractional: less than 40°C apart

As the liquid boils, a **condensation line** of vapor can be observed as it moves up the distilling head. Once these vapors reach the thermometer bulb, a dramatic temperature increase is observed. The temperature of the vapors in the distilling head provides information regarding the progress of the distillation. Initially, the vapors are rich in the more volatile compound, and the observed temperature is close to the boiling point of that compound. In a distillation with an efficient separation, the initial temperature remains relatively constant until all of that compound is collected. After the compound with the lower boiling point is completely distilled, the temperature rises sharply as the vapors of the higher-boiling compound reach the thermometer bulb. At this time, the boiling point of the higher-boiling compound is observed as it distills into the receiver.

When no fractionating column is used, or when the fractionating column is inefficient, mixtures of the distilled compounds are incompletely separated. This inefficiency is indicated by a very gradual increase in the temperature measured during the distillation. Samples collected at temperatures between the boiling points of the two compounds will consist of mixtures of the two compounds. A comparison of the results of simple and fractional distillation is shown in Figure 6.

Microscale Distillation

Distillation is a difficult organic laboratory technique to use when separating microscale volumes, because significant amounts of distillate are commonly left adhering to the glass surfaces of the apparatus. However, specialized equipment has been designed to permit the simple distillation of volumes less than one milliliter. One such apparatus, the Hickman still, is shown in Figure 10 later in this module. Another apparatus for microscale distillations uses special glassware with elastomeric connectors, as shown in Figure 8 later in this module. Microscale distillations may also be conducted in a test tube using a Pasteur pipet as a condenser and receiver.

Microscale distillations are especially useful when small volumes of a liquid must be purified for spectral or refractive index analyses. The relative amounts of cyclohexane and toluene present in a sample may be determined by measuring the refractive index of the sample. Figure 7 shows a graph that correlates the refractive index of mixtures of cyclohexane and toluene with their composition.

Refractive index measurements are typically reported at 20 °C. A refractive index measured at a temperature higher or lower than 20 °C must

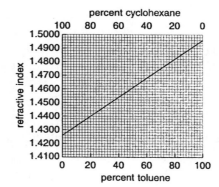

Figure 7
A correlation curve relating refractive index to the composition of cyclohexane–toluene mixtures

be corrected to 20 °C. To make this correction, Equation 2 is used, where n^{20} is the refractive index at 20 °C, n^T is the refractive index at the measured temperature, and T is the measured temperature.

$$n^{20} = n^T + 0.00045(T - 20 \text{ °C}) \qquad \text{(Eq. 2)}$$

For example, if the refractive index of a cyclohexane–toluene mixture is measured as 1.4752 at 26 °C, then the refractive index at 20 °C can be calculated:

$$n^{20} = 1.4752 + 0.00045(26 - 20 \text{ °C}) = 1.4779$$

Locating the point on the graph in Figure 7 corresponding to $n^{20} = 1.4779$ indicates that the sample contains 74 percent toluene and 26 percent cyclohexane.

Macroscale Distillation

Equipment

aluminum foil	2 support rings
boiling chips	2 support stands
copper metal sponge*	2 utility clamps
electric flask heater, with regulator	wire gauze, ceramic center*
50-mL graduated cylinder	
standard taper glassware:	

    condenser, with adapter and rubber tubing
    distilling head
    fractionating column*
    100-mL round-bottom flask
    −10 to 260 °C thermometer, with adapter†

*for fractional distillation
†adapter may be required to hold thermometer in place

Reagents and Properties

Substance	Quantity (mL)	mol mass (g/mol)	bp (°C)
cyclohexane	25	84.16	80.7
toluene	25	92.14	110.6

Preview

- Assemble macroscale simple distillation apparatus
- Place cyclohexane–toluene mixture in pot
- Distill the mixture, recording the temperature at 5-mL intervals
- Assemble macroscale fractional distillation apparatus and repeat as for simple distillation

PROCEDURE

General Considerations

CAUTION

Wear departmentally approved safety goggles at all times while in the chemistry laboratory.

Always use caution in the laboratory. Many chemicals are potentially harmful. Prevent contact with your eyes, skin, and clothing. Avoid ingesting any of the reagents.

Exercise care when assembling a distillation apparatus. Support the flask heater with a support ring attached to a support stand so that the heater can be quickly lowered away from the apparatus, if necessary.

Use a utility clamp to attach the neck of the pot to the support stand to support the apparatus in the event you remove the flask heater. Support the condenser with a second clamp and support stand.

Carefully adjust the angle of the clamp supporting the condenser. Lubricate the joints by using your finger to apply stopcock grease lightly along the interior joint section. Rotate the joint after connection to distribute the grease uniformly. Check the joints immediately before beginning the distillation, and reconnect any joints that are loose.

Select a pot size so that the pot is one-half to two-thirds full of liquid. Add two boiling chips to the pot.

NOTE: Overfilling the pot can result in bumping or foaming of material into the receiver. Boiling chips provide a surface on which vapor bubbles can form. This bubble formation helps prevent superheating and bumping of the liquid.

Insert the thermometer into a thermometer adapter so that the top of the thermometer bulb is even with or slightly below the bottom of the side arm on the distilling head, as shown in Figure 3 earlier in this module.

NOTE: Carefully positioning the thermometer ensures that the bulb is submerged in any vapors that pass through the distilling head and that the vapor temperature is measured accurately.

Use rubber tubing to attach the condenser to a water tap and to discharge water from the condenser to the drain.

NOTE: Water should enter the condenser at the bottom and exit from the top so that no air remains in the cooling jacket. A moderate flow of water is sufficient for cooling.

Place the end of the adapter inside the receiver to minimize the release of vapors into the room.

CAUTION

Heating a closed apparatus can cause the apparatus to rupture. Make certain the distillation apparatus has an opening to the atmosphere. *Do not heat a closed container.*

Discontinue the distillation before all of the liquid is gone from the pot. Some organic compounds explode when heated to dryness. *Do not distill to dryness.*

1. Conducting Simple Distillation

CAUTION

Cyclohexane is flammable and irritating. Toluene is flammable and toxic. If possible, use a *fume hood*.

Do not add boiling chips to a hot liquid. The large surface area of the boiling chip can cause the hot liquid to foam out of the apparatus and cause burns.

Assemble the simple distillation apparatus shown in Figure 3 earlier in this module, using a 100-mL round-bottom flask for the pot and a 50-mL graduated cylinder for the receiver. Place two boiling chips and 25 mL each of cyclohexane and toluene into the pot, taking care not to spill any chemicals onto the flask heater. Start the flow of water through the condenser. Check the apparatus and reconnect any joints that are loose.

Heat the mixture to boiling. Adjust the heater to produce distillate at a rate that is no greater than one drop per s. Record the temperature when you collect the first drop of distillate and again after every 5 mL of distillate you collect. Continue the distillation until the temperature reaches 110 °C or until fewer than 5 mL of liquid remains in the pot.

NOTE: As the liquid boils, watch for the condensation line of vapor as it moves up the distilling head. To observe and record an accurate temperature reading, the *entire thermometer bulb* must be immersed in vapor.

Turn off the heater and lower it away from the pot. Allow the pot to cool for a few minutes. Then turn off the water to the condenser.

CAUTION

2. Conducting Fractional Distillation

2 mL   73°

4 mL   76°

6 mL   78°

8 mL   80°

10 mL   80°

12 mL   80°

14 mL   80°

16 mL   80°

18 mL   80°

20 mL 80°

22 mL 81°

24 mL 83°

26 mL 85°

28 mL 87°

30 mL

3. Cleaning Up

CAUTION

Cyclohexane is flammable and irritating. Toluene is flammable and toxic. If possible, use a *fume hood*.

Do not add boiling chips to a hot liquid. The large surface area of the boiling chip can cause the hot liquid to foam out of the apparatus and cause burns.

Assemble the fractional distillation apparatus shown in Figure 4 earlier in this module, using a 100-mL round-bottom flask for the pot and a 50-mL graduated cylinder for the receiver. Pack the fractionating column with copper metal sponge, as directed by your laboratory instructor.

NOTE: Be careful to position the fractionating column vertically to promote mixing of the liquid and vapor phases. The fractionating column looks much like a condenser, but has indentations in the inner jacket to support the column packing. Be careful; these indentations are easily broken. The outer jacket insulates against heat loss from the inner jacket during distillation. *Do not pass water through the fractionating column.*

Place two boiling chips and 25 mL each of cyclohexane and toluene into the pot. Start the water flow through the condenser. Check the apparatus and reconnect any joints that are loose.

Heat the mixture in the pot to boiling. Observe the condensation line as it moves up the fractionating column.

When the vapors reach the top of the column packing, reduce the heating rate so the vapor condensation line remains just above the column packing and below the side arm of the distilling head. Maintain the vapor condensation line in this position for 5 min to allow the vapor and liquid in the column to reach equilibrium.

Wrap the fractionating column and distilling head with aluminum foil to minimize the temperature fluctuations during the distillation. Then adjust the heating rate to produce distillate at a rate no greater than 1 drop per s.

Record the temperature when you collect the first drop of distillate and again after every 5 mL of distillate you collect. Continue the distillation until the temperature reaches 110 °C or until fewer than 5 mL of liquid remains in the pot.

Turn off the heater and lower it from the pot. Allow the pot to cool for a few minutes. Then turn off the water to the condenser.

Use the labeled collection containers provided by your laboratory instructor. Clean your glassware with soap or detergent.

CAUTION

Wash your hands thoroughly with soap or detergent before leaving the laboratory.

MICROSCALE DISTILLATIONS

A. Using Glassware with Elastomeric Connectors

Equipment

aluminum foil	microspatula
100-mL beaker	2 receiver vials, 5-mL,
boiling chips	with screw caps
copper metal sponge*	sand bath[†]
glassware with elastomeric	2 support rings
connectors	support stand
5-mL boiling flask	−10 to 260 °C thermometer,
distilling head with	with adapter
air condenser	2 utility clamps
distilling column*	wire gauze, ceramic center

*for fractional distillation
[†]sand in crystallizing dish on electric hot plate or sand in electric heating well with heat controller

Reagents and Properties

Substance	Quantity (mL)	mol mass (g/mol)	bp (°C)
cyclohexane	1.5	84.16	80.7
toluene	1.5	92.14	110.6

Preview

- Assemble microscale simple distillation apparatus
- Place cyclohexane-toluene mixture in pot
- Distill the mixture
- Collect the distillate, recording the temperature as a function of the number of drops
- Assemble microscale fractional distillation apparatus and repeat as for simple distillation

PROCEDURE

CAUTION

Wear departmentally approved safety goggles at all times while in the chemistry laboratory.

Always use caution in the laboratory. Many chemicals are potentially harmful. Prevent contact with your eyes, skin, and clothing. Avoid ingesting any of the reagents.

General Considerations

Exercise care when assembling a distillation apparatus. Support the flask heater with a support ring attached to a support stand so that the heater can be quickly lowered away from the apparatus, if necessary.

Use a utility clamp to attach the neck of the pot to the support stand to support the apparatus in the event you remove the flask heater.

Select a pot size so that the pot is one-half to two-thirds full of liquid. Add a boiling chip to the pot.

NOTE: Overfilling the pot can result in bumping or foaming of material into the receiver. A boiling chip provides a surface on which vapor bubbles can form. This bubble formation helps prevent superheating and bumping of the liquid.

Insert the thermometer into a thermometer adapter so that the top of the thermometer bulb is even with or slightly below the bottom of the side arm on the distilling head-condenser, as shown in Figure 8.

NOTE: Carefully positioning the thermometer ensures that the bulb is submerged in any vapors that pass through the distilling head and that the vapor temperature is measured accurately.

Place the end of the distilling head-condenser side arm inside the receiver to minimize the release of vapors into the room. Support the ice-filled beaker with wire gauze on a support ring.

CAUTION ⚠

Heating a closed apparatus can cause the apparatus to ruptur. Make certain the distillation apparatus has an opening to the atmosphere. *Do not heat a closed container.*

Discontinue the distillation before all of the liquid is gone from the pot. Some organic compounds explode when heated to dryness. *Do not distill to dryness.*

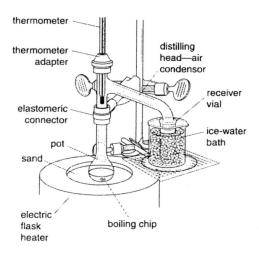

Figure 8

An apparatus using elastomeric connectors for microscale simple distillation

1. Conducting Simple Distillation

CAUTION

Cyclohexane is flammable and irritating. Toluene is flammable and toxic. If possible, use a *fume hood*.

Assemble the simple distillation apparatus as shown in Figure 8, using a 5-mL boiling flask for the pot and a 5-mL vial for the receiver. Place a boiling chip and 1.5 mL each of cyclohexane and toluene into the pot.

Position the thermometer bulb below the side arm of the distilling head–condenser, and place the end of the air condenser as deeply as possible into the receiver. Place the receiver into a 100-mL beaker and surround the receiver with ice. Check the apparatus and reconnect any joints that are loose.

Heat the mixture to boiling. Adjust the heating rate by using a spatula to move the hot sand either around or away from the pot. Control the heating rate to produce distillate at a rate of about 2–4 drops per min.

NOTE: As the liquid boils, watch for the condensation line of vapor as it moves up the distilling head. To observe and record an accurate temperature reading, the *entire thermometer bulb* must be immersed in vapor.

Read and record the temperature when you collect the first drop of distillate and again after every 5 drops of distillate you collect. Continue the distillation until the temperature remains constant at 110 °C or until the pot is almost dry. Discontinue the heating before all of the mixture distills and the pot becomes completely dry. Lower the heater away from the pot.

2. Conducting Fractional Distillation

CAUTION

Cyclohexane is flammable and irritating. Toluene is flammable and toxic. If possible, use a *fume hood*.

Assemble the fractional distillation apparatus shown in Figure 9, using a 5-mL boiling flask for the pot and a 5-mL vial for the receiver. Place a boiling chip and 1.5 mL each of cyclohexane and toluene into the pot. Tightly pack the fractionating column with copper metal sponge.

Position the thermometer bulb below the side arm of the distilling head–condenser, and place the end of the air condenser as deeply as possible into the receiver. Place the receiver into a 100-mL beaker and surround the receiver with ice. Check the apparatus and reconnect any joints that are loose.

Heat the mixture to boiling. Observe the condensation line as it moves up the fractionating column. When the vapors reach the top of the column packing, reduce the heating rate so the vapor condensation line remains just above the column packing and below the side arm of the distilling head. Maintain the vapor condensation line in this position for about 5 min to allow the vapor and liquid in the column to reach equilibrium.

Wrap the fractionating column and distilling head with aluminum foil to minimize the temperature fluctuations during the distillation. Then adjust the heating rate to produce distillate at a rate of about 2–4 drops per min.

Read and record the temperature when you collect the first drop of distillate and again after every 5 drops of distillate you collect. Continue the distillation until the temperature remains constant at 110 °C or until the

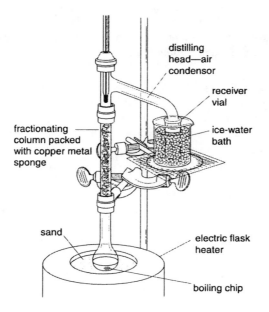

Figure 9
An apparatus using elastomeric connectors for microscale fractional distillation

pot is almost dry. Discontinue the heating before the boiling flask becomes completely dry, and lower the heater away from the pot.

3. Cleaning Up   Use the labeled collection containers provided by your laboratory instructor. Clean your glassware with soap or detergent.

> **CAUTION**
>
> **Wash your hands thoroughly with soap or detergent before leaving the laboratory.**

MICROSCALE DISTILLATIONS

B. Using the Hickman Still   *Equipment*

boiling chips	support stand
2 conical vials, 3-mL	−10 to 150 °C thermometer, small size to fit Hickman still
Hickman still	
magnetic spinning band*	−10 to 260 °C thermometer, for sand bath
microburner	
microspatula	tongs
3 Pasteur pipets, with latex bulb	3 utility clamps
sand bath†	6 vials, 2-mL, with screw caps

*for fractional distillation
†sand in crystallizing dish on electric hot plate or sand in electric heating well with heat controller

Reagents and Properties

Substance	Quantity (mL)	mol mass (g/mol)	bp (°C)
cyclohexane	1.0	84.16	80.7
toluene	1.0	92.14	110.6

Preview

- Prepare a bent-tip Pasteur pipet
- Assemble Hickman apparatus and add cyclohexane–toluene mixture
- Conduct the distillation, collecting samples from 80–90 °C, 90–100 °C, and 100–110 °C
- Repeat the Procedure using a Teflon spinning band for fractional distillation
- Determine the percent composition of the samples, using refractive index

PROCEDURE

CAUTION

Wear departmentally approved safety goggles at all times while in the chemistry laboratory.

Always use caution in the laboratory. Many chemicals are potentially harmful. Prevent contact with your eyes, skin, and clothing. Avoid ingesting any of the reagents.

CAUTION

Cyclohexane is flammable and irritating. Toluene is flammable and toxic. If possible, use a *fume hood*.

1. Conducting a Simple Distillation

Prepare a bent-tip Pasteur pipet by heating the pipet in a microburner flame. Use tongs to bend the pipet to a 30° angle 1 cm from the tip.

NOTE: A standard Pasteur pipet can be used in a Hickman still model that has a built-in side port.

Transfer 1.0 mL each of cyclohexane and toluene into a 3-mL conical vial, and add a small boiling chip. Attach the Hickman still head and clamp the apparatus vertically in a sand bath, as shown in Figure 10.

Place a thermometer through the center opening of the still head so that the thermometer bulb is positioned as shown in Figure 10. Raise the sand-bath temperature to about 90 °C. Then gradually increase the sand-bath temperature at a rate of 2 °C per min. Collect the material that distills when the Hickman still thermometer registers 80–90 °C. Using a bent-tip Pasteur pipet, remove the distillate that condenses in the collar of the still head. Transfer the distillate to an appropriately labeled sample vial.

NOTE: Cyclohexane and toluene are quite volatile. Cap the vials to ensure that the small samples do not evaporate.

Collect a second sample that distills in the range 90–100 °C and a third sample in the range 100–110 °C.

2. Conducting Fractional Distillation

Transfer 1.0 mL each of cyclohexane and toluene into a 3-mL conical vial. Attach the Hickman still head containing a magnetic spinning band, and clamp the apparatus vertically in a sand bath, as shown in Figure 11.

Place a thermometer through the center opening of the still head so that the thermometer bulb is positioned, as shown in Figure 11. Raise the sand-bath temperature to 90 °C. When the mixture begins to boil, turn on the magnetic stirrer to a low setting to start the spinning band. Then gradually increase the sand-bath temperature at a rate of 2 °C per min. As the vapor enters the bottom of the still column, increase the spinning band rate to a middle range setting. Once liquid begins to collect in the collar of the still, increase the spinning band rate to the maximum setting.

Collect the material that distills when the Hickman still thermometer registers in the range 80–90 °C. Using a bent-tip Pasteur pipet, remove the distillate that condenses in the collar of the still head. Transfer the distillate to an appropriately labeled sample vial.

NOTE: Cyclohexane and toluene are quite volatile. Cap the vials to ensure that the small samples do not evaporate.

Collect a second sample that distills in the range 90–100 °C and a third that distills in the range 100–110 °C.

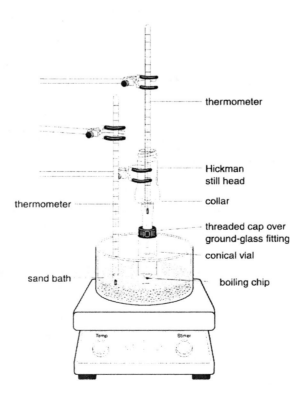

Figure 10

A Hickman still assembly for simple distillation

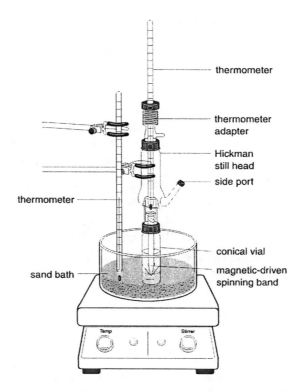

thermometer

thermometer adapter

Hickman still head

side port

thermometer

conical vial

sand bath

magnetic-driven spinning band

Figure 11
A Hickman still assembly for fractional distillation

3. Measuring Refractive Index

Using a refractometer, measure the refractive index of the compounds in each vial. Correct the refractive indices for temperature, using Equation 2.

Using the correlation curve shown in Figure 7 earlier in this experiment and the corrected refractive index for the solution in each collection vial, determine the percent of cyclohexane and toluene in each sample.

4. Cleaning Up

Use the labeled collection containers provided by your laboratory instructor. Clean your glassware with soap or detergent.

CAUTION

Wash your hands thoroughly with soap or detergent before leaving the laboratory.

MICROSCALE DISTILLATIONS

C. Using Test Tube Reflux

Equipment

boiling chips	support stand
copper metal sponge*	2 test tubes, 13 × 100-mm
microspatula	−10 to 260 °C thermometer
2 Pasteur pipets, with latex bulb	utility clamp
sand bath†	6 vials, 2-mL, with screw caps

*for fractional distillation
†sand in crystallizing dish on electric hot plate or sand in electric heating well with heat controller

Reagents and Properties

Substance	Quantity (mL)	mol mass (g/mol)	bp (°C)
cyclohexane	1.0	84.16	80.7
toluene	1.0	92.14	110.6

Preview

- Assemble apparatus and add cyclohexane–toluene mixture
- Save sample of original simple distillation mixture for analysis
- Distill approximately half of the mixture
- Transfer residue to vial
- Using refractive index, analyze the composition of the original mixture, the distillate, and the pot residue
- Repeat the Procedure for fractional distillation, using a test tube packed with copper metal sponge

PROCEDURE

CAUTION

Wear departmentally approved safety goggles at all times while in the chemistry laboratory.

Always use caution in the laboratory. Many chemicals are potentially harmful. Prevent contact with your eyes, skin, and clothing. Avoid ingesting any of the reagents.

CAUTION

Cyclohexane is flammable and irritating. Toluene is flammable and toxic. If possible, use a *fume hood*.

1. Conducting Simple Distillation

Place 1.0 mL each of cyclohexane and toluene into a 13 × 100-mm test tube. Mix well and add one small boiling chip. Using a Pasteur pipet, remove about 5 drops of the mixture, and place the drops into a small vial labeled "Original Mixture–Simple".

NOTE: Cyclohexane and toluene are volatile. Cap the vials to ensure that the small samples do not evaporate.

Clamp the test tube in a vertical position. Use a sand bath to heat the liquid until the liquid boils and the condensation line for the vapor is about 2 cm from the top of the test tube, as shown in Figure 12.

Squeeze the bulb of a Pasteur pipet, place the pipet tip into the hot vapors, and *very slowly* draw the vapors into the cool pipet, where the vapors will condense. Transfer this distillate to a small vial labeled "Distillate–Simple". Repeat the process until you collect about half of the mixture in the distillate vial.

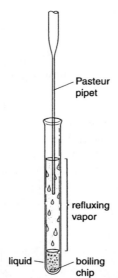

Figure 12
Simple distillation of very small samples using a test tube and a Pasteur pipet

Remove the test tube from the sand bath, allow it to cool, and transfer the remaining liquid into a vial labeled "Pot Residue–Simple".

2. Conducting Fractional Distillation

Place 1.0 mL each of cyclohexane and toluene into a 13 × 100-mm test tube, mix well, and add one small boiling chip. Using a Pasteur pipet, remove 5–10 drops of the mixture and place the drops into a small vial labeled "Original Mixture–Fractional".

Prepare a plug of copper sponge approximately 4 cm long. Tightly pack the copper plug into the test tube so that the bottom of the plug is about 1 cm above the top of the liquid and 3 cm below the mouth of the test tube, as shown in Figure 13.

Clamp the test tube in a vertical position and heat the liquid with a sand bath until the liquid boils. Observe the vapor condensation line as it moves through the copper sponge, and adjust the heat so that the condensation line reaches a point about 1 cm above the top of the copper.

Squeeze the bulb of a Pasteur pipet, place the tip into the hot vapors, and *very slowly* draw the vapors into the cool pipet, where they will

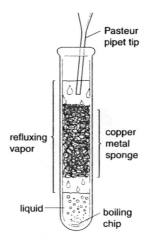

Figure 13
A test tube reflux apparatus for conducting a fractional distillation

© 2004 Cengage Learning

condense. Transfer this distillate to a small vial labeled "Distillate–Fractional", and repeat the process until you collect about half of the mixture in the distillate vial.

Remove the test tube from the sand bath. Cool the test tube, remove the copper plug, and transfer the remaining liquid into a vial labeled "Pot Residue–Fractional".

3. Measuring Refractive Index

Using a refractometer, measure the refractive index of the compounds in each vial. Correct the refractive indices for temperature, using Equation 2.

Using the correlation curve shown in Figure 7 earlier in this module and the corrected refractive index for the solution in each collection vial, determine the percent of cyclohexane and toluene in each sample. Compare your results for simple and fractional distillation.

4. Cleaning Up

Use the labeled collection containers provided by your laboratory instructor. Clean your glassware with soap or detergent.

CAUTION

Wash your hands thoroughly with soap or detergent before leaving the laboratory.

_____   _____   _____

Post-Laboratory Questions

1. For macroscale distillations, or for microscale distillations using glassware with elastomeric connectors, plot the data for simple distillation and for fractional distillation on one graph. Plot temperature on the vertical axis and total volume of distillate on the horizontal axis, as shown in Figure 6 earlier in this module. Draw a smooth curve through the data points for each distillation.

2. (a) At what temperatures were the first drop of distillate collected in the simple and fractional distillations?

   (b) Using Figure 1, estimate the composition of these initial samples of distillate. Based on the results, what conclusion can you draw regarding the relative efficiencies of the two separations?

3. For macroscale distillations, or for microscale distillations using glassware with elastomeric connectors, compare the plot from your simple distillation with that from your fractional distillation. In which case do the changes in temperature occur more gradually? Which method is more effective in achieving separation? Briefly explain.

4. For Hickman still or for test tube microscale distillations, compare the refractive index data for simple and fractional distillations. Do the data suggest which distillation procedure is more efficient? Briefly explain.

_____   _____   _____
name   *section*   *date*

Pre-Laboratory Assignment

1. Briefly explain why you should not add boiling chips to a boiling liquid.

2. (a) Briefly explain how and why you should position the thermometer in the distillation head during a distillation.

(b) What is the purpose of the outer jacket on a fractionating column?

(c) How is the rate of heating adjusted when using a sand bath as a heat source?

(d) How is the distillate collected in a test tube microscale distillation?

3. What effect does an increase in the heating rate have on the boiling temperature during a distillation?

4. As molecules move up a fractional distillation column, they condense and then revaporize. During which of these steps is the concentration of the more volatile compound of the mixture increased? Briefly explain.

5. Using Figure 2, estimate the composition of a cyclohexane-toluene distillate that is collected

   at 85 °C;

   at 95 °C;

   at 105 °C.

Purifying Acetanilide by Recrystallization

Prepared by Carl Wigal, Lebanon Valley College

PURPOSE OF THE EXPERIMENT

Select an appropriate recrystallizing solvent. Separate and purify acetanilide from a mixture by recrystallization. Compare the melting points of impure and recrystallized acetanilide.

BACKGROUND REQUIRED

You should know how to measure mass, in milligrams, and volume, in milliliters. You should know how to measure melting points.

BACKGROUND INFORMATION

Impurities often contaminate organic compounds that have been synthesized in the laboratory or isolated from natural sources. **Recrystallization** is a purification process used to remove impurities from organic compounds that are solid at room temperature. This process is based on the premise that the solubility of a compound in a solvent increases with temperature. Conversely, the solubility of the compound decreases as the solution cools, and crystals form.

Very pure compounds can be produced by recrystallization. As a heated solution of the desired compound cools, a small, pure seed crystal of the compound forms in the solution. Layer by layer, additional molecules attach to this crystal, forming a growing crystal lattice, as shown in Figure 1. The molecules in the crystal have a greater affinity for other molecules of the same kind than they do for any impurities present in the solution. In effect, the process of crystal formation removes one kind of molecule from the solution.

Choosing a Recrystallizing Solvent

Selecting an appropriate recrystallizing solvent to use is probably the most difficult step of recrystallization. The primary consideration when choosing a recrystallizing solvent is the extent to which the compound and impurities

Figure 1

(a) Identical molecules attach to one another, forming a crystal lattice; (b) impurities have different shapes or sizes and do not layer

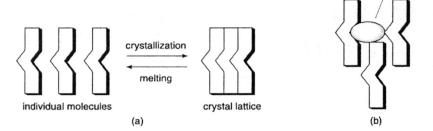

Figure 2

Ideal solubility patterns of a compound, line A, and accompanying impurities, lines B and C, at varying temperatures

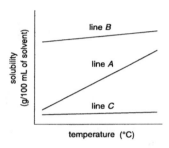

are soluble in the solvent at high and low temperatures. The graph in Figure 2 shows three possible scenarios for how the solubilities of the compound and the impurities depend on temperature.

Ideally, the compound to be recrystallized should be very soluble in the chosen solvent at elevated temperatures, but almost insoluble in the cold solvent, as shown by line *A*. Impurities should be soluble in the chosen solvent at all temperatures so that impurities stay in solution, as shown by line *B*. Alternatively, impurities should be insoluble at all temperatures so they can be filtered from the hot solution, as shown by line *C*.

Experimentation is needed to select an appropriate recrystallizing solvent. Typically, several solvents are used to test the extent of solubility of the compound. A small amount of the compound is mixed with a few milliliters of each solvent. The compound's solubility is observed at room temperature and near the solvent's boiling point. If the compound is soluble in a solvent at room temperature, the solvent is not suitable. If the compound is insoluble at room temperature and soluble near the solvent's boiling point, the solvent is a suitable candidate.

"Insoluble" is a relative term. All compounds are soluble to some extent in every solvent. For example, benzoic acid in water has a solubility of 6.80 grams per 100 milliliters at 100 °C. However, benzoic acid has a solubility of only 0.34 gram per 100 milliliters in water at 25 °C. Benzoic acid is typically listed as insoluble in 25 °C water.

When considering the solubility of an organic compound, a general rule is *like dissolves like*. Polar organic molecules contain functional groups that can hydrogen bond, such as $-OH$, $-NH_2$, and $-CO_2H$. Polar molecules are generally most soluble in polar solvents. Many organic molecules are nonpolar. Nonpolar molecules are most soluble in nonpolar solvents. A list of commonly used recrystallization solvents is shown in Table 1.

The boiling point of the recrystallization solvent should be lower than the melting point of the compound to be recrystallized. If the solvent's boiling point is higher than the compound's melting point, the compound will oil out. **Oiling out** occurs when a compound is insoluble in a solution at a temperature above the compound's melting point. As a result, the compound is deposited as an oil, and not as crystals.

Another important criterion for selecting a recrystallizing solvent relates to recovery of the compound. An abundant quantity of crystals must be produced as the solution cools to room temperature or below.

The four major criteria for selecting a recrystallizing solvent are summarized in Table 2.

Table 1 *Commonly used recrystallization solvents, in order of decreasing polarity*

Solvent	bp(°C)	Solvent	bp(°C)
Water	100	Ethyl ether	35
Methanol	65	Dichloromethane	40
Ethanol (95%)	78	Toluene	111
Acetone	56	Petroleum ether	35–60
Ethyl acetate	77		

Table 2 *Criteria for selecting a recrystallizing solvent*

(1) Compound being purified must be insoluble in solvent at room temperature
(2) Compound must be soluble in boiling solvent
(3) Solvent's boiling point must be lower than the compound's melting point
(4) An abundant quantity of crystals must be recoverable from the cool solvent

Often, the requirements necessary for successful recrystallization are not met by a single solvent. In these cases, a mixture of two solvents, called a **solvent pair,** is used. Two solvents are selected that are miscible with each other, but have opposite abilities to dissolve the compound. The compound to be recrystallized should be soluble in one solvent (*A*) of the pair and should be relatively insoluble in the second solvent (*B*).

To determine the proper combinations of the two solvents, the compound is dissolved in a minimum volume of solvent *A* near the boiling temperature of this solvent. Next, solvent *B* is added to the boiling mixture until the mixture becomes cloudy, indicating that the compound is precipitating from solution. A few drops of solvent *A* are added to redissolve the precipitate, producing a clear solution. Then the solvent pair is treated just like a single recrystallization solvent. Common solvent pairs are ethanol and water, acetone and ether, and acetic acid and water.

Dissolving the Compound

Once a suitable solvent is found, the recrystallization process is continued by dissolving the compound in a minimum volume of boiling solvent. Then a five percent excess of the solvent is added to the saturated solution to prevent premature crystallization. For example, if 10 mL of a boiling solvent is required to *just* dissolve a compound, five percent of 10 mL or 0.5 mL would be added to bring the total volume to 10.5 mL.

Decolorizing the Solution

Occasionally, a sample may contain a soluble impurity that produces a colored solution, and that solution colors crystals that would otherwise be colorless. In that case, activated carbon, or decolorizing carbon, is used to remove these colored impurities from solution. Activated carbon has a

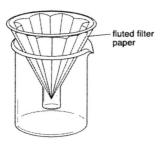

Figure 3
A gravity filtration apparatus used to filter undissolved impurities

surface area that adsorbs dissolved organic substances. Adding an excess of carbon must be avoided, because carbon can also adsorb the compound that is being recrystallized, reducing the percent recovery.

The hot solution is filtered by gravity filtration through a funnel containing a fluted filter paper to remove any insoluble compound, including the carbon. If no undissolved impurities are present, or if carbon has not been added, the filtration step is omitted. A typical gravity filtration apparatus is shown in Figure 3. The funnel, filter paper, and collection flask are heated with boiling solvent prior to filtering the solution to prevent premature crystal formation.

Using a *fluted* filter paper increases surface area inside the funnel and speeds the filtering process. Figure 4 on the next page shows how to produce a fluted filter paper.

Recrystallizing Pure Compound

After the compound is dissolved in a minimal amount of boiling solvent and the solution is filtered, as necessary, the solution is allowed to slowly cool to room temperature. If crystal formation occurs too rapidly, impurities may become trapped in the crystals. Then the filtered solution is cooled in an ice-water bath for a few minutes to maximize crystal formation. Crystals usually form as the solution temperature decreases.

Sometimes, crystals do not form in the cooled solution. In this case, two methods can be used to induce crystallization. One method involves scratching the inside of the flask with a glass stirring rod. The freshly scratched glass supplies sites for seed crystal formation. Alternatively, a seed crystal of the pure compound can be placed into the solution to promote crystal growth.

Collecting, Washing, and Drying the Crystals

Vacuum filtration is the best method for separating the crystals from the **mother liquor,** or remaining solvent. A typical vacuum filtration apparatus is shown in Figure 5 on the next page.

In vacuum filtration, a receiver flask with a sidearm, called a **filter flask,** is connected by heavy-walled vacuum tubing to a vacuum source. A Büchner funnel is fitted to the filter flask with a rubber stopper or filter adapter.

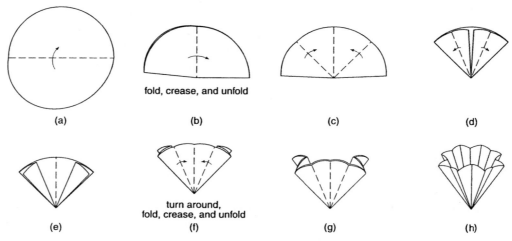

Figure 4
Folding a fluted filter paper

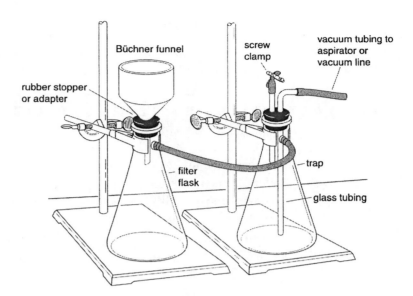

Figure 5
A typical vacuum filtration apparatus

The most common source of vacuum is a **water aspirator.** In a water aspirator, water moves past a small hole leading into a sidearm that can be attached to a trap. A partial vacuum is created because of the reduced pressure at the point where the rapidly moving water passes the hole. At that point, air is pulled into the aspirator sidearm. This phenomenon is called the **Bernoulli effect**.

A **trap** can be used in tandem with a water aspirator to prevent contamination of the solution in the filter flask with water. Sudden drops in water pressure can cause water to be drawn into the filter flask. Fitting a trap between the filter flask and the aspirator prevents any reverse water flow from reaching the filter flask.

To recover the pure crystals, the perforated Büchner funnel plate is covered with a filter paper disk, which is moistened with recrystallization solvent. With vacuum applied, the solution containing the suspended crystals is poured onto the filter paper so that a uniform thickness of crystals collects on the paper. After the mother liquor has been pulled through the filter, the crystals are washed with small portions of cold solvent. Then the crystals are dried and their mass is measured.

Calculating Percent Recovery

Percent recovery is calculated by dividing the mass of the recrystallized compound by the mass of the crude compound before recrystallization, as shown in Equation 1.

$$\% \text{ recovery} = \left(\frac{\text{mass of recrystallized compound. g}}{\text{mass of crude compound. g}}\right)(100\%) \quad \text{(Eq. 1)}$$

Assessing Purity

Purity of a recrystallized compound is assessed by observing its color and by measuring its melting point range. If a compound is described in the chemical literature as having white crystals, the recrystallized compound should appear white. If the compound has an off-white color, the compound should again be recrystallized using activated carbon.

A pure compound melts over a narrow range of 1–3 °C near its reported melting point. If a *dry* recrystallized compound has a melting point range of four degrees or more, it should be recrystallized again.

PURIFYING ACETANILIDE BY RECRYSTALLIZATION

Equipment

2 beakers, 100-mL	Microspatula
250-mL beaker[†]	Pasteur pipet, with latex bulb
Büchner funnel, with filter paper	Sand bath[*]
2 graduated Erlenmeyer flasks, 25-mL	Screw clamp
	Stirring rod, glass
11-cm fluted filter paper	2 support stands
125-mL filter flask, with 1-hole stopper	5 test tubes, 13 × 100-mm
	2 utility clamps
Short-stem filter funnel	Vacuum trap
10-mL graduated cylinder	250-mL filter flask
25-mL graduated cylinder	2-hole stopper
Hot plate	2 pieces glass or plastic tubing
Labels	Vacuum tubing

[*]or crystallizing dish on electric hot plate or electric heating well with heat controller
[†]for ice bath

Reagents and Properties

Substance	Quantity	Molar mass (g/mol)	mp (°C)	bp(°C)
Acetanilide	1 g	135.17	113–115	
Acetone	2 mL	58.08		56
Carbon, activated	60 mg			
Ethanol	2 mL	46.07		78
Petroleum ether	2 mL	*		35–60

*mixture of hydrocarbons

Preview

- Check solubility of acetanilide in four solvents
- Choose a recrystallizing solvent
- Weigh the acetanilide
- Dissolve the acetanilide in the hot recrystallizing solvent
- Add activated carbon to remove dissolved impurities and filter the hot solution

- Recrystallize the pure acetanilide
- Collect the crystals of acetanilide
- Wash, dry, and weigh the crystals
- Measure the melting points of crude and recrystallized acetanilide

PROCEDURE

CAUTION

Wear departmentally approved safety goggles at all times while in the chemistry laboratory.

Always use caution in the laboratory. Many chemicals are potentially harmful. Prevent contact with your eyes, skin, and clothing. Avoid ingesting any of the reagents.

1. Choosing a Recrystallizing Solvent

CAUTION

Acetanilide is toxic and irritating. Acetone and ethanol are flammable and irritating. Petroleum ether is flammable and toxic. Use these compounds in a *fume hood*.

Label four 13 × 100-mm test tubes "acetone", "water", "ethanol", and "petroleum ether". Place approximately 100 mg of acetanilide into each test tube. Use a microspatula to pulverize the acetanilide. Place 2.0 mL of the appropriate solvent into each test tube. Thoroughly stir each mixture. Record whether the acetanilide is soluble or insoluble in each solvent at room temperature.

NOTE: Lumps of acetanilide may be slow to dissolve, interfering with the correct solvent selection.

CAUTION

Heated test tubes containing solvent boil over easily. Be careful to avoid burns from the hot solvent.

Select the test tube(s) containing the solvent(s) in which acetanilide did not dissolve at room temperature. Using a sand bath, heat the mixture(s) to boiling. Record whether acetanilide is soluble or insoluble in each hot solvent.

Allow the heated solvent(s) to cool slowly to room temperature. Prepare an ice–water bath by half filling a 250-mL beaker with equal volumes of ice and water. Place the tube(s) into the bath for 5 min, and observe whether recrystallization occurs. Record your observations.

Based on your observations, choose an appropriate solvent from which to recrystallize acetanilide. Consult your laboratory instructor concerning your solvent choice before proceeding to Part 2. Place the solvents in the test tubes into appropriate containers labeled "Recovered Acetone", "Recovered Ethanol", "Recovered Water", and "Recovered Petroleum Ether", provided by your laboratory instructor.

Insoluble
—water
—ether
coluble
—acetone
—ethanol

© 2004 Cengage Learning

2. Dissolving the Compound

watch glass

53.4g

wg+ acetanalide

1.305g

Weigh 500 mg of acetanilide and place it into a 25-mL Erlenmeyer flask. Place 15 mL of the appropriate recrystallizing solvent into a second 25-mL Erlenmeyer flask. Add a boiling chip. Using a hot plate, heat the solvent to boiling.

Using beaker tongs, pick up the hot flask containing the boiling solvent. Use a Pasteur pipet to add 0.5–1 mL of boiling solvent to the flask containing the acetanilide. Swirl the flask with each addition. Keep the solvent in both flasks at boiling by placing the flasks on the hot plate. Continue the solvent additions until the acetanilide *just* dissolves.

Using beaker tongs, remove the flasks from the hot plate. Allow the acetanilide solution to cool below the solvent boiling point. Observe the solution color. Record your observations. Measure and record your solvent volume.

Calculate the additional solvent volume needed to have a 5% excess. Measure and add that solvent volume to the acetanilide flask.

3. Decolorizing the Solution

while boiling

water soluble
ether insoluble

ice bath

water insoluble
ether soluble

$-\frac{1}{2}$ mL

$-\frac{1}{2}$ mL

$-\frac{1}{2}$ mL

$-\frac{1}{2}$ mL

$-\frac{1}{2}$ mL

$-\frac{1}{2}$ mL

$-\frac{1}{2}$

CAUTION ⚠

Activated carbon is an irritant. Prevent eye, skin, and clothing contact. Avoid inhaling dust and ingesting the carbon. *Do not add carbon to a boiling solution.* This addition will cause the solution to boil over and burn your skin. Also, do not boil a solution containing carbon too vigorously, or the solution may boil over.

Assemble a gravity filtration apparatus, as shown in Figure 3 earlier in this module. Weigh 60 mg of activated carbon. *Conduct the Procedure in Parts A and B simultaneously.*

NOTE: So that crystals will not form in the funnel, plan to filter the boiling solution from Part *B* using the filter apparatus from Part *A* while the filter apparatus is still hot.

A. Heating the Gravity Filtration Apparatus

Place 20 mL of the recrystallizing solvent into a 100-mL beaker. Add a boiling chip. Heat the solvent to boiling on a hot plate. Using beaker tongs, pick up the hot beaker containing the boiling solvent. Preheat the filtration apparatus by pouring the solvent through the funnel containing a fluted filter paper. Do not allow the boiling chip to go into the funnel. Collect the solvent in another beaker. Place the gravity filtration apparatus on the hot plate to keep the solvent hot.

B. Adding the Activated Carbon

At the same time, add the 60 mg of activated carbon to the Erlenmeyer flask with the acetanilide solution. Reheat the solution to boiling.

When you have completed Parts A and B, pour the boiling solvent from the filtration apparatus beaker into the other 100-mL beaker. *While the gravity filtration apparatus is still hot from the recrystallizing solvent,* filter the boiling solution containing the carbon through the gravity filtration apparatus. Collect the liquid in the 25-mL receiving flask. Observe the color of the filtered solution. Record your observations.

−6mL −12
−10mL

4. Recrystallizing Pure Acetanilide

Allow the decolorized solution containing the acetanilide to cool to room temperature. When the solution has reached room temperature, place the Erlenmeyer flask into an ice–water bath for 5 min to complete the crystallization.

5. Collecting, Washing, and Drying the Crystals

While the solvent and solution are cooling in the ice bath, assemble a vacuum filtration apparatus as shown in Figure 5 earlier in this module, using a 125-mL filter flask. Also prepare a washing solvent by placing 5 mL of the recrystallizing solvent into a test tube. Cool the tube and its contents in the ice-water bath.

Weigh a filter paper and record its mass. Once crystallization is complete, turn on the water to the aspirator, and moisten the filter paper with a few drops of recrystallizing solvent. Swirl the flask containing the acetanilide, and pour the crystals and mother liquor into the Büchner funnel, using a glass rod to direct the crystals to the middle of the filter paper.

After the mother liquor has been pulled into the filter flask, release the vacuum by loosening the screw clamp on the trap. Remove the Büchner funnel from the filter flask and pour the mother liquor into a beaker. Tighten the screw clamp and reattach the Büchner funnel.

Use 4–5 mL portions of the mother liquor to rinse the remaining crystals of acetanilide from the Erlenmeyer flask. Pour the rinses into the Büchner funnel.

Wash the crystals in the Büchner funnel with the cold recrystallizing solvent. Allow the crystals to dry by pulling air through the funnel for 10 min. Then disconnect the vacuum tubing and turn off the aspirator. Remove the filter paper and crystals. Disassemble the filtration apparatus.

Weigh your dried crystals and filter paper, and record the mass. Observe the color and shape of the crystals and record your observations.

Measure and record the melting point ranges of both crude and recrystallized acetanilide. If your laboratory instructor directs you to do so, place your crystals into a labeled sample vial to turn in.

6. Cleaning Up

Use the labeled collection containers provided by your laboratory instructor. Clean your glassware with soap or detergent.

CAUTION

Wash your hands thoroughly with soap or detergent before leaving the laboratory.

© 2004 Cengage Learning

_____ _____ _____
name   *section*   *date*

Post-Laboratory Questions

1. The solubility of benzoic acid in water is 6.80 g per 100 mL at 100 °C and 0.34 g per 100 mL at 25 °C.

   (a) Calculate the minimum volume of water needed to dissolve 1.00 g of benzoic acid at 100 °C.

   (b) Calculate the maximum theoretical percent recovery from the recrystallization of 1.00 g of benzoic acid from 15 mL of water, assuming the solution is filtered at 25 °C.

2. The solubility of acetanilide in your recrystallizing solvent is 5.0 mg per mL at 10 °C.

   (a) Calculate the maximum percent recovery in this experiment, assuming a 15.0-mL recrystallizing solution is filtered at 10 °C.

   (b) Calculate the percent recovery of the acetanilide produced in your experiment.

   (c) How do your results compare to the maximum percent recovery? Briefly explain.

3. A student rushed through this experiment. Describe the effect that the following procedural changes would have on the percent recovery of acetanilide. Briefly explain the basis of each answer.

   (a) Rather than adding 0.5-mL portions of boiling solvent to the acetanilide, the student added 5-mL portions of boiling solvent.

   (b) The student did not pre-heat the gravity filtration apparatus in Part 3.

   (c) The student forgot to cool 5 mL of solvent in Part 5 and washed the crystals with room-temperature solvent.

_____   _____   _____
name   *section*   *date*

Pre-Laboratory Assignment

1. Briefly explain why
   (a) you should not heat organic solvents over a Bunsen burner flame.

   (b) you should add activated carbon to a cool solution and then heat the mixture to boiling rather than add the carbon to a boiling solution.

2. Indicate a procedure to solve the following recrystallization problems.
   (a) oiling out

   (b) lack of crystal formation

   (c) presence of colored impurities

   (d) premature recrystallization in the funnel stem during gravity filtration

3. Compound *A*, a white crystalline solid with a melting point of 75 °C, has the solubility profile shown in the following table. Which of the solvents listed would be a good recrystallizing solvent for Compound *A*? Briefly explain. The boiling points for these solvents are shown in Table 1 earlier in this module.

Compound A solubility profile

Solvent	Solubility at 25 °C	Solubility at boiling point
Water	I	S
Methanol	I	S
Acetone	S	S
Ethyl ether	S	S

4. A student purified a 500-mg sample of phthalic acid by recrystallization from water. The published solubility of phthalic acid in 100 mL of water is 0.54 g at 14 °C and 18 g at 99 °C.

  (a) What is the smallest volume of boiling water the student could use to dissolve 500 mg of phthalic acid?

  Dissolution of phthalic acid in boiling water produced a dark-colored solution. The student allowed the solution to cool, added several spatulas full of activated carbon, and heated the mixture to boiling. After gravity filtration, the clear and colorless solution was allowed to cool to room temperature. Crystals formed, and the student isolated 380 mg of phthalic acid.

  (b) Calculate the percent recovery of phthalic acid in this experiment.

  (c) Suggest one or more procedural errors the student made that could be responsible for some loss of phthalic acid.

Separating Ferrocene and Acetylferrocene by Adsorption Column Chromatography

Prepared by Joe Jeffers, Ouachita Baptist University

PURPOSE OF THE EXPERIMENT

Prepare an adsorption chromatography column. Separate a two-compound mixture using column chromatography and calculate percent recovery for each compound.

EXPERIMENTAL OPTIONS

Using the Dry Pack Method
Using the Slurry Pack Method

BACKGROUND REQUIRED

You should know how to weigh milligram quantities. You should know how to use air or nitrogen to speed evaporation of volatile solvents.

BACKGROUND INFORMATION

The term **chromatography** refers to several related techniques for analyzing, identifying, or separating mixtures of compounds. All chromatographic techniques have a two-part operation in common. In each technique a sample mixture is placed into a liquid or gas, called a **mobile phase**. The mobile phase carries the sample through a solid support, called the **stationary phase**, which contains an adsorbent or another liquid. The different compounds in the sample mixture move through the stationary phase at different rates, due to different attractions for the mobile and stationary phases. Thus, individual compounds in the mixture separate as they move through the stationary phase. The separate compounds can be collected or detected, depending on the particular chromatographic technique involved.

Adsorption column chromatography is a technique that uses a solid stationary phase, the **adsorbent**, packed in a glass column, and a solvent, the mobile phase, that moves slowly through the packed column. A solvent used as a mobile phase is called an **eluent**.

In an adsorption column chromatography experiment, a mixture of compounds is added to the eluent. As the eluent moves through the column, the stationary phase and the mobile phase interact with the compounds in the mixture. The differences in attraction of the compounds to the stationary and mobile phases result in the compounds moving at different rates through the packed column, separating from one another.

A compound attracted more strongly by the mobile phase will move rapidly through the column, and **elute** from, or come off, the column dissolved in the eluent. In contrast, a compound more strongly attracted to the stationary phase will move slowly through the column.

Alumina (Al_2O_3) and silica gel ($SiO_2 \cdot xH_2O$) are the most commonly used adsorbents for adsorption column chromatography. Alumina is generally suitable for chromatography of less polar compounds. Silica gel gives good results with compounds containing polar functional groups.

Even within a mixture of relatively low polarity compounds, the more polar compounds of the mixture bind tightly to the adsorbent; less polar ones bind more loosely. Separation occurs when an eluent of low to moderate polarity is passed through the column. Less polar compounds of the mixture readily dissolve in the eluent and move through the column. More polar compounds have a stronger attraction to the adsorbent than to the moving eluent. When differences in attraction are great enough, the compounds can be separated.

A mobile phase consisting of a single eluent may be sufficient to separate and elute each compound of a mixture. However, if the mixture to be separated includes compounds with a wide range of polarities, two eluents may have to be used. In such a case, the eluent of lower polarity is used first.

Table 1 shows the relative polarity of various eluents used as mobile phases. Eluents more polar than ethers should not be used with alumina

Table 1 *Relative polarities of various eluents*

hexane	
tetrachloroethane	
benzene	
toluene	
trichloroethane	
dichloroethane	*increasing*
diethylether	*polarity*
tert-butyl methyl ether	
ethyl acetate	
acetone	
ethanol	
methanol	
water	▼

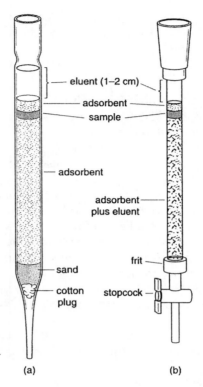

eluent (1–2 cm)

adsorbent

sample

adsorbent

adsorbent plus eluent

frit

sand

cotton plug

stopcock

(a)   (b)

Figure 1
Microscale column chromatography usually employs either (a) the Pasteur pipet column, or (b) the microscale chromatography column

because such eluents either react on the alumina surface or they dissolve the alumina.

Preparing Adsorption Chromatography Columns

Figure 1 shows the two most common types of columns employed in microscale column chromatography. The packed adsorbent is called the **column bed**. A typical column has a bed height ten times the column diameter.

There are two satisfactory methods for packing adsorption chromatography columns, the dry pack method and the slurry pack method.

Using the Dry Pack Method

The dry pack method, shown in Figure 1(a), uses a short-stem Pasteur pipet as a column. A small cotton or glass wool plug at the pipet bottom, layered with a small amount of sand, provides a level base for the adsorbent. Dry adsorbent is added.

A sample mixture containing the compounds to be separated must also be added to the column in a dry form. Typically, the mixture is dissolved in a minimum volume of a moderately polar eluent, the solution is mixed with a small amount of adsorbent, and the eluent is removed by evaporation. The dry sample-adsorbent powder is added to the top of the column bed. Finally, a small amount of pure adsorbent is placed on top of the sample to prevent any disruption of the sample layer with the addition of eluent.

Separation of the sample mixture compounds is achieved by adding eluent to the top of the column bed. Eluent is collected as it elutes from the bottom of the column.

Using the Slurry Pack Method

A microscale chromatography column, shown in Figure 1(b), contains a stopcock to control eluent flow and a glass frit to support the adsorbent. Although such a column could be packed using the dry pack method, the slurry pack method is more commonly used.

The **slurry** used is a mixture of adsorbent and the chosen eluent. The column is packed by closing the stopcock, filling the column half full with the eluent, and adding the adsorbent–eluent slurry. During the addition of the slurry, the stopcock is opened to allow eluent to drain slowly through the column as the adsorbent bed packs.

Air bubbles must not be allowed to form in the bed. Such bubbles cause the bed to be irregular and interfere with the uniform movement of the mixture compounds through the column. The mixture sample is added to the column either dissolved in a minimum volume of a moderately polar eluent or as a dry sample–adsorbent powder, as described in the dry pack method.

Separation of the mixture compounds is achieved by adding eluent to the top of the column bed. Eluent is collected as it elutes from the bottom of the column.

If the separation requires more than one eluent, the column is packed using the less polar eluent. For example, hexane is less polar than *tert*-butyl methyl ether (TBME), as shown in Table 1. If both hexane and TBME are to be used, the column is packed with hexane.

Detecting the Separated Compounds

Each compound forms a **band,** or area of concentration, when a mixture is placed on the column. As a compound is attracted to the eluent, that band moves through the column. The column must be vertical at all times, as shown in Figure 2(a). If the column is not kept upright, Figure 2(b), bands may elute unevenly, preventing effective separation.

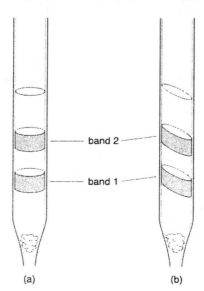

band 2

band 1

(a)   (b)

Figure 2

(a) A vertical column allows good separation of compounds, while (b) a nonvertical column causes non-horizontal bands and poor compound separation

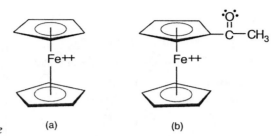

Figure 3
*Molecular structure of
(a) ferrocene, (b) acetylferrocene*

(a)   (b)

Colored bands are visible as they move through the column. For example, if the experiment involves a mixture of ferrocene, Figure 3(a), and acetylferrocene, Figure 3(b), the less polar ferrocene will move down the column as a yellow band, leaving behind the orange band of the more polar acetylferrocene.

If the bands are not visible, the eluent is collected in small volumes, such as one-milliliter amounts. Each volume is tested to determine whether it contains a mixture compound. The test method will depend on the properties of the mixture compounds.

Calculating Percent Recovery

To calculate the percent recovery of the mixture compounds, the recovered mass of each compound must be measured. The percent recovery for each compound can be calculated, as shown in Equation 1.

$$\text{percent recovery} = \left(\frac{\text{mass of recovered compound, mg}}{\text{mass of compound in original mixture}} \right)(100\%)$$

(Eq. 1)

Using the Dry Pack Method

Equipment

2 beakers, 50-mL	2 Pasteur pipets, with latex bulbs
3-mL conical vial	9-mm Pasteur pipet
cotton or glass wool	sand bath, with thermometer*
4 Erlenmeyer flasks, 50-mL	#1 stopper
fine sand	support stand
labels	utility clamp
marking pen	20-cm wire
microspatula	

*sand in crystallizing dish or sand in electric heating well with heat controller

Reagents and Properties

Substance	Quantity	Molar mass (g/mol)	mp (°C)	bp (°C)
acetylferrocene	35 mg	228	81–83	
alumina	3.3 g	102	2054	
tert-butyl methyl ether	20 mL	88		55–56
ferrocene	35 mg	186	174–176	
hexane	20 mL	86		69

Preview

- Prepare dry pack column
- Prepare ferrocene–acetylferrocene sample
- Apply sample to column
- Elute ferrocene
- Elute acetylferrocene
- Evaporate eluents from ferrocene and acetylferrocene
- Measure masses of separated compounds

PROCEDURE

Chemical Alert

acetylferrocene—*toxic*
tert-butyl methyl ether—*flammable and irritant*
hexane—*flammable and irritant*

CAUTION

Wear departmentally approved safety goggles at all times while in the chemistry laboratory.

1. Labeling and Weighing Collection Containers

Label four 50-mL Erlenmeyer flasks "hexane", "hexane eluent", "TBME", and "TBME eluent", respectively. Label two 50-mL beakers "ferrocene" and "acetylferrocene", respectively. Weigh each beaker and record the masses.

2. Preparing a Dry Pack Column

Prepare a column in a short-stem, wide-bore, 9-mm Pasteur pipet by placing a small plug of cotton at its tip. Use a wire to push the cotton into place. Do not make the cotton plug too tight or eluent flow will be restricted.

Using a utility clamp, attach the column to a support stand, making certain the column is vertical. If the utility clamp is too large to firmly hold the column, use paper towels or a split stopper to hold the column in the clamp.

Pour approximately 50 mg of sand on top of the cotton plug. Then slowly pour 3 g of alumina on top of the sand. Tap the side of the pipet to pack the column as you add the alumina.

3. Preparing a Sample

CAUTION

***tert*-Butyl methyl ether (TBME) is flammable and irritating. Keep TBME away from flames and other heat sources. Use TBME under a *fume hood*. Acetylferrocene is highly toxic. Prevent eye, skin, and clothing contact. Avoid ingesting and inhaling these compounds.**

Weigh 70 mg of a 50:50 mixture of ferrocene and acetylferrocene. Place the mixture into a 3-mL vial. Add 800 μL of TBME to the vial and swirl the vial to dissolve the mixture. Add 100 mg of alumina to the solution and mix. Note that the alumina does not dissolve.

Evaporate the mixture to dryness by placing the vial in a 60 °C sand bath under a fume hood. Use a *gentle* stream of air or nitrogen to speed the evaporation.

4. Applying the Sample to the Column

Add the dry alumina–sample mixture to the top of the column. Add an additional 200 mg of alumina on top of the sample to protect the sample layer from disruptions when adding eluent.

5. Eluting Ferrocene

CAUTION

Hexane is flammable and irritating. Keep hexane away from flames and other heat sources. Use hexane under a *fume hood*. Prevent eye, skin, and clothing contact. Avoid ingesting and inhaling this compound.

Half-fill the 50-mL flask labeled "hexane" with hexane. Use this hexane as your working stock of eluent. Refill if necessary.

Place the flask labeled "hexane eluent" under the column. Using a Pasteur pipet, *slowly* add hexane, in 1-mL increments, to the top of the column. Allow the liquid to flow down the side of the column, taking care not to disturb the alumina bed. Collect the hexane as it elutes from the column.

NOTE: Do not allow the column to go dry. If necessary, place a #1 stopper in the top of the column to stop the eluent flow for *short* time periods.

Continue to add hexane to the top of the column until the bottom of the yellow ferrocene band is at the bottom of the column bed.

NOTE: When the bottom edge of the colored band reaches the bottom edge of the alumina (the top edge of the sand), the ferrocene is ready to elute. Elution of the band is complete when the top edge of the colored band has eluted from the bottom tip of the column.

Remove the hexane eluent flask from under the column, and replace it with the *preweighed* 50-mL beaker labeled "ferrocene". Collect the hexane containing the ferrocene, using this beaker.

After all the ferrocene has eluted from the bottom of the column, remove the beaker from under the column. Place the hexane eluent flask under the column and proceed immediately to Part 6.

6. Eluting Acetylferrocene

Half-fill the 50-mL flask labeled "TBME" with TBME. Use this TBME as your working stock eluent. Refill if necessary.

Allow the hexane above the column bed to flow into the bed. When the top of the bed *just* begins to appear dry, use a Pasteur pipet to carefully add 1 mL of TBME to the top of the column.

Remove the hexane eluent flask from under the column, and replace it with the flask labeled "TBME eluent". Collect the eluent in this flask.

Continue adding TBME, in 1-mL increments, until the bottom of the orange acetylferrocene band is at the bottom of the column bed.

Remove the TBME eluent flask from under the column. Replace the flask with the *preweighed* 50-mL beaker labeled "acetylferrocene". Collect the TBME containing the acetylferrocene, using this beaker.

If crystals of acetylferrocene form at the tip of the column, fill a Pasteur pipet with TBME. Use the TBME to rinse the acetylferrocene into the labeled beaker.

After all the acetylferrocene has eluted from the column, remove the acetylferrocene beaker from under the column. Collect any additional eluent in the TBME eluent flask.

7. Drying and Weighing Compounds

Evaporate the eluents from the ferrocene and acetylferrocene beakers by placing them in a 60 °C sand bath under the fume hood. Use a *gentle* stream of air or nitrogen to speed evaporation.

When the eluents have evaporated, allow the beakers to cool. Weigh each beaker. Record the masses. Subtract the masses of the respective empty beakers.

8. Cleaning Up

Use the labeled collection containers provided by your laboratory instructor. Transfer the contents of the hexane and hexane eluent flasks to the container labeled "Recovered Hexane". Transfer the contents of the TBME and TBME eluent flasks to the container labeled "Recovered *tert*-Butyl Methyl Ether". Scrape the recovered ferrocene and acetylferrocene from their respective beakers, and place the compounds in the containers labeled "Recovered Ferrocene" and "Recovered Acetylferrocene", respectively.

Remove the column from the utility clamp and place the column in the container labeled "Used Columns". Place the Pasteur pipets into the container labeled "Used Pasteur Pipets". Clean your glassware with soap or detergent.

CAUTION ⚠️

Wash your hands thoroughly with soap or detergent before leaving the laboratory.

Using the Slurry Pack Method

Equipment

3 beakers, 50-mL	microspatula
3-mL conical vial	2 Pasteur pipets, with latex bulbs
chromatography column	sand bath*
4 Erlenmeyer flasks, 50-mL	support stand
labels	utility clamp
marking pen	

*sand in crystallizing dish or sand in electric heating well with heat controller

Reagents and Properties

Substance	Quantity	Molar mass (g/mol)	mp (°C)	bp (°C)
acetylferrocene	35 mg	228	81–83	
alumina	3.3 g	102	2054	
tert-butyl methyl ether	20 mL	88		55–56
ferrocene	35 mg	186	174–176	
hexane	50 mL	86		69

Preview

- Prepare slurry pack column
- Prepare ferrocene-acetylferrocene sample
- Apply sample to column
- Elute ferrocene
- Elute acetylferrocene
- Evaporate eluents from ferrocene and acetylferrocene
- Measure masses of separated compounds

PROCEDURE

Chemical Alert

acetylferrocene—*toxic*
tert-butyl methyl ether—*flammable and irritant*
hexane—*flammable and irritant*

CAUTION

Wear departmentally approved safety goggles at all times while in the chemistry laboratory.

1. Labeling and Weighing Collection Containers

Label four 50-mL Erlenmeyer flasks "hexane", "hexane eluent", "TBME", and "TBME eluent", respectively. Label two 50-mL beakers "ferrocene" and "acetylferrocene", respectively. Weigh each beaker and record the masses.

2. Preparing a Slurry Pack Column

CAUTION

Hexane is flammable and irritating. Keep hexane away from flames and other heat sources. Use hexane under a *fume hood*. Prevent eye, skin, and clothing contact. Avoid ingesting and inhaling this compound.

Using a utility clamp, attach a chromatography column equipped with a stopcock and a glass frit to a support stand, making certain the column is vertical.

Fill the 50-mL flask labeled "hexane" with hexane. Use this hexane as your working stock of eluent. Refill if necessary.

Close the stopcock, and half-fill the column with hexane. Mix 3 g of alumina with approximately 20 mL of hexane in a 50-mL beaker. Swirl the beaker to form a slurry. Pour the slurry into the column. At the same time, open the stopcock slightly to allow hexane to *drip* from the bottom of the column.

As the column bed packs, tap the sides of the column to ensure good adsorbent packing and to dislodge any air bubbles that may be present. Continue adding the slurry, with tapping, until all of the alumina is in the column.

Rinse the beaker with hexane, and add the rinses to the column. *Do not allow the column to go dry.* After the bed has packed, close the stopcock, making certain that hexane is present above the top of the column bed.

3. Preparing a Sample

CAUTION ⚠

If possible, use *tert*-butyl methyl ether (TBME) under a *fume hood*. TBME is flammable and irritating. Keep TBME away from flames and other heat sources. Acetylferrocene is highly toxic. Prevent eye, skin, and clothing contact. Avoid ingesting and inhaling these compounds.

Weigh 70 mg of a 50:50 mixture of ferrocene and acetylferrocene. Place the mixture into a 3-mL vial. Add 800 μL of TBME to the vial, and swirl the vial to dissolve the mixture. Add 100 mg of alumina to the solution and mix. Note that the alumina does not dissolve.

Evaporate the mixture to dryness by placing the vial in a 60 °C sand bath under a fume hood. Use a *gentle* stream of air or nitrogen to speed the evaporation.

4. Applying the Sample to the Column

Open the column stopcock to allow the hexane level to reach the top of the alumina bed. When the top of the bed *just* begins to appear dry, close the stopcock.

NOTE: No excess hexane should be visible above the column bed. No air bubbles should be present in the bed. Only the *very top* of the bed should appear dry.

Add the dry alumina-sample mixture to the top of the column. Add an additional 200 mg of alumina on top of the sample to protect the sample layer from disruptions when adding eluent.

5. Eluting Ferrocene

Place the flask labeled "hexane eluent" under the column. Open the stopcock and collect the hexane as it elutes from the column. Using a Pasteur pipet, carefully add hexane, in 1-mL increments, to the top of the column, taking care not to disturb the alumina bed.

NOTE: Do not allow the column to go dry. When air bubbles are allowed to form in the alumina bed, eluent will flow around the bubbles, leaving sample on the alumina. Large air bubbles may stop the eluent flow completely.

Continue to add hexane to the top of the column until the bottom of the yellow ferrocene band is at the bottom of the column bed.

NOTE: When the bottom edge of the colored band reaches the bottom edge of the alumina (the top edge of the glass frit), the ferrocene is ready to elute. Elution of the band is complete when the top edge of the colored band has eluted from the bottom tip of the column.

Remove the hexane eluent flask from under the column, and replace the flask with the *preweighed* 50-mL beaker labeled "ferrocene". Collect the hexane containing the ferrocene, using this beaker.

After all the ferrocene has eluted from the bottom of the column, remove the beaker from under the column. Place the hexane eluent flask under the column and proceed immediately to Part 6.

6. Eluting Acetylferrocene

Allow the hexane above the column bed to flow into the bed. When the top of the bed *just* begins to appear dry, close the stopcock. Remove the hexane eluent flask from under the column, and replace it with the flask labeled "TBME eluent".

Half-fill the 50-mL flask labeled "TBME" with TBME. Use this TBME as your working stock eluent. Refill if necessary.

Use a Pasteur pipet to carefully add 1 mL of TBME to the top of the column. Open the stopcock and collect the eluent in the flask. Continue adding the TBME, in 1-mL increments, until the orange acetylferrocene band is at the bottom of the column bed.

Remove the TBME eluent flask from under the column. Replace the flask with the *preweighed* 50-mL beaker labeled "acetylferrocene". Collect the TBME containing the acetylferrocene, using this beaker.

If crystals of acetylferrocene form at the tip of the column, fill a Pasteur pipet with TBME. Use the TBME to rinse the acetylferrocene into the labeled beaker.

After all the acetylferrocene has eluted from the column, close the stopcock. Remove the acetylferrocene beaker from under the column. Place the TBME eluent flask under the column. Open the stopcock, and collect any additional eluent in the flask.

7. Drying and Weighing Compounds

Evaporate the eluents from the ferrocene and acetylferrocene by placing the beakers in a 60 °C sand bath under the fume hood. Use a *gentle* stream of air or nitrogen to speed evaporation.

When the eluents have evaporated, allow the beakers to cool. Weigh each beaker. Record the masses. Subtract the masses of the respective empty beakers.

8. Cleaning Up

Use the labeled collection containers provided by your laboratory instructor. Transfer the contents of the hexane and hexane eluent flasks to the container labeled "Recovered Hexane". Transfer the contents of the TBME and TBME eluent flasks to the container labeled "Recovered *tert*-Butyl Methyl Ether". Scrape the recovered ferrocene and acetylferrocene from their respective beakers, and place the compounds in the containers labeled "Recovered Ferrocene" and "Recovered Acetylferrocene", respectively.

Remove the column from the utility clamp and place the column in the container labeled "Used Columns". Place the Pasteur pipets into the container labeled "Used Pasteur Pipets". Clean your glassware with soap or detergent.

CAUTION

Wash your hands thoroughly with soap or detergent before leaving the laboratory.

Post-Laboratory Questions

1. Using Equation 1, calculate your percent recoveries of ferrocene and acetylferrocene.
2. Describe the movement of acetylferrocene during the addition of hexane to the column.
3. Explain what would happen if you had used only hexane as the eluent in this experiment.
4. Explain what would happen if you had used only the more polar TBME as the eluent in this experiment.

_____   _____   _____
name   *section*   *date*

Pre-Laboratory Assignment

1. Briefly describe the hazards associated with the compounds used in this experiment.

2. Why is it important to prevent air bubbles from forming in the column bed?

3. Briefly explain why the chromatography column should be kept absolutely vertical while it is being packed and used.

4. How will you know when you should begin to collect the acetylferrocene sample as it elutes from the column?

5. What is the purpose of adding alumina on top of the sample?

Separating a Mixture of Biphenyl, Benzhydrol, and Benzophenone by Thin-Layer Chromatography

Prepared by Ronald J. Wikholm, University of Connecticut

PURPOSE OF THE EXPERIMENT

Select a solvent to separate a mixture of biphenyl, benzhydrol, and benzophenone by thin-layer chromatography. Identify the mixture compounds by comparing R_f values with reference compounds. Use thin-layer chromatography to investigate solvent polarity effects on the relative mobilities of these compounds in a mixture. Use thin-layer chromatography to identify the specific compounds in an unknown mixture containing any combination of biphenyl, benzhydrol, and benzophenone.

BACKGROUND REQUIRED

You should know how to use a microburner or a Bunsen burner.

BACKGROUND INFORMATION

Thin-layer chromatography (TLC) is a simple and inexpensive analytical technique that can quickly and efficiently separate quantities of less than ten micrograms (µg) of material. TLC has many applications in the organic laboratory. TLC is used for the rapid analysis of reagent and product purity, or to quickly determine the number of compounds in a mixture. Also, by comparing an unknown compound's behavior to the behaviors of known standard compounds, mixture compounds can be tentatively identified.

Chemists frequently use TLC to follow the progress of a reaction by monitoring the disappearance of a reactant or the appearance of a product. Also, TLC often is used to select a suitable solvent before attempting a larger scale column chromatography separation. Then, during the column chromatography experiment, TLC is frequently used to monitor the separation.

The term chromatography refers to several related techniques for analyzing, identifying, or separating mixtures of compounds. All chromatographic techniques have a two-part operation in common. In each technique a sample mixture is placed into a liquid or gas, called a **mobile phase**. The mobile phase carries the sample through a solid support, called the **stationary phase**, which contains an adsorbent or another liquid. The different compounds in the sample mixture move through the stationary phase at different rates, due to different attractions for the mobile and stationary phases. Thus, individual compounds in the mixture separate as they move through the stationary phase. The separate compounds can be collected or detected, depending on the particular chromatographic technique involved.

In TLC, capillary action allows a liquid (mobile phase) to ascend a solid (stationary phase) coated on a support **plate**. A sample of the compound mixture is applied near the bottom of a dry TLC plate, as shown in Figure 1(a). The plate is placed into a **developing chamber**, a covered container with a shallow layer of mobile phase liquid in the bottom. As the mobile phase ascends the plate, the mixture compounds dissolve in the mobile phase to different extents, due to differences in their relative attractions for the mobile and stationary phases. After the separation is complete, the TLC plate is called a **chromatogram**, as shown in Figure 1(b).

During the TLC process, the solid stationary phase, called the **adsorbent**, adsorbs the mixture compounds. As the mobile phase, called the **eluent**, travels up over the adsorbent the compounds within the mixture move at different rates. A reversible and continuous competitive attraction between the eluent and the adsorbent for the mixture compounds causes this rate difference.

Compounds with less attraction for the adsorbent move rapidly with the eluent. Compounds with more attraction for the adsorbent move slowly with the eluent. Because TLC adsorbents are typically very polar, the more polar is a compound in the mixture, the more strongly it adheres to the adsorbent and the more slowly it moves.

Similarly, intermolecular attractions between the eluent and the compounds determine the solubility of the compounds in the mobile

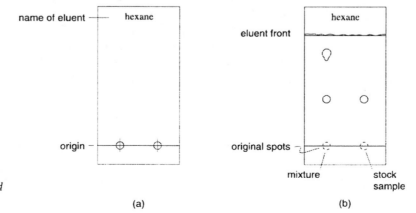

Figure 1
A TLC plate (a) labeled for identification and spotted, and (b) as a chromatogram

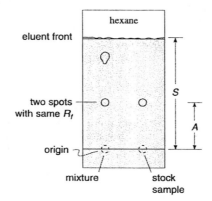

Figure 2
A chromatogram showing measurements for R_f calculations

phase. In general, the more polar the eluent, the more rapidly a given compound moves. Polar compounds, which are strongly attracted to the adsorbent, require polar eluents to attract them away from the adsorbent.

Determining a Retention Factor

The ratio of the distance that a compound moves to the distance that the eluent front moves is called the **retention factor**, denoted as R_f. A calculation for R_f is shown in Equation 1.

$$R_f = \frac{\text{distance traveled by compound, mm}}{\text{distance traveled by eluent front, mm}} \qquad \text{(Eq. 1)}$$

For example, in Figure 2 the stock sample compound moved distance A while the eluent front traveled distance S. If distance A is 25 millimeters (mm) and distance S is 55 mm, then the R_f is calculated as shown in Equation 2.

$$R_f = \frac{A}{S} = \frac{25 \text{ mm}}{55 \text{ mm}} = 0.45 \qquad \text{(Eq. 2)}$$

The chromatographic behavior of individual compounds is reproducible as long as the stationary and mobile phases and the temperature are kept constant. Therefore, an R_f can be used for identification purposes.

When a compound is strongly attracted to the adsorbent and does not travel very far from the **origin**, or point of application, the R_f is small. An increase in eluent polarity would probably increase the attraction of the compound for the eluent. As a result, the compound would move farther up the plate, resulting in a larger R_f.

Identical R_fs for a known compound and an unknown compound on the same chromatogram suggest that the known and the unknown compounds are the same. However, two different compounds can have the same R_f in a given eluent. Additional evidence that two samples are the same compound can be obtained by comparing their mobilities in several eluent systems of varying polarities. Two different compounds that have the same R_f in one eluent are unlikely to have the same R_f in other eluents of different polarities, while two different samples of the same compound will have the same R_f in every eluent.

Choosing Adsorbents and Eluents

Alumina (Al_2O_3) and silica gel ($SiO_2 \cdot x \, H_2O$) are the most commonly used adsorbents in TLC and column chromatography. However, for use in TLC,

Table 1 *Approximate order of polarity of eluents used in chromatography*

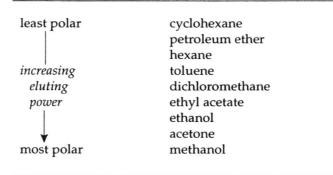

a binder such as calcium sulfate is added to these adsorbents to hold them onto the plate. For this reason, commercially prepared adsorbents may not be used interchangeably between TLC and column chromatography.

Alumina is generally suitable for chromatography of less polar compounds. Silica gel gives good results with compounds containing polar functional groups.

Water content affects adsorbent activity by occupying polar sites on the surface. The greater the water content, the lower the adsorbent activity. For reproducible results, the plates are dehydrated by heating in a drying oven and then stored in a desiccator.

The eluents are organic compounds of various structures and polarities, as shown in Table 1 above. The more polar an eluent, the greater is its **eluting power**, that is, its ability to move compounds over the adsorbent surface.

Combining eluents of low polarity with those of high polarity allows the preparation of mixed eluents of practically any eluting power. For example, the eluting power of a 1:1 mixture of hexane and ethyl acetate would be between the eluting powers of pure hexane and pure ethyl acetate. Eluent selection is usually a matter of trial and error until a separation or desired mobility is achieved.

Using TLC in an Experiment

A TLC experiment has three general stages: spotting, developing, and visualizing.

Spotting a Plate

The origin is marked, usually by drawing a thin line across the bottom of the plate with a pencil, as shown in Figure 3. The sample compound or mixture should be dissolved in a volatile solvent such as acetone or dichloromethane. A glass capillary tube is used to apply a small amount of sample solution onto the plate, keeping the sample in as small an area as possible. With practice, spots with diameters of 1–2 mm can be produced.

After the solvent evaporates, additional sample solution can be applied to the same spot. Application of too much sample can lead to "tailing" and poor separation, as shown in Figure 3. Varying amounts of a sample can be spotted on the same plate to determine which application gives the best results.

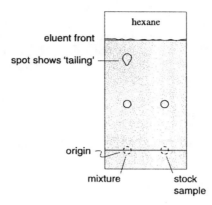

Figure 3
A completed chromatogram

Developing a Plate

To develop the chromatogram, a piece of filter paper is placed along the walls of the developing chamber, which contains a shallow layer of the appropriate eluent. The paper acts as a wick that absorbs the eluent and ensures that, when the chamber is closed, its atmosphere is saturated with eluent vapor, minimizing evaporation from the plate.

When the spotted plate is placed into the chamber, the origin marked on the plate must be higher than the level of the eluent, to prevent the sample from dissolving from the plate into the eluent layer. When the eluent reaches a point approximately 10 mm from the top of the plate, the plate is removed from the chamber. The point that the eluent has reached is called the **eluent front** and is immediately marked with a pencil, as shown in Figure 3. The plate is dried by allowing the eluent to evaporate from the plate.

If the eluent front is allowed to reach the top of the plate, the mixture compounds may continue to move along the plate. An R_f measured under these circumstances is not valid.

Visualizing the Compound

Upon development, a successful separation of colored compounds will reveal distinct spots, indicating that the mixture compounds have separated, as shown in Figure 3. To make separated colorless compounds observable to the eye, the spots are treated in some way to make them visible. The process is called **visualization**.

Some compounds fluoresce. Such compounds can be visualized by viewing the TLC plate under an ultraviolet (UV) lamp. Frequently, the adsorbent contains a chemically inert fluorescent material. When viewed under UV light, compounds that absorb the UV light appear as dark spots that may be outlined with a pencil.

Another simple method for visualizing organic compounds is to place the chromatogram in a chamber containing iodine (I_2) crystals and vapor. The I_2 vapor forms a colored complex with many compounds and allows detection of their spots. The spot location must be marked immediately because the I_2 will eventually sublime from the plate.

In some instances, a reagent such as phosphomolybdic acid solution is sprayed on the plate. This reagent forms a colored product with the compound of interest.

Equipment

5 beakers, 250-mL, with plastic wrap to cover each	5–6 melting point capillary tubes microburner or Bunsen burner
12-cm filter paper,* cut to fit developing chamber	pencil
glass stirring rod	5 rubber bands
10-mL graduated cylinder	ruler
labels	9 thin-layer chromatography plates, silica gel, 2.5 × 7.5-cm,
marking pen	with fluorescent indicator

*or paper toweling

Reagents and Properties

Substance	Quantity	Molar mass (g/mol)	mp (°C)	bp (°C)
benzhydrol		184.24	65–67	
benzophenone		182.22	49–51	
biphenyl		154.21	69–72	
dichloromethane	5 mL	84.93		40
ethyl acetate	5 mL	88.11		77
hexane	5 mL	86.18		69
iodine		253.81	113	184
methanol	5 mL	32.04		65
toluene	5 mL	92.14		111

Preview

- Prepare micropipets from capillary tubes
- Prepare five developing chambers, each containing one of the eluents to be investigated
- Label and mark TLC plates
- Spot stock solution on TLC plate
- Develop TLC plate and mark eluent front
- Visualize and mark chromatogram under UV light
- Repeat spotting, developing, and visualizing in each of the other eluents
- Using eluent that separates the three compounds, spot known compound alongside the mixture
- Repeat with other compounds
- Use iodine chamber to visualize one chromatogram
- Analyze an unknown mixture

Handwritten margin notes:

measure top and bottom

Stock and turn in w/ lab all

R_f : $\frac{2.7}{5.3}$ xxx

R_f : $\frac{2.8}{5.4}$ xx

Unknown ↓

x   x

z
benzophenone: $\frac{2.8}{5.4}$

x biphenyl: $\frac{4.1}{5.3}$

y: benzohydrol: $\frac{1.0}{5.3}$

PROCEDURE

Chemical Alert

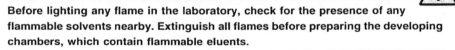

benzhydrol in acetone—*Flammable and irritant*
benzophenone in acetone—*flammable and irritant*
biphenyl in acetone—*flammable and irritant*
dichloromethane—*toxic and irritant*
ethyl acetate—*flammable and irritant*
hexane—*flammable and irritant*
iodine—*toxic and corrosive*
methanol—*flammable and toxic*
toluene—*flammable and toxic*

CAUTION

Wear departmentally approved safety goggles at all times while in the chemistry laboratory.

1. Preparing Micropipets for Spotting

CAUTION

Before lighting any flame in the laboratory, check for the presence of any flammable solvents nearby. Extinguish all flames before preparing the developing chambers, which contain flammable eluents.

Prepare micropipets for spotting the TLC plates by drawing out melting point capillary tubing. Draw out the tubing using a small flame from a microburner or a Bunsen burner to heat the midpoint of a melting point capillary. Slowly rotate the tubing until a yellow flame indicates the tube is softened. Remove the tubing from the flame and *immediately* draw out the ends of the tubing about 5–10 cm to form a very fine open capillary.

Break the capillary into two micropipets. Prepare 5–10 micropipets. Use a new micropipet for each solution.

2. Preparing the Developing Chamber

CAUTION

Ethyl acetate and hexane are flammable and irritating. Dichloromethane is toxic and irritating. Methanol and toluene are flammable and toxic. Do not use these compounds near flames or other heat sources. Use a *fume hood*. Prevent eye, skin, and clothing contact. Avoid inhaling vapors and ingesting the compounds. *Do not use these eluents until all students have prepared their micropipets and all burners have been removed.*

Obtain five 250-mL beakers and label each beaker with the name of one of the eluents: "ethyl acetate", "hexane", "methanol", "dichloromethane", and "toluene". Obtain five rubber bands and five pieces of plastic wrap, each large enough to cover a 250-mL beaker.

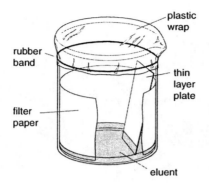

Figure 4
Developing chamber for TLC

NOTE: Your laboratory instructor will tell you if you are to coordinate your work with other students.

Cut a piece of filter paper into a rectangle wide enough so that the paper extends nearly to the top of the slide and only long enough so the paper covers three-quarters of the beaker wall, as shown in Figure 4. Cut papers to fit the other four beakers.

Using a glass stirring rod to direct the flow, pour 5 mL of the appropriate eluent into each labeled beaker to moisten the filter paper liner and to form a layer 3–4 mm deep. Cover each developing chamber with plastic wrap and set aside.

Spotting the TLC Plates

Obtain five 2.5 × 7.5-cm TLC silica gel plates. With a *pencil*, label each plate at the top with the name of one of the five eluents.

NOTE: Avoid touching the coated surface of the TLC plate with your fingers. Hold the plate at the top or by the sides. *Use a pencil to mark on the TLC plate.* Inks dissolve in the eluents.

Mark the origin on each of the five plates by making a *very faint* pencil line across the plate 1 cm from the bottom. Faintly mark two cross-hatch lines on the origin line to indicate where the solution will be spotted, as shown in Figure 1(a) earlier in this module.

NOTE: Do not bear down with the pencil when marking the origin. The pencil lead can cut completely through the adsorbent, forming a gap that may stop the flow of eluent.

⚠ CAUTION

Benzhydrol, benzophenone, and biphenyl in acetone solutions are flammable and irritating. Do not use these compounds near flames or other heat sources. Prevent eye, skin, clothing, and combustible materials contact. Avoid inhaling vapors or ingesting these compounds.

Obtain a vial of the stock solution mixture containing biphenyl, benzhydrol, and benzophenone. Place the drawn-out end of a micropipet into the stock solution and allow the liquid to rise by capillary action. Spot the solution onto one TLC plate by quickly and lightly touching the end of the micropipet to the surface of the adsorbent at each cross-hatch. Transfer an amount of liquid to the plate that produces a spot with a diameter less than 2 mm.

NOTE: Allow the solvent to dry completely between applications to the same spot. Otherwise, the spot will become too large.

After the sample solvent has evaporated, make a second application to one of the two spots to increase the sample amount. Allow the solvent to evaporate.

4. Developing TLC Plates

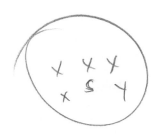

Check to be certain that the eluent level in each developing chamber is *below* the point where the samples have been spotted. Place the spotted TLC plate into the ethyl acetate developing chamber. Use the chamber wall to support the plate, as shown in Figure 4. Cover the chamber with a piece of plastic wrap, secured with a rubber band.

NOTE: Avoid leaning the plate against the filter paper. Eluent on the filter paper can be adsorbed by the adsorbent on the plate and interfere with the ascending eluent. Such extraneous eluent may prevent the mixture compounds from moving up the plate in a straight line.

When the eluent front rises to within 1 cm of the top of the plate, remove the plate from the chamber and *immediately* mark the eluent front with a pencil. Allow the eluent to evaporate from the plate under a fume hood.

NOTE: Mark the eluent front immediately after removing the plate from the chamber. Many eluents evaporate quickly and leave no trace.

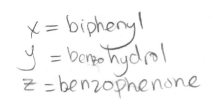

x = biphenyl
y = benzohydrol
z = benzophenone

—Toulene best solvent

CAUTION

Ultraviolet radiation can cause severe damage to the eyes. Wear goggles. Do not look directly into the UV lamp.

Examine the developed TLC plate under an ultraviolet light. Use a pencil to circle any visualized spots.

Using each of the four other eluents and new TLC plates, repeat the procedures for spotting the stock solution and developing the chromatogram. Use the same micropipet to spot the stock solution on each plate.

Compare the chromatograms from each eluent chamber. Compare the spots from both single and double sample applications. Record the name of the eluent that gives the best separation of the mixture. Use this eluent in Parts 5 and 6. Record whether a single sample application or a double sample application gives better results.

Use a ruler to measure the distance from the origin to the center of each spot on the plate developed with the chosen eluent. Measure the distance from the origin to the eluent front. Use Equation 1 to calculate the R_f for each spot.

5. Identifying the Compounds in a Mixture

Obtain a solution of biphenyl from your laboratory instructor. Using a new micropipet for each new solution, spot the biphenyl alongside the stock solution mixture on a new TLC plate.

NOTE: Your laboratory instructor may have you spot all three compounds and the stock solution mixture on one TLC plate.

Develop the plate in the eluent identified in Part 4 that gives the most efficient separation. Visualize the chromatogram using ultraviolet light. Use a pencil to outline the spots.

Repeat this procedure for benzhydrol and benzophenone. Calculate the R_f for each compound. Record each R_f and the identity of each compound.

CAUTION ⚠

Iodine (I₂) is toxic and corrosive. Avoid inhaling vapors when using the I₂ chamber.

Place one of the developed chromatograms into an I_2 chamber prepared by your laboratory instructor. Allow the chromatogram to remain in the chamber for 5 min. Describe the appearance of the plate after visualization with I_2.

handwritten: A little bit darker yellow appeared in the middle of the stock like the bottom of the plate. Rest is all light yellow throughout

6. Analyzing an Unknown Mixture

Obtain an unknown solution and a new TLC plate. Spot the unknown solution and the stock solution mixture onto the plate. Develop the plate in the eluent identified in Part 4. Visualize the spots with either ultraviolet light or I_2. *handwritten: unknown is biphenyl!*

Calculate R_fs for each compound in the mixture. Record the compounds present in the unknown solution.

7. Cleaning Up

Use the labeled collection containers provided by your laboratory instructor. When you are finished with the developing chambers, pour any remaining eluent into the appropriate containers labeled "Recovered Dichloromethane", "Recovered Ethyl Acetate", "Recovered Hexane", "Recovered Methanol", and "Recovered Toluene". Place your used TLC plates and micropipets into the container labeled "Used TLC Plates and Micropipets."

CAUTION ⚠

Wash your hands thoroughly with soap or detergent before leaving the laboratory.

handwritten left margin:

on back page ←

unknown $R_f = \dfrac{3.9}{5.1}$

stock $R_f = \dfrac{2.5}{5.1}$

Post-Laboratory Questions

1. (a) List the five eluents in order of increasing polarity.

   (b) With regard to your experimental results, briefly describe the effect of eluent polarity on the R_f of each stock solution mixture compound.

   (c) In the Pre-Laboratory Assignment, you listed biphenyl, benzhydrol, and benzophenone in order of increasing polarity. What conclusion can you draw about the effect of compound polarity on R_f in the chosen eluent? Briefly explain.

2. Briefly explain why you selected the eluent you used to separate your unknown mixture, and why you rejected each of the other eluents.

3. Briefly describe the effect of the following procedural errors on a thin-layer chromatogram.

   (a) Applying too large a sample when spotting the plate.

   (b) Placing the spotted plate into a developing chamber containing an eluent level above the level of the origin.

   (c) Allowing the plate to remain in the developing chamber until the eluent front reaches the top of the plate.

   (d) Removing the plate from the developing chamber when the eluent front has moved only half-way up the plate.

   (e) Developing the plate in an uncovered chamber.

4. Suppose you prepared benzhydrol by the reduction of benzophenone with sodium borohydride. Briefly describe how you could use TLC to decide when the reaction was complete.

_____   _____   _____
name   *section*   *date*

Pre-Laboratory Assignment

1. (a) Briefly describe why all burners must be turned off before any developing chambers are prepared.

(b) Briefly explain why it is important to work in a fume hood when you pour the eluents used in this experiment.

2. Briefly define or describe each of the following terms as they pertain to this experiment.

(a) spotting a plate

(b) developing a plate

(c) visualizing

(d) R_f

3. Use your textbook or an appropriate reference to determine the structural formulas of biphenyl, benzhydrol, and benzophenone.

   (a) Draw the structural formulas of these compounds.

   (b) Based on these structures, list the three compounds in order of increasing polarity.

Separating and Identifying Mixtures by Gas Chromatography

Prepared by L. G. Wade, Jr., Whitman College

PURPOSE OF THE EXPERIMENT

Separate, detect, and identify volatile compounds of mixtures by gas chromatography. Calculate response ratios of separated compounds. Analyze an unknown mixture to identify and quantify its compounds.

BACKGROUND REQUIRED

You should know how to fill a microsyringe properly and how to read accurately the volume of liquid it contains.

BACKGROUND INFORMATION

Organic chemists routinely analyze a wide variety of mixtures. Syntheses often produce mixtures containing products, by-products, starting materials, and solvents. Natural products such as turpentine and perfumes can be complex mixtures of compounds. Crude oil, gasoline, and other fuels are mixtures of hydrocarbons that are graded according to their composition. Chemical wastes must be analyzed for proper disposal. Gas chromatography is frequently the cheapest, fastest, and easiest method for separating, identifying, and quantifying the compounds of a complex mixture.

The term **chromatography** refers to several related techniques for analyzing, identifying, or separating mixtures of compounds. All chromatographic techniques have a two-part operation in common. In each technique a sample mixture is placed into a liquid or gas, called a **mobile phase**. The mobile phases carries the sample through a solid support, called the **stationary phase**, which contains an adsorbent or another liquid. The different compounds in the sample mixture move through the stationary phase at different rates, due to different attractions for the mobile and stationary phases. Thus, individual compounds in the mixture separate as they move through the stationary phase. The separate compounds can be collected or detected, depending on the particular chromatographic technique involved.

Gas chromatography (GC) uses an inert gas as the mobile phase moving through a column containing a liquid stationary phase. The separations are based on differences in attraction of the mixture compounds to the gas and liquid phases. Gas chromatography is also known by the following terms: gas–liquid chromatography (GLC), gas–liquid phase chromatography (GLPC), gas–liquid partition chromatography (GLPC), and vapor–phase chromatography (VPC).

The Gas Chromatograph

A simplified diagram of a gas chromatograph appears in Figure 1. In a gas chromatographic analysis, 0.1–10 microliters (µL) of a mixture of compounds is injected into a heated **injector**, where all of the compounds vaporize. A gentle stream of the **carrier gas**, usually helium, moves the entire mixture onto the column. The compounds of the mixture separate as they pass through the column. The process can be considered as an exceptionally good fractional distillation using a superb fractionating column.

The separated compounds pass from the column into a **detector** that produces an electrical signal proportional to the amount of compound passing through the detector. A **recorder** provides a graph, the **gas chromatogram**, of the detector signal versus time. The gas chromatogram shows a peak for each compound of the mixture. The **retention time**, which is the amount of time required for a compound to pass through the column, can be measured from the chromatogram. Under identical operating conditions, retention times for specific compounds are reproducible and can be compared with standard, known compounds.

An **integrator** measures the areas under the peaks in the gas chromatogram. Because peak areas are proportional to the amounts of the compounds present, the relative amounts of the compounds in the original mixture can be calculated.

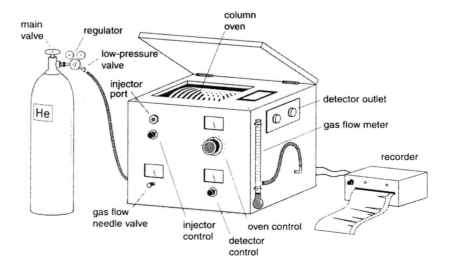

Figure 1

A typical gas chromatograph

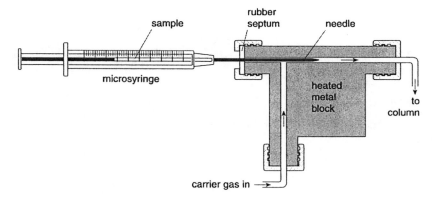

Figure 2
A gas chromatograph injector

Most gas chromatographs require very small samples, and no attempt is made to collect the separated compounds. However, large columns are available that separate samples up to one gram. Receivers attached to the outside of the gas chromatograph can collect the individual compounds after they pass through the detector.

The Injector

Samples are introduced into the gas chromatograph at the injector, shown in Figure 2. It consists of a heated block of metal with passages through which the carrier gas flows. A replaceable rubber **septum** at the injection port allows a microsyringe needle to be inserted to introduce the sample directly into the heated stream of carrier gas. To achieve the best separations with the sharpest peaks, the injector must instantly vaporize all the compounds of the sample and send the mixture onto the column as a very narrow band. Therefore, the injector is generally kept at a higher temperature than the column temperature.

If the injector temperature is lower than the boiling point of any compound of the mixture, that compound will not be instantly vaporized. As a result, the compound will slowly move onto the column in a broad band, making separation and quantification difficult.

The Column

The heart of the gas chromatograph is the column that separates the compounds of the sample. The carrier gas, acting as a mobile phase, passes over a liquid stationary phase that has an affinity for the compounds being separated. Each compound of the mixture **partitions**, or reaches equilibrium distribution, between the mobile phase and the stationary phase. The more time a compound spends in the mobile phase, the more quickly the compound passes through the column.

The amount of time a compound spends in each phase depends on several factors. The relationship between the column temperature and a compound's boiling point is crucial. At low column temperatures, compounds with lower boiling points spend more time in the mobile phase than do compounds with higher boiling points. Therefore, these lower-boiling compounds tend to move faster and come off the column sooner than higher-boiling compounds. On the other hand, high column

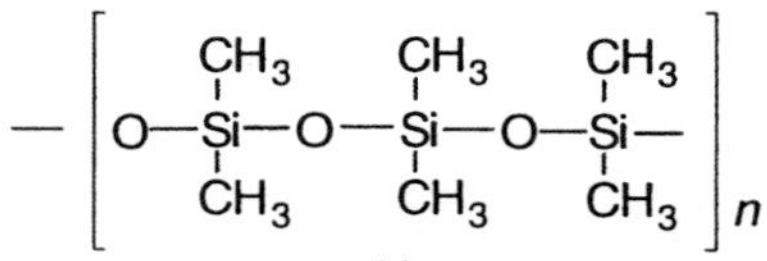

$$-\left[\begin{array}{ccc} CH_3 & CH_3 & CH_3 \\ | & | & | \\ O-Si-O-Si-O-Si- \\ | & | & | \\ CH_3 & CH_3 & CH_3 \end{array}\right]_n$$

(a)

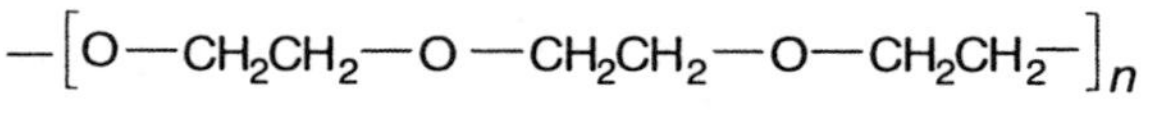

$$-\left[O-CH_2CH_2-O-CH_2CH_2-O-CH_2CH_2-\right]_n$$

(b)

Figure 3

Two common liquid coatings for the stationary phase: (a) poly(dimethylsiloxane), a silcone rubber; and (b) poly(ethylene glycol), Carbowax

temperatures cause all compounds to spend more time in the mobile phase, causing all compounds to move through the column faster.

A compound's affinity for the stationary phase also helps to determine how fast it moves. Nonpolar stationary phases, such as SE-30 silicone rubber, tend not to discriminate among compounds and give separations that depend mostly on boiling points. Polar stationary phases, such as Carbowax, tend to bind more strongly with polar compounds, retarding their movement through the column. For example, an alkane and an alcohol with identical boiling points move together and do not separate on a nonpolar column. A polar column, however, binds the alcohol more strongly, causing it to move more slowly than the alkane. Structures for these stationary phase materials are shown in Figure 3.

A gas chromatograph column is coiled so that a long column fits into a small column oven. **Packed columns** are usually made of copper or stainless steel tubing, with 1/8-inch or 1/4-inch diameters common for analytical columns. Preparative instruments may use columns as large as four inches in diameter. Column lengths are generally between 30 centimeters and 10 meters, with 1.5–3-meter lengths most common.

A packed column contains a solid support, generally an inert, granular solid. The solid support is coated with the stationary phase, a relatively nonvolatile liquid such as silicone rubber SE-30 or Carbowax.

Capillary columns are commonly made of fused silica, with 0.2–0.8-mm inside diameters. The inside surface of the column serves as the solid support. This surface is coated with the stationary phase liquid. Then UV light or heat is used to make the liquid polymerize on the surface of the tube. The outside of the tube is coated with another polymer to make it less fragile. While many chemists make their own packed columns, most chemists buy capillary columns because of the special techniques that are needed to make them.

Capillary columns give better separations than packed columns of the same length, and capillary columns are more compact, allowing longer columns, typically 12–30 meters. Capillary columns can separate complex mixtures containing many compounds. Capillary columns require much smaller samples than do packed columns, however. Smaller samples require the use of more sensitive detectors. Figure 4 shows both packed and capillary columns.

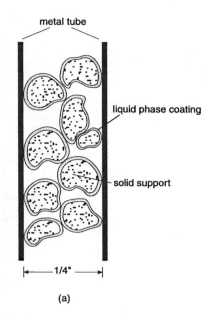

(a)

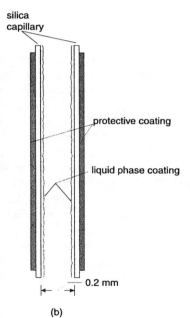

Figure 4

Comparison of a packed column and a capillary column (enlarged): (a) packed column; and (b) capillary column

(b)

The Detector

A wide variety of detectors can be used in gas chromatographs. The two most common types are the thermal conductivity detector and the flame ionization detector.

A **thermal conductivity detector (TCD)**, shown in Figure 5(a), compares the temperatures of two heated filaments: a sample filament and a reference filament. The filaments are made from an alloy whose resistance varies with temperature. The filaments are heated by an electrical current.

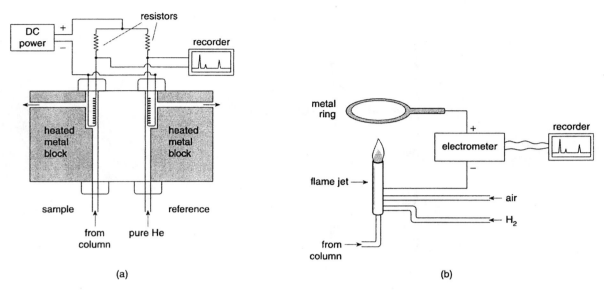

Figure 5
The most common types of GC detectors: (a) a thermal conductivity detector (TCD); and (b) a flame ionization detector (FID)

The effluent gas from the column containing carrier gas and sample compounds passes over the sample filament. Only pure carrier gas, usually helium, passes over the reference filament. Because helium has a higher thermal conductivity than any organic compound, pure helium cools a filament more quickly than a mixture of helium and an organic compound.

When only pure helium **elutes** from, or comes off, the column, the sample and reference filaments are at the same temperature. When an organic compound elutes from the column, the sample filament is cooled less efficiently. The sample filament temperature rises above that of the reference filament. As a result, the sample filament's resistance drops. The difference in resistance between the two filaments is transmitted as an electronic signal that is sent to the recorder. The recorder displays the signal as a peak on the chart paper.

The advantages of TCD are its simplicity, low cost, and, in certain cases, its ability to detect all impurities, including air and water. The disadvantages of TCD are its relatively low sensitivity and its variable sensitivity to different kinds of compounds. Also, TCD filaments quickly burn out if the current to the filaments is turned on without helium flowing to cool them.

A **flame ionization detector** (FID), shown in Figure 5(b), burns the effluent coming off the column in a hydrogen–air flame. The combustion of an organic compound produces ions. These ions conduct a current between the metal flame jet and a metal ring placed above the flame jet. FID is sufficiently sensitive for use with either packed columns or capillary columns. Either helium or nitrogen can serve as the carrier gas. FID does not detect stable inorganic substances such as air and water.

Some gas chromatographs are connected to specialized detectors that provide additional analytical data to identify compounds of a mixture. A GC-MS and a GC-IR use a mass spectrometer and an infrared spectrometer, respectively, as detectors.

The detector temperature must be higher than the boiling points of all compounds in the mixture. Otherwise, a low-boiling compound could condense and clog the detector.

The Gas Chromatogram

When the gas chromatograph separates a sample mixture, the recorder produces a gas chromatogram of the detector output with respect to time. A gas chromatogram of a four-compound mixture is shown in Figure 6. Each peak in the gas chromatogram represents one compound of the sample mixture. The two most important features of these peaks are their retention times and their peak areas.

Retention Times

Retention times depend on the physical properties of the compounds to be separated and the instrument parameters. Table 1 summarizes the most important factors affecting retention times. For rapid analyses, the GC is set for short retention times. For more difficult separations, the GC is set for longer retention times.

Pure compounds can be injected as standards, and their retention times measured. Then the sample mixture is injected and the retention times of the mixture compounds are measured. By comparing the retention times of the sample compounds with the pure standards, each compound can be identified.

For manual recorders, the point of injection is marked on the chart paper when the injection is made. Retention times are obtained by

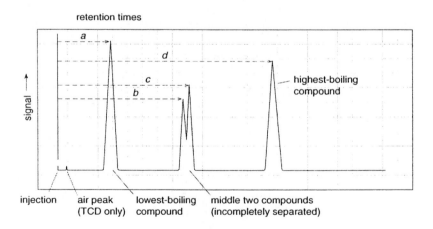

Figure 6
A typical gas chromatogram

Table 1 *Factors affecting retention time*

	Shorter (faster) retention times	*Longer (slower) retention times*
instrument parameters		
column length	short column	long column
column temperature	higher temperature	lower temperature
helium flow	high flow rate	low flow rate
properties of the compound		
volatility	high volatility	low volatility
affinity for column	nonpolar	polar (with polar column)

measuring the distance from the point of injection to the center of the peak, and dividing by the chart speed.

Pressing the "start" button on a digital recorder automatically marks the point of injection. Digital recorders usually calculate and print the retention times next to the peaks on the chart paper.

A small amount of air often accompanies the sample when the sample is injected into the column. Air gives a peak in a chromatogram using TCD because air has a lower thermal conductivity than helium. Air is not attracted to the stationary phase, so the retention time of the air peak is the same as the time for carrier gas to pass through the column. Some operators intentionally introduce a bubble of air into the sample and measure retention times using the distance from the air peak to the peaks of the sample mixture.

In some cases, another standard compound, such as an alkane, is added to the sample. Then retention times are measured from the standard peak. Such **relative retention times** are very accurate if the instrumental settings are carefully standardized and controlled.

Peak Areas

For a given compound, the area under its peak on a chromatogram is proportional to the amount of that compound in the sample. Most GC recorders have digital integrators that calculate peak areas. Before digital integrators were available, chemists used simple mechanical integrators, or they cut out the peaks from the chart paper and weighed the paper.

Direct comparison of peak areas for different compounds is unreliable because detectors do not have the same sensitivity to all compounds. Different compounds have different thermal conductivities, and they give different numbers and kinds of ions in a flame. For example, heptane has a lower thermal conductivity than hexane. A GC with TCD that separates an equimolar mixture of heptane and hexane shows a larger peak for heptane.

Accurate quantitative gas chromatography requires the calculation of **response ratios**, ratios of peak areas for equal amounts of all compounds in a mixture. To obtain accurate relative amounts of the compounds in a sample, peak areas must be divided by the corresponding response ratios. Response ratios are used to quantify separated compounds in a mixture when the amounts of the compounds are not known.

Consider a three-compound mixture separated into three peaks by GC. Assume that equimolar amounts of the compounds make up the mixture. Integration of the peaks gives peak areas, or **integrals**, of 9600, 8000, and 6400 for peaks 1, 2, and 3, respectively.

To calculate response ratios, the middle peak is usually selected as a reference peak. The other two peaks are compared to the middle peak. The areas of peaks 1 and 3 are divided by the area of peak 2 to obtain response ratios for the three compounds.

Peak 1 is 1.20 times as large as peak 2 (9600/8000), so the response ratio for the first compound is 1.20. A response ratio of 1.20 indicates that the detector is 1.20 times as sensitive to the first compound as it is to the second compound.

Similarly, the response ratio for peak 3 is obtained by dividing its area by that of peak 2 (6400/8000). The calculated response ratio of 0.80 indicates that the detector is 0.80 times as sensitive to the third compound as it is to the second. The response ratio for peak 2 is 1.00 (8000/8000).

If the first compound has a response ratio of 1.20 and the third has a response ratio of 0.80, the first peak area is divided by 1.20 and the third peak area by 0.80 to get corrected areas that represent the amounts of compounds present. For peak 1, the corrected area is 9600/1.20 = 8000; for peak 3, the corrected area is 6400/0.80 = 8000. In this way, the areas of the compounds used are corrected to give equal responses, which reflect the equal quantities of the compounds in the mixture. In subsequent analyses of mixtures that have unequal molar amounts of each compound, the use of response ratios allows accurate quantitative comparison of the compounds.

Consider the following example for the quantitative analysis of an unknown mixture of these three compounds. GC analysis gives integrals of 6500, 9000, and 7500 for peaks 1, 2, and 3, respectively. Each compound is divided by its response ratio to obtain the corrected integral. Peak 1 (6500/1.20) gives a corrected integral of 5417; peak 2 (9000/1.00) stays at 9000; and peak 3 (7500/0.80) gives a corrected integral of 9375. The corrected ratio is 5417:9000:9375 for compounds 1:2:3.

The percent composition for each compound of the mixture is calculated by dividing the corrected integral for each compound by the total of the corrected integrals for all three compounds and multiplying by 100, as shown in Equation 1.

$$\% \text{ composition} = \frac{\text{corrected integral of compound}}{\text{total of all corrected integrals}} (100\%) \qquad \text{(Eq. 1)}$$

The composition of the example mixture is compound 1 (5417/23,792), 22.8 percent; compound 2 (9000/23,792), 37.8 percent; and compound 3 (9375/23,792), 39.4 percent.

Attenuation

If peaks on the chart paper are too small, they are difficult to see and difficult to integrate accurately. If they are too large, they extend beyond the ability of the paper to display them, and a flat top is drawn for the peaks. The display of peaks can be adjusted by selecting the appropriate attenuations.

Detector attenuation is the setting that selects the amount of detector signal that is sent to the recorder. The recorder has a range of acceptable electronic signals that it can receive. The detector attenuation can be adjusted to provide a signal within that range.

Recorder attenuation is the setting that determines the amount of full-scale display on the recorder. For example, a recorder attenuation that displays 10 millivolts (mV) full scale is appropriate if the largest peak produces an electronic output that is 8 to 10 mV. In this case, the large peak would extend to 80–100 percent of the available chart space. If, however, the largest peak output is 2 mV, that peak would extend to only 20 percent of the available chart space, and the peaks would be too small. Changing the attenuation setting to give 2 mV full scale would allow the 2 mV peak to extend to 100 percent of the available chart space and display the peaks appropriately.

If, on the other hand, the largest peak produces an output of 20 mV, and the attenuation is 10 mV full scale, the peak is too tall for the display. By changing the attenuation to give 20 mV full scale, the entire peak can be displayed.

Equipment

labels	3 Pasteur pipets, with latex bulb
marking pen	5-mL screw-cap vial
microsyringe	

Reagents and Properties

	quantity (g)	molar mass (g/mol)	bp (°C)
butyl acetate	1.32	116.16	124–126
ethyl acetate	1.00	88.11	76–77
propyl acetate	1.16	102.13	102

Preview

- Weigh butyl acetate, ethyl acetate, and propyl acetate, and mix the compounds in 5-mL vial
- Receive GC operation instructions from your laboratory instructor
- Mark the chart paper with sample information
- Rinse the syringe with sample mixture and fill the syringe with the appropriate amount of sample
- Inject the sample mixture into the GC injector
- Start the integrator or mark the recorder
- Monitor the peaks on the recorder
- After the compounds elute, stop the integrator or recorder
- Adjust the attenuation or gain, if necessary
- Repeat the sample injection, if necessary
- Read the retention times for the three compounds
- Read the peak areas for the three compounds
- Obtain an unknown mixture from your laboratory instructor
- Inject the unknown mixture into the GC

PROCEDURE

Chemical Alert

Butyl acetate—Flammable and irritant
Ethyl acetate—Flammable and irritant
Propyl acetate—Flammable and irritant

CAUTION

Wear departmentally approved safety goggles at all times while in the chemistry laboratory.

1. Preparing the Sample Mixture

CAUTION

Butyl acetate, ethyl acetate, and propyl acetate are flammable and irritating. Keep these compounds away from flames and other heat sources. Prevent eye, skin, and clothing contact. Avoid breathing vapors or ingesting these compounds. If possible, use them under a *fume hood*.

Using a Pasteur pipet to dispense the liquids, weigh 1.32 g butyl acetate, 1.00 g ethyl acetate, and 1.16 g propyl acetate into a 5-mL vial. Close the vial after each weighing to minimize evaporation.

2. Setting Up the Equipment

Obtain a microsyringe from your laboratory instructor. Check to make certain the syringe is clean and the plunger moves freely inside the bore. If the syringe is not clean, carefully clean it as your laboratory instructor directs.

Turn on the GC detector and recorder as directed by your laboratory instructor. Mark the recorder paper with the following information: names of mixture compounds; volume of sample injection; oven temperature; attenuation setting; chart speed, for manual recorders; date; and your name. If you are using a manual recorder, turn on the integrator and start the chart paper moving.

NOTE: Your laboratory instructor will provide specific instructions for using your gas chromatograph and will indicate the settings and any adjustments necessary for its operation. *Do not make adjustments without approval of your laboratory instructor.*

3. Analyzing a Standard Mixture

Slowly half-fill the syringe with sample mixture. Then expel the sample into a vial labeled "Sample Rinses", provided by your laboratory instructor. Repeat the sample rinse 3–4 times. Half-fill the syringe with sample, and then expel all but the amount you want to inject.

NOTE: Your laboratory instructor will tell you the appropriate sample volume for your instrument, usually about 1 μL for packed columns and 0.1 μL for capillary columns. The volume of injected sample should be less than half the total volume of the syringe. The plunger can then be withdrawn slightly to draw air into the syringe, if an air peak is desired.

CAUTION

When making an injection, avoid touching the hot injection port with your fingers or with the glass barrel of the syringe. The hot port can burn your fingers or crack the syringe barrel.

Inject the mixture of the three compounds. Make the injection quickly, but carefully, to avoid bending the needle. *Use two hands* as indicated in Figure 7. Hold the syringe in one hand, with the thumb against the plunger to keep the gas pressure from expelling the plunger. Use your other hand to hold the needle and guide it into the septum. *Do not bend the needle.* Insert the needle into the septum until the syringe barrel is about 1 cm from the injector. If a needle stop is used, insert the needle into the septum until the needle stop touches the injector.

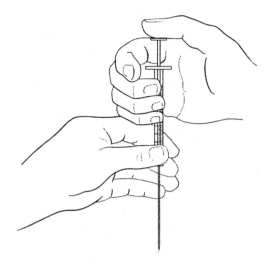

Figure 7
Two-hand injection technique

Gently depress the plunger fully. At *exactly* the same time, mark the start position if using a manual recorder, or press the "start" button if using a digital integrator. Withdraw the needle.

Record the chart speed. After peaks for all three compounds appear on the recorder, press the "stop" button on a digital integrator. The integrator will print the peak areas for each compound. If you are using a manual recorder, stop the recorder. Measure the distance from the injection point to the center of each peak and record the results.

Repeat the analysis until your results are consistent.

NOTE: If your peaks are poorly shaped or vary in size from one injection to another, the cause is usually poor injection technique. You may be injecting too slowly, or touching the needle to the hot injection port, or failing to fill the syringe properly. Your laboratory instructor can help you use the proper injection technique to transfer consistent volumes of sample into the column quickly without bending the needle.

---

4. Analyzing an Unknown Mixture

Obtain from your laboratory instructor an unknown mixture containing two or three of the esters analyzed in Part 3. Thoroughly rinse the syringe 4–5 times with your unknown sample. Expel the rinses into the vial labeled "Sample Rinses".

Inject your sample into the GC. Analyze as before.

5. Cleaning Up

Use the labeled collection containers provided by your laboratory instructor. Place unused samples and unknowns into the container labeled "Recovered Acetate Mixtures". Place used Pasteur pipets into the container labeled "Used Pasteur Pipets".

⚠

Wash your hands thoroughly with soap or detergent before leaving the laboratory.

Post-Laboratory Questions

1. Calculate retention times and response ratios for each peak in the standard mixture from Part 3.
2. Using the response ratios from Part 3, calculate the corrected integral for each compound in your unknown mixture.
3. Identify the compounds present in your unknown mixture.
4. Calculate the percent composition of the unknown mixture.

_____   _____   _____
name   section   date

Pre-Laboratory Assignment

1. What precautions are necessary when working around the GC injection port?

2. What problems result if the temperature is set too low for
   (a) the injector?

   (b) the column?

   (c) the detector?

3. For each parameter listed, explain whether or not a change in the parameter will have an effect on the retention time of a compound.

(a) injector temperature

(b) column temperature

(c) detector temperature

(d) length or type of column

(e) size of injected sample

(f) detector attenuation

Separating Acids and Neutral Compounds by Solvent Extraction

Prepared by Jerry Manion, University of Central Arkansas

PURPOSE OF THE EXPERIMENT

Use solvent extraction techniques to separate a mixture consisting of a carboxylic acid, a phenol, and a neutral compound.

EXPERIMENTAL OPTIONS

Microscale Extraction
Macroscale Extraction

BACKGROUND REQUIRED

You should be familiar with the experimental techniques used to determine melting points, to test for acidity using pH paper, and to separate a solid from a solution using vacuum filtration. You should know how to speed solvent evaporation using air or nitrogen.

BACKGROUND INFORMATION

Frequently, organic chemists must separate an organic compound from a mixture of compounds, often derived from natural sources or as products of synthetic reactions. One technique used to separate the mixture compounds is called extraction. **Extraction** is a process that selectively dissolves one or more of the mixture compounds into an appropriate solvent. The solution of these dissolved compounds is often referred to as the **extract**.

Extraction processes include removal of soluble compounds from a solid matrix, such as occurs in brewing coffee or tea or in decaffeinating coffee with liquid carbon dioxide. In the organic chemistry laboratory,

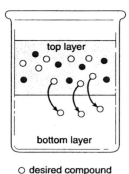

○ desired compound
● impurities

Figure 1
Extraction occurs when the desired compound changes layers, leaving impurities behind

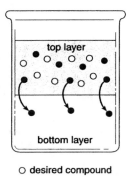

○ desired compound
● impurities

Figure 2
Washing occurs when impurities change layers, leaving the desired compound behind

however, extraction almost always refers to the transfer of compounds from one liquid solvent to another liquid solvent.

A compound can be separated from impurities in a solution by extracting the compound from the original or first solvent into a second solvent. The compound must be more soluble in the second solvent than in the first solvent, and the impurities must be insoluble in the second solvent.

Also, to effect the extraction, the two solvents selected must be **immiscible**, or not soluble in one another, so that they produce two separate solvent layers. After dissolving the mixture in the first solvent, the solution is added to the second solvent. The two layers are vigorously mixed to maximize the surface area between them. This mixing facilitates the transfer of a dissolved compound from one layer to another. Once the transfer process is complete, the layers are again allowed to form, as shown in Figure 1. Separation of the two layers then completes the separation of the desired compound from the impurities.

Washing is the reverse process, in which the impurities are removed to the second solvent, leaving the desired compound in the original solvent, as shown in Figure 2.

Selecting the Appropriate Scale

The amount of compound to be extracted determines whether macroscale or microscale techniques should be employed for the extraction. The chemical principles associated with the extractions are identical, but the techniques are somewhat different.

Extractions using larger quantities of solvents, tens or hundreds of milliliters, require a separatory funnel, as shown in Figure 3. The solvent layers are mixed by shaking the separatory funnel. Then the layers are allowed to reform. The bottom layer is drained through the stopcock; the top layer is poured from the top of the separatory funnel.

Microscale extractions can be conducted using a test tube or a centrifuge tube. Mixing and separating the layers can be done using a Pasteur pipet.

Choosing Solvents

The first requirement in the extraction process is to select two immiscible solvents. One solvent, usually water, should be polar in nature. The second solvent should be nonpolar and might be a hydrocarbon, an ether, or a

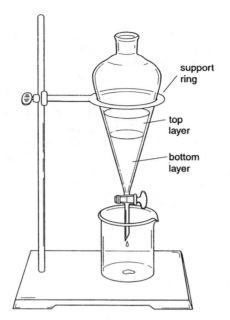

Figure 3
A separatory funnel used for macroscale extractions

Figure 4
Ethers and hydrocarbons are less dense than water

© 2004 Cengage Learning

Figure 5
Dichloromethane is more dense than water

chlorinated solvent, such as dichloromethane. When the two immiscible solvents are placed into a container, two liquid layers result. The more dense solvent is always the bottom layer.

It is important to identify the solvent in each layer. Hydrocarbons and ethers are *less dense* than water or the dilute aqueous solutions used in extractions. When one of these nonpolar solvents is used, the *water* layer is the *bottom* layer, as shown in Figure 4.

However, dichloromethane is more dense than water. When dichloromethane is used as the nonpolar solvent, the *water* layer will be the *top* layer, as shown in Figure 5.

Although the identity of each layer can be established from the density of each solvent, their identities should be confirmed. To confirm the identities of the layers, one or two drops of water are introduced *just below* the surface of the top layer. If the drops of water mix with the top layer, then the top layer is the water layer. If the drops of water fall through the top layer to the layer below, then the water layer is the bottom one. *It is a good practice to save all layers in labeled containers until the experiment is complete and the desired product is isolated.*

Often the two solvents will not completely separate after shaking, due to the formation of an emulsion at the interface between them. An **emulsion** is a suspension of small droplets of one liquid in another liquid. Emulsions are generally opaque or cloudy in appearance and are often mistaken as a third layer.

The small size of the droplets in an emulsion causes the separation of the two solvents to take place very slowly. Several procedures may be helpful to facilitate this separation. For example, gentle swirling of the container, addition of a few drops of saturated aqueous sodium chloride (NaCl) or ethanol, or addition of more solvent to dilute the solutions may help. In particularly difficult cases, it may be necessary to filter the mixture to remove small solid particles that promote emulsion formation.

A simple, but useful, guide to solubility is *like dissolves like*. That is, nonpolar compounds, including most organic compounds, are more soluble in nonpolar solvents than in polar solvents. On the other hand, ionic and polar compounds are more soluble in polar solvents, such as water. These solubility differences can be exploited to separate nonpolar compounds from ionic or polar compounds.

For example, synthetic reactions often produce ionic, inorganic salts as by-products of the desired nonpolar organic product. In such cases, these salts are removed by washing the nonpolar solvent with water. The organic compound remains dissolved in the nonpolar solvent.

Some organic compounds are sufficiently polar to be quite soluble in water. Extraction of such polar compounds into a nonpolar solvent is often difficult. The process can be facilitated by using the technique called **salting out**. Inorganic salts, such as NaCl, are dissolved in water to reduce the solubility of the organic compound in the aqueous layer. Under these conditions, the organic compound preferentially dissolves in the nonpolar layer.

Extraction is a particularly effective means of separating organic compounds if one compound in the mixture can be chemically converted to an ionic form. The ionic form is soluble in an aqueous layer and can be extracted into it. Other non-ionized organic compounds in the mixture will remain dissolved in the nonpolar solvent layer. Separation of the two layers results in the separation of the dissolved compounds.

Ionic forms of some organic compounds can be produced by reacting them with aqueous acids or bases (see Figure 6 below). Reacting organic acids with bases such as sodium hydroxide (NaOH) converts these acids to water-soluble anions. Reacting basic amines with dilute aqueous acid solutions such as hydrochloric acid (HCl) converts the amines to water-soluble cations.

The extent to which an acid-base reaction proceeds to completion depends upon the relative acidity and basicity of the reactants and products. Reactions occur so that stronger acids and bases react to produce weaker conjugate bases and acids. Recall that the pK_a is a measure of the acidity of an acid, as shown in Equation 1.

$$pK_a = -\log K_a \qquad \text{(Eq. 1)}$$

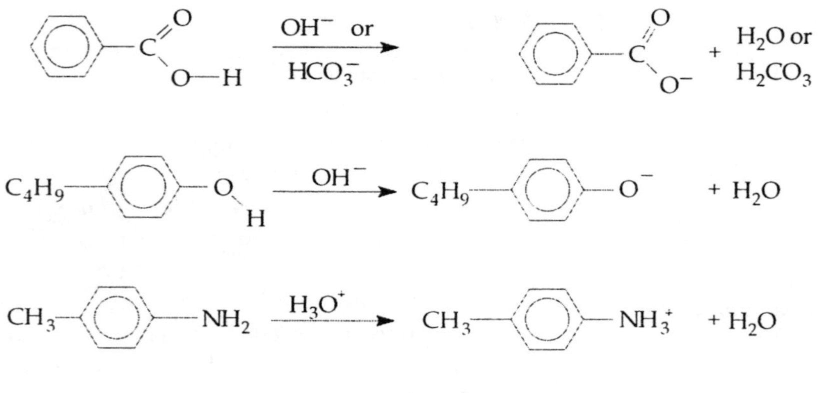

Figure 6

Organic compounds can be converted to ionic forms by reactions with aqueous solutions of acid or base

Stronger acids have smaller pK_as and their conjugate bases are inherently weaker. The position of an acid–base equilibrium can then be predicted from a knowledge of the pK_as of the acids involved. Stronger acids, those with a smaller pK_a, will react with the conjugate bases of weaker acids, those with a larger pK_a.

An analysis of Figure 7 indicates that aqueous NaOH can be used to extract both *p*-toluic acid and *p-tert*-butylphenol from a nonpolar solvent, as shown in Equations 2 and 3. The stronger base, OH$^-$, removes a hydrogen ion, H$^+$, from *p*-toluic acid to form the salt, *p*-toluate. The polar salt is soluble in aqueous solution. Both OH$^-$ and *p*-toluate are bases. The pK_a of 16 indicates that OH$^-$ is a stronger base than *p*-toluate, with a pK_a of 4.2. The stronger base takes H$^+$ from the weaker base.

Similarly, OH$^-$ is a stronger base than *p-tert*-butylphenoxide ion, with a pK_a of 10.2. So OH$^-$ takes H$^+$ from *p-tert*-butylphenol to form the water soluble *p-tert*-butylphenoxide ion.

Sodium hydrogen carbonate (NaHCO$_3$), with a pK_a of 6.4, is a weaker base than *p-tert*-butylphenoxide ion, so HCO$_3^-$ will not take H$^+$ from *p-tert*-butylphenol, as shown in Equation 4. As a result, *p-tert*-butylphenol is not converted to a salt in aqueous sodium hydrogen carbonate and does not become water soluble.

Although aqueous NaHCO$_3$ is not sufficiently basic to react with *p-tert*-butylphenol, NaHCO$_3$ will react with *p*-toluic acid to form the water soluble *p*-toluate, as shown in Equation 5.

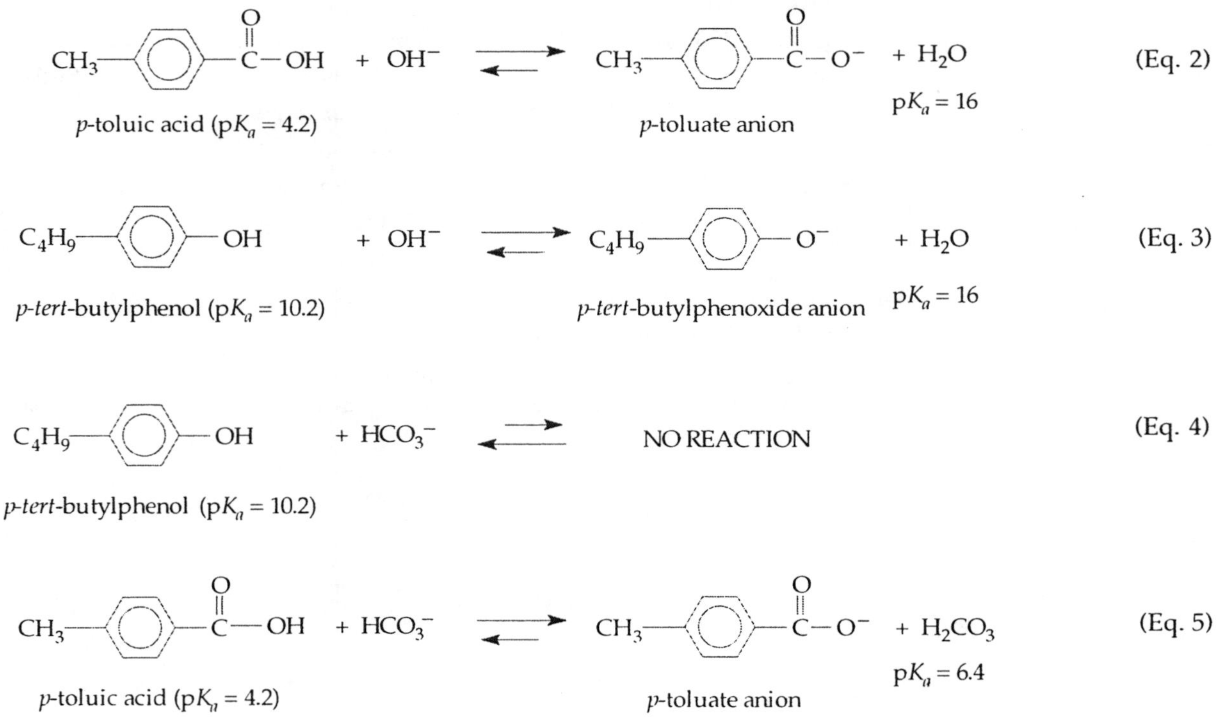

Figure 7
The position of an acid–base equilibrium is determined by the relative acidity of the reactant acid and the product acid

The *p*-toluic acid and the *p-tert*-butylphenol can be recovered by adding HCl to the aqueous solutions. The *p*-toluate and *p-tert*-butylphenoxide ions are stronger bases than is Cl$^-$, so each one takes H$^+$ from HCl. The acid forms are not water soluble, so they precipitate from solution.

The procedure you will use in this experiment exploits the differences in these reactions to separate *p*-toluic acid and *p-tert*-butylphenol from the nonpolar solvent in which they are dissolved. First, you will extract only *p*-toluic acid into NaHCO$_3$ solution. Then, you will extract *p-tert*-butylphenol into NaOH solution. Next, you will add HCl to each of the extracts to precipitate the water-insoluble *p*-toluic acid and *p-tert*-butylphenol. You will isolate the precipitates from the solutions by vacuum filtration, then air dry them. A flowchart for the separations is shown in Figure 8 on the next page.

A third compound, acetanilide, does not react with either NaOH or NaHCO$_3$ and remains dissolved in the nonpolar solvent. To recover acetanilide, you will dry the nonpolar layer with anhydrous sodium sulfate (Na$_2$SO$_4$) and evaporate the solvent in a fume hood. You will recrystallize the acetanilide in an ice bath.

After you dry the compounds, you will measure the mass of each isolated compound. Finally, you will measure the melting point of each compound and assess its purity by comparing the experimentally measured melting point with the literature value.

Microscale Extraction

Equipment

3 beakers, 50-mL	hot plate
2 beakers, 250-mL*	melting point capillary tubes
15-mL centrifuge tube,	5 Pasteur pipets, with latex bulb
with plastic cap	pH test paper
filter paper, to fit	sand bath†
Hirsch filter funnel	thermometer, −10 to 110 °C
glass stirring rod	2 watch glasses
10-mL graduated cylinder	weighing paper
Hirsch filter funnel, with	
50-mL filter flask and gasket	

*one for the ice bath, the other to support the centrifuge tube
†sand in crystallizing dish on electric hot plate or sand in electric heating well with heat controller

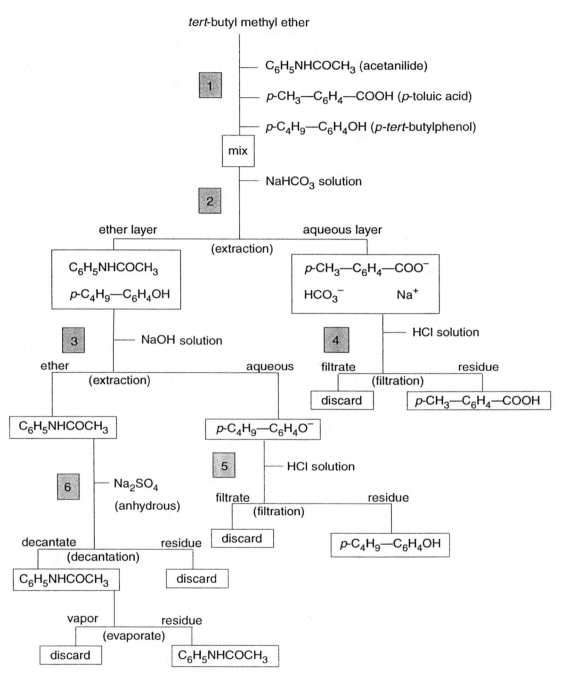

Figure 8
Flowchart for separations using microscale techniques

Reagents and Properties

Substance	Quantity	Molar mass (g/mol)	mp (°C)	bp (°C)
acetanilide	60 mg	135.16	113–115	
tert-butyl methyl ether	5 mL	88.15		55–56
p-tert-butylphenol	100 mg	150.22	98–101	
3M hydrochloric acid	2mL			
0.5M sodium hydrogen carbonate	6 mL			
0.5M sodium hydroxide	6 mL			
sodium sulfate, anhydrous	0.5 g			
p-toluic acid water, distilled or deionized	100 mg	136.15	180–182	

Preview

- Dissolve acetanilide, *p*-toluic acid, and *p-tert*-butylphenol in *t*-butyl methyl ether (see Figure 8)
- Extract *p*-toluic acid from the ether layer with $NaHCO_3$ solution, separating the layers
- Extract *p-tert*-butylphenol from the ether layer with NaOH solution, separating the layers
- Isolate *p*-toluic acid by adding HCl solution to the aqueous $NaHCO_3$ layer
- Isolate *p-tert*-butylphenol by adding HCl solution to the aqueous NaOH layer
- Isolate acetanilide by drying the ether solution, then evaporating *t*-butyl methyl ether in a fume hood
- Dry the isolated compounds and measure their masses
- Measure the melting point of each compound, and compare to literature value

PROCEDURE

CAUTION

Wear departmentally approved safety goggles at all times while in the chemistry laboratory.

Always use caution in the laboratory. Many chemicals are potentially harmful. Prevent contact with your eyes, skin, and clothing. Avoid ingesting any of the reagents.

1. Preparing the Extraction Mixture

CAUTION

Acetanilide is toxic and irritating. *tert*-Butyl methyl ether is flammable and irritating.

Weigh 50–70 mg of acetanilide and 80–120 mg each of *p*-toluic acid and *p-tert*-butylphenol. Record the exact mass of each solid. Place 5 mL of *tert*-butyl methyl ether into a 15-mL centrifuge tube. Add the three solids to the *tert*-butyl methyl ether in the centrifuge tube and mix to dissolve.

2. Extracting *p*-Toluic Acid

CAUTION

Reactions between sodium hydrogen carbonate (NaHCO₃) and acids produce carbon dioxide (CO₂) gas, which can result in foaming.

Add 2 mL of 0.5M aqueous $NaHCO_3$ to the ether solution in the centrifuge tube. Gently and thoroughly mix the two layers in the centrifuge tube.

NOTE: To ensure complete reaction, it is important to mix the layers well. If you are using a centrifuge tube with a tightly fitted cap that does not leak, vigorous shaking can achieve this mixing. An alternative technique is to repeatedly draw the mixture into a Pasteur pipet and then to forcefully discharge the mixture back into the tube.

Once any initial reaction has subsided, place the plastic cap on the centrifuge tube and shake gently. Remove the cap to allow any CO_2 gas to escape. Repeat this process several times, gradually increasing the intensity with which you shake the tube. Shake vigorously, because thorough mixing of the layers is essential.

Support the centrifuge tube in a beaker or flask and allow the liquid layers to separate. Confirm the identity of the layers by using a Pasteur pipet to introduce one or two drops of water *just below* the surface of the top layer. Make certain no air is in the pipet tip. Closely observe what happens to the drops.

Using a Pasteur pipet, carefully remove the aqueous layer and transfer it to a labeled 50-mL beaker.

To remove any toluic acid remaining in the ether layer, add a second 2-mL $NaHCO_3$ portion to the tube containing the ether mixture. Shake the tube vigorously. Remove the aqueous layer and combine it in the beaker with the first extract. Repeat with a third 2-mL $NaHCO_3$ portion.

Add 1 mL of distilled or deionized water to the centrifuge tube and mix. Remove the aqueous layer and combine it with the three $NaHCO_3$ solution extracts in the 50-mL beaker. Save this aqueous solution for Part 4.

3. Extracting *p-tert*-Butylphenol

CAUTION

0.5M Sodium hydroxide (NaOH) is toxic and corrosive.

Add 2 mL of 0.5M NaOH to the ether solution remaining in the centrifuge tube. Shake the tube vigorously.

Using a Pasteur pipet, remove the aqueous layer and transfer the layer into a clean, labeled, 50-mL beaker. Repeat the extraction of the ether layer with a second 2-mL NaOH portion. Remove the second NaOH layer and combine it with the first. Repeat with a third 2-mL NaOH portion.

Add 1 mL of water to the ether remaining in the centrifuge tube and mix. Remove the aqueous layer and combine it with the three NaOH extracts.

Save the NaOH extracts in the 50-mL beaker for Part 5. Save the ether layer remaining in the centrifuge tube for Part 6.

4. Isolating *p*-Toluic Acid

Select the 50-mL beaker containing the NaHCO$_3$ extracts from Part 2. Add 3M HCl dropwise to the NaHCO$_3$ solution to precipitate the *p*-toluic acid. Notice that foaming occurs and a precipitate of *p*-toluic acid forms. Continue to add the 3M HCl, dropwise with stirring, until no more solid is produced and the solution tests acidic (pH $\leq$ 3).

NOTE: To test for acidity, remove a drop of the solution with a stirring rod and place the drop on a small piece of pH test paper.

Weigh a filter paper and record its mass. Using the weighed filter paper, separate the crystals from the solution using vacuum filtration with a Hirsch funnel. Support the crystals and paper on a watch glass and allow the crystals to air dry.

5. Isolating *p-tert*-Butylphenol

Select the 50-mL beaker containing the NaOH extracts from Part 3. To remove any remaining traces of *tert*-butyl methyl ether that might inhibit the crystallization of the phenol, heat the NaOH solution to about 60 °C on a hot plate in a *fume hood*. Remove the beaker from the hot plate and allow the solution to cool.

To precipitate *p-tert*-butylphenol, add 3M HCl dropwise to the cooled solution until it tests acidic. If the phenol separates as an oil, cool the mixture in an ice bath to facilitate crystallization.

Weigh a filter paper and record its mass. Using the weighed filter paper, separate the *p-tert*-butylphenol crystals from the solution by filtration with a Hirsch funnel. Support the crystals and paper on a watch glass and allow the crystals to air dry.

6. Isolating Acetanilide

Select the centrifuge tube containing the ether layer from Part 3. Add approximately 0.5 g of anhydrous Na$_2$SO$_4$ to the centrifuge tube to remove any traces of water from the ether–acetanilide solution. Cap the tube, shake it, and allow it to stand for 5 min.

NOTE: After anhydrous Na$_2$SO$_4$ adsorbs water, it will look like salt or sugar.

Weigh a 50-mL beaker and record its mass. Decant the dried ether–acetanilide solution into the 50-mL beaker, leaving the Na$_2$SO$_4$ in the centrifuge tube.

Evaporate the ether, in a *fume hood*, by warming the beaker on a 50 °C sand bath while *gently* blowing air or nitrogen over the solution. Avoid overheating.

NOTE: Too much heat causes acetanilide to sublime. When the ether has evaporated, a small amount of oil will remain, and the container will feel hot to the touch.

Crystallize the oil residue, the acetanilide, by cooling the beaker in an ice bath. If necessary, scratch the bottom of the beaker with a glass stirring rod, or add a seed crystal, to induce crystallization. Allow the acetanilide crystals to dry.

7. Measuring Product Mass and Melting Point

When all of the samples are dry, measure the mass of each compound. Measure the melting point of each compound, and assess its purity by comparing the measured melting point with the literature value.

8. Cleaning Up

Use the labeled collection containers provided by your laboratory instructor. Clean your glassware with soap or detergent.

> **CAUTION**
>
> Wash your hands thoroughly with soap or detergent before leaving the laboratory.

Macroscale Extraction

Equipment

4 beakers, 100-mL	melting point capillary tubes
400-mL beaker, with ice	2 Pasteur pipets, with latex bulb
5.5-cm Büchner funnel	pH test paper
125-mL Erlenmeyer flask	125-mL separatory funnel
250-mL filter flask*	support ring
filter paper to fit Büchner funnel	support stand
glass stirring rod	thermometer, −10 to 110 °C
25-mL graduated cylinder	2 watch glasses
hot plate	weighing paper

*with gasket or other adapter

Reagents and Properties

Substance	Quantity	Molar mass (g/mol)	mp (°C)	bp (°C)
acetanilide	0.3 g	135.16	113–115	
tert-butyl methyl ether	25 mL	88.15		55–56
p-tert-butylphenol	0.5 g	150.22	98–101	
3M hydrochloric acid	2 mL			
0.5M sodium hydrogen carbonate	6 mL			
0.5M sodium hydroxide	6 mL			
sodium sulfate, anhydrous	1 g			
p-toluic acid	0.5 g	136.15	180–182	
water, distilled or deionized				

Preview

- Dissolve acetanilide, *p*-toluic acid, and *p-tert*-butylphenol in *t*-butyl methyl ether (See Figure 8 earlier in this module)
- Extract *p*-toluic acid from the ether layer with $NaHCO_3$ solution, separating the layers
- Extract *p-tert*-butylphenol from the ether layer with NaOH solution, separating the layers
- Isolate *p*-toluic acid by adding HCl solution to the aqueous $NaHCO_3$ layer
- Isolate *p-tert*-butylphenol by adding HCl solution to the aqueous NaOH layer
- Isolate acetanilide by drying the ether solution, then evaporating *t*-butyl methyl ether in a fume hood
- Dry the isolated compounds and measure their masses
- Measure the melting point of each compound and compare to literature value

PROCEDURE

CAUTION

Wear departmentally approved safety goggles at all times while in the chemistry laboratory.

Always use caution in the laboratory. Many chemicals are potentially harmful. Prevent contact with your eyes, skin, and clothing. Avoid ingesting any of the reagents.

1. Preparing the Extraction Mixture

CAUTION

Acetanilide is toxic and irritating. *tert*-Butyl methyl ether is flammable and irritating.

Weigh 0.25–0.35 g of acetanilide and 0.4–0.6 g each of *p*-toluic acid and *p-tert*-butylphenol. Record the exact mass of each compound. Place 25 mL of *tert*-butyl methyl ether into a 100-mL beaker. Add the three solids to the *tert*-butyl methyl ether and mix to dissolve. Pour this solution into a 125-mL separatory funnel supported by a support ring, as shown in Figure 3 earlier in this module.

NOTE: Be sure to close the stopcock at the bottom of the separatory funnel before adding solutions.

2. Extracting *p*-Toluic Acid

CAUTION

Reaction of sodium hydrogen carbonate ($NaHCO_3$) with acids produces carbon dioxide (CO_2) gas, which can result in foaming.

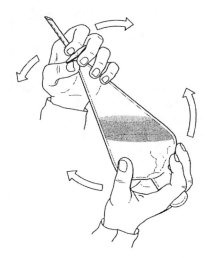

Figure 9
Mixing solutions in a separatory funnel

Add 10 mL of 0.5*M* aqueous $NaHCO_3$ to the ether solution in the separatory funnel. Place the glass stopper in the top of the separatory funnel, and invert the funnel while holding the stopper in place, as shown in Figure 9. Gently mix the two layers by rocking the separatory funnel back and forth.

With the funnel inverted, open the stopcock to vent any gas that is generated. Listen for the gas as it exits through the stopcock. Continue this mixing process, gradually increasing the force of the mixing, until the funnel can be shaken quite vigorously with no gas being produced upon venting. Place the funnel in the support ring and allow the layers to separate.

Confirm the identity of the layers by using a Pasteur pipet to introduce one or two drops of water *just below* the surface of the top layer. Make certain no air is in the pipet tip. Closely observe what happens to the drops.

water went →
into the
bottom layer

Remove the glass stopper from the top of the funnel, and open the stopcock to allow the aqueous layer to drain into a clean, labeled 100-mL beaker. When the interface between the layers *just* reaches the bottom of the funnel (top of the stopcock), close the stopcock to retain the ether layer in the funnel.

NOTE: If you open the stopcock while the glass stopper is in the top of the separatory funnel, a slight vacuum will be created, and the bottom layer will not drain from the funnel.

Add a second 10-mL $NaHCO_3$ portion to the funnel to remove any *p*-toluic acid remaining in the ether layer. Mix with frequent venting. After the layers have separated, drain the aqueous layer into the beaker with the first extract. Repeat with a third 10-mL $NaHCO_3$ portion.

Add 5 mL of distilled or deionized water to the separatory funnel and mix. Drain the water layer into the beaker containing the three $NaHCO_3$ solution extracts. Save this aqueous solution for Part 4.

3. Extracting p-tert-Butylphenol

CAUTION

0.5M Sodium hydroxide (NaOH) is toxic and corrosive.

Add 10 mL of 0.5M NaOH to the ether solution remaining in the separatory funnel. Mix the layers as before so that the NaOH and the p-tert-butylphenol can react. Remember to mix cautiously at first with frequent venting through the stopcock. Allow the layers to separate, and drain the aqueous NaOH layer into a clean, labeled 100-mL beaker.

Repeat the extraction of the ether layer with a second 10-mL NaOH portion. Drain the NaOH layer from the separatory funnel into the 100-mL beaker containing the first NaOH extract. Repeat with a third 10-mL NaOH portion.

Add 5 mL of water to the ether remaining in the separatory funnel and mix. Allow the layers to separate. Drain the water layer into the 100-mL beaker containing the three NaOH extracts.

Save the NaOH extracts for Part 5. Save the ether layer remaining in the separatory funnel for Part 6.

4. Isolating p-Toluic Acid

CAUTION

3M Hydrochloric acid (HCl) is toxic. Adding 3M HCl to the NaHCO₃ solution will produce CO₂, causing a large amount of foaming.

Select the 100-mL beaker containing the NaHCO₃ extracts from Part 2. To precipitate the p-toluic acid, carefully add 3M HCl to the NaHCO₃ solution. Notice that foaming occurs, and a precipitate of p-toluic acid forms. Continue to add the 3M HCl, dropwise with stirring, until no more solid is produced and the solution tests acidic (pH $\leq$ 3).

NOTE: To test for acidity, remove a drop of the solution with a stirring rod and place the drop on a small piece of pH test paper.

Weigh a filter paper and record its mass. Using the weighed filter paper, separate the crystals from the solution using vacuum filtration with a Büchner funnel. Support the crystals and paper on a watch glass and allow the crystals to air dry.

5. Isolating p-tert-Butylphenol

Select the 100-mL beaker containing the NaOH extracts from Part 3. To remove any remaining traces of tert-butyl methyl ether that might inhibit the crystallization of the phenol, heat the NaOH solution to about 60 °C on a hot plate in a **fume hood**. Remove the beaker from the hot plate and allow the solution to cool.

To precipitate crystals of p-tert-butylphenol, carefully add 3M HCl to the cooled solution until it is acidic. If the phenol separates as an oil, cool the mixture in an ice bath to facilitate crystallization.

Weigh a filter paper and record its mass. Using the weighed filter paper, separate the p-tert-butylphenol crystals from the solution by filtration with a Büchner funnel. Support the crystals and paper on a watch glass and allow the crystals to air dry.

6. Isolating Acetanilide

Anhydrous sodium sulfate (Na$_2$SO$_4$) is irritating and hygroscopic.

Select the separatory funnel containing the ether layer from Part 3. Transfer the ether–acetanilide solution from the separatory funnel to a clean 125-mL Erlenmeyer flask. Add approximately 1 g of anhydrous Na$_2$SO$_4$ to the flask to remove any traces of water from the solution. Stopper the flask and allow it to stand for 5 min with occasional swirling.

NOTE: After anyhydrous Na$_2$SO$_4$ adsorbs water, it will look like salt or sugar.

57.443g ←   round-bottom flask

Weigh a 100-mL ~~beaker~~ and record its mass. Decant the clear, dried ether–acetanilide solution into the 100-mL beaker.

Evaporate the ether, in a *fume hood*, by warming the beaker on a hot plate while a stream of air passes over the solution. Avoid overheating.

NOTE: Too much heat causes acetanilide to sublime. When the ether has evaporated, a small amount of oil will remain, and the container will feel hot to the touch.

Crystallize the oil residue, the acetanilide, by cooling the beaker in an ice bath. If necessary, scratch the bottom of the beaker with a glass stirring rod, or add a seed crystal, to induce crystallization. Allow the acetanilide crystals to dry.

7. Measuring Product Mass and Melting Point

When all of the samples are dry, measure the mass of each compound. Measure the melting point of each compound, and assess its purity by comparing the measured melting point with the literature value.

8. Cleaning Up

Use the labeled collection containers provided by your laboratory instructor. Clean your glassware with soap or detergent.

Wash your hands thoroughly with soap or detergent before leaving the laboratory.

Post-Laboratory Questions

1. Calculate the percent recovery of each of the compounds recovered from the original mixture.

2. If you mistakenly extracted the ether solution first with NaOH solution and then with $NaHCO_3$ solution, no crystals would be produced upon acidification of the $NaHCO_3$ layer. Briefly explain.

3. What product would you obtain if you evaporated the water from the NaOH layer prior to acidifying the layer?

4. Suppose that you used dichloromethane instead of *tert*-butyl methyl ether as the nonpolar solvent in this experiment. What changes in the procedure would you make in view of the fact that dichloromethane is more dense than water?

5. Benzoic acid (C_6H_5–COOH) is a weak acid (pK_a = 4.2) and naphthalene is neutral, neither acidic or basic. Prepare a flowchart for the separation and recovery of benzoic acid and naphthalene.

	Molar mass (g/mol)	mp (°C)	bp (°C)	pK_a
benzoic acid	122.12	122.4	249.2	4.2
naphthalene	128.16	80.2	217.9	neutral

6. After comparing the melting points of each of your compounds to their respective literature values, comment on the purity of each compound.

name section date

Pre-Laboratory Assignment

1. Briefly describe the hazards you should be aware of when you work with:
   (a) *tert*-butyl methyl ether

   (b) 3*M* HCl

2. Briefly explain or describe the following:
   (a) What is the difference between extraction and washing?

   (b) How would you determine which layer is the aqueous layer after you add $NaHCO_3$ solution to the ether solution of your compounds?

   (c) Why is the NaOH extract heated before acidification?

   (d) What two visible evidences of reaction will you see when you acidify the $NaHCO_3$ extract with HCl solution?

   (e) In which layer would *p*-toluic acid be more soluble if *p*-toluic acid were added to a two-layer mixture of *tert*-butyl methyl ether and water?

(f) How would the results differ if you added sodium *p*-toluate instead of *p*-toluic acid to the two-layer mixture of *tert*-butyl methyl ether and water?

3. Briefly explain how you will isolate *p-tert*-butylphenol after you have extracted it into NaOH solution.

4. Write the equation for the chemical reaction that will occur for the organic compound when you perform the following steps in this experiment.
(a) Add HCl solution to the NaHCO$_3$ extract.

$$CH_3-\!\!\!\bigcirc\!\!\!-\overset{\overset{O}{\|}}{C}-O^- \ + \ HCl \longrightarrow$$

(b) Add HCl solution to the NaOH extract.

$$\underset{CH_3}{\overset{CH_3}{CH_3-\overset{|}{\underset{|}{C}}}}-\!\!\!\bigcirc\!\!\!-O^- \ + \ HCl \longrightarrow$$

Isolating Clove Oil from Cloves Using Steam Distillation

Prepared by Joseph W. LeFevre, SUNY Oswego

PURPOSE OF THE EXPERIMENT

Isolate clove oil from cloves by steam distillation and extraction. Use reactions with bromine, potassium permanganate, and iron(III) chloride to characterize the product. Analyze the product purity by thin-layer chromatography.

EXPERIMENTAL OPTIONS

Semi-Microscale Steam Distillation
Microscale Steam Distillation
    Using Glassware with Elastomeric Connectors
    Using the Hickman Still
Characterizing the Product

BACKGROUND REQUIRED

You should be familiar with distillation, extraction, drying organic solvents, speeding evaporation of organic solvents, thin-layer chromatography, and general microscale techniques.

BACKGROUND INFORMATION

Simple and fractional distillations are carried out on miscible mixtures. Ideal mixtures follow **Raoult's law:** The total vapor pressure of the system is determined by adding together the products of the vapor pressure and the respective mole fraction of each compound. For a two-compound system, this relationship is shown in Equation 1, where P_T is the total vapor pressure, P_1^0 and P_2^0 are the vapor pressures of pure compounds 1 and 2, and X_1 and X_2 are the respective mole fractions.

$$P_T = P_1^0 X_1 + P_2^0 X_2 \qquad \text{(Eq. 1)}$$

Distillation can also be performed on mixtures in which the two compounds are *not* miscible. This process is called **codistillation**. When one of the compounds is water, the process is called **steam distillation**.

When two immiscible liquids are distilled, the total vapor pressure P_T above the liquid is equal to the sum of the vapor pressures of each compound. This relationship, known as **Dalton's law**, is shown in Equation 2.

$$P_T = P_1^0 + P_2^0 \qquad \text{(Eq. 2)}$$

The respective mole fractions are *not* included in this equation because, in an ideal situation, each liquid vaporizes independently of the other. When P_T is equal to atmospheric pressure of 760 torr, compounds 1 and 2 begin to codistill, with each compound contributing to P_T.

Consider water as compound 1. The vapor pressure of pure water at its boiling point of 100 °C is 760 torr. Because compound 2 also contributes to P_T, the mixture will distill at a temperature less than 100 °C. The actual distillation temperature will depend on the vapor pressure of compound 2. Steam distillation offers an advantage in that volatile compounds that are unstable or have high boiling points can codistill with water at relatively low temperatures. This process avoids decomposition that might occur at the normal boiling point of the compound of interest. For example, eugenol, the major compound of clove oil, boils at a relatively high temperature of 254 °C. Steam distillation avoids this high temperature and results in the distillation of eugenol at a temperature slightly less than 100 °C.

In practice, steam distillation is usually carried out by one of two methods. In the first method, an excess of water is added to the compound of interest in a distilling flask. The mixture is then heated to the boiling point. The resulting vapor is condensed and collected in a receiving flask. The compound of interest is then separated from the water, often by extraction. In the second method, steam is bubbled into the compound of interest to effect the distillation. In this experiment, you will use the first method because it is easier to set up.

Clove oil belongs to a large class of natural products called the **essential oils**. Many of these compounds are used as flavorings and perfumes and, in the past, were considered to be the "essence" of the plant from which they were derived.

Cloves are the dried flower buds of the clove tree, *Eugenia caryophyllata*, found in India and other locations in the Far East. Steam distillation of freshly ground cloves results in clove oil, which consists of several compounds. Eugenol is the major compound, comprising 85–90 percent. Eugenol acetate comprises 9–10 percent. These structures are shown in Figure 1.

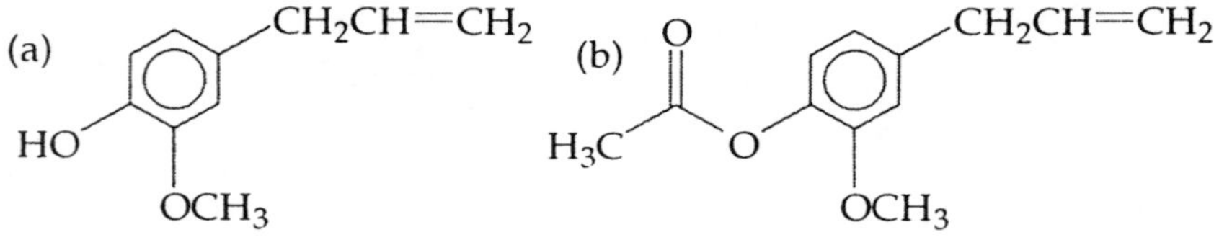

Figure 1
Structures for (a) eugenol and (b) eugenol acetate

Qualitative Tests

Eugenol contains a carbon–carbon double bond and an aromatic hydroxyl group called a phenol. These functional groups provide the basis for simple chemical tests used to characterize the clove oil. A solution of bromine (Br_2) in dichloromethane decolorizes as Br_2 reacts with the double bond to form a colorless compound, as shown in Equation 3. A positive test is the disappearance of the red Br_2 color.

$$\text{(red)} \qquad\qquad\qquad\qquad\qquad\qquad \text{1,2-dibromo compound} \atop \text{(colorless)} \qquad \text{(Eq. 3)}$$

A potassium permanganate ($KMnO_4$) solution can oxidize a double bond at room temperature to form a 1,2-diol with the simultaneous reduction of Mn^{7+} in $KMnO_4$ to Mn^{4+} in manganese dioxide (MnO_2), as shown in Equation 4. A positive test is the disappearance of the purple $KMnO_4$ and the appearance of MnO_2 as a muddy brown precipitate.

$$3 \quad + 2\ KMnO_4 + 4\ H_2O \longrightarrow 3 \quad + 2MnO_2 + 2\ KOH$$
$$\text{(purple)} \qquad\qquad\qquad\qquad \text{1,2 diol} \quad \text{(brown)} \qquad\qquad \text{(Eq. 4)}$$

Phenols (Ar–OH) react with the Fe^{3+} ion in iron(III) chloride ($FeCl_3$) to give complexes that are blue, green, red, or purple, as shown in Equation 5. The color may last for only a few seconds or for many hours, depending on the stability of the complex.

$$6\ ArOH \quad + \quad Fe^{3+} \rightleftharpoons \left[\begin{array}{c} OAr \\ ArO\,\cdots\!\mathop{Fe}\!\cdots OAr \\ ArO \quad OAr \\ OAr \end{array} \right]^{3-} + \quad 6\ H^+$$
$$\text{(yellow)} \qquad\qquad \text{(blue, green, red, or purple)} \qquad\qquad \text{(Eq. 5)}$$

In this experiment, you will steam distill clove oil from freshly ground cloves. Following the distillation, clove oil and water will be present in the receiving flask. Because clove oil will be a minor fraction of the distillate, the clove oil must be extracted from the water into an organic solvent such as dichloromethane. Removing the dichloromethane layer leaves clove oil as the product.

Semi-Microscale Steam Distillation

Equipment

boiling chips	sand bath[†‡]
Bunsen burner	125-mL separatory funnel[§]
cotton[*]	standard-taper glassware
electric flask heater	Claisen connecting tube
50-mL Erlenmeyer flask,	condenser,
with stopper	with adapter and tubing
glass stirring rod	distilling head
10-mL graduated cylinder	100-mL round-bottom flask
50-mL graduated cylinder	2 round-bottom flasks, 50-mL
marking pen	thermometer, −10 to 260 °C,
microspatula	with adapter
mortar and pestle	support ring
3 Pasteur pipets, with latex bulb	2 support stands
powder funnel	3 utility clamps

[*] for Pasteur filter pipet
[†] or hot-water bath
[‡] sand in crystallizing dish on electric hot plate or sand in electric heating well with heat controller
[§] also use as addition funnel

Reagents and Properties

Substance	Quantity	Molar mass (g/mol)	bp (°C)
cloves	5 g		
dichloromethane	21 mL	84.93	40
eugenol[*]		164.20	254
methanol	10 mL	32.04	64.7
sodium chloride, sat. solution	10 mL	58.44	
sodium sulfate, anhydrous	0.5 g	142.04	

[*] product

Preview

- Grind the cloves with a mortar and pestle
- Place the ground cloves and water in the distilling flask
- Assemble the steam distillation apparatus
- Distill the mixture
- Extract the clove oil into dichloromethane
- Dry the dichloromethane layer with anhydrous Na_2SO_4
- Remove the dichloromethane from the clove oil by distillation
- Weigh the clove oil

PROCEDURE

Chemical Alert

dichloromethane—*toxic and irritant*

eugenol—*irritant*

methanol—*flammable and toxic*

anhydrous sodium sulfate—*irritant and hygroscopic*

CAUTION

Wear departmentally approved safety goggles at all times while in the chemistry laboratory.

---

1. Conducting Steam Distillation

Weigh 5 g of whole cloves. Grind them to a coarse powder, using a mortar and pestle. Reweigh the powder and record the mass. 10.19 500

Use a powder funnel to transfer the ground cloves to a ~~100-mL~~ round-bottom flask. Add ~~40 mL~~ of deionized or distilled water and a boiling chip 150 mL to the flask. Mix well with a glass stirring rod. Mark the level of the mixture on the side of the flask.

Add 30 mL of water to a 50-mL round-bottom flask. Mark the level of the water on the side of the flask. Then discard the water from the flask.

Assemble the steam distillation apparatus shown in Figure 2. Use the 500 ~~100~~-mL round-bottom flask as the pot. Use the 50-mL round-bottom flask as the receiver. If a vacuum adapter is not used, *make certain there is an opening to the atmosphere.* Pour 100 mL of water into the addition funnel. Start the flow of water through the condenser.

Adjust a Bunsen burner flame to lessen the hot central cone. Heat the pot by waving the flame back and forth under the pot. Maintain a distillation rate of approximately one drop every 3–5 s.

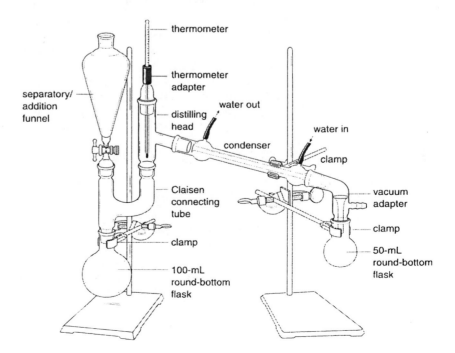

thermometer

thermometer adapter

separatory/ addition funnel

water out

distilling head

condenser

water in

clamp

Claisen connecting tube

vacuum adapter

clamp

clamp

100-mL round-bottom flask

50-mL round-bottom flask

Figure 2
Semi-microscale steam distillation apparatus

NOTE: Do not heat the mixture too rapidly. The clove mixture tends to foam when rapidly heated. The burner flame can easily be added and withdrawn to control the heating rate.

Add water to the pot at 10-min intervals to keep the water level at the mark. Stop the distillation when approximately 30 mL of distillate has been collected.

2. Extracting the Clove Oil

C A U T I O N

Dichloromethane is toxic and irritating. Use a *fume hood*. Clove oil (eugenol) is irritating. Prevent eye, skin, and clothing contact.

Allow the receiver to cool to room temperature. Carefully pour the distillate from the receiver into a 125-mL separatory funnel. Add 10 mL of saturated NaCl solution.

Using a Pasteur pipet, carefully rinse the condenser and the inside neck of the receiving flask with 5 mL of dichloromethane. Swirl the flask gently to dissolve the remaining clove oil. Add this dichloromethane to the distillate in the separatory funnel.

NOTE: Significant amounts of clove oil will adhere to the condenser and the sides and neck of the receiving flask.

Cap the separatory funnel and gently swirl the contents for several seconds. *Vent the separatory funnel frequently.* After the pressure has been vented, shake the contents vigorously to thoroughly mix the two layers.

Swirl the separatory funnel. At the same time, gently tap the outside of the separatory funnel with your index finger to force into the bottom layer any droplets of dichloromethane that are adhering to the sides of the funnel.

Allow the layers to separate. Drain the lower dichloromethane layer into a 50-mL Erlenmeyer flask, making certain that none of the aqueous layer is transferred to the flask.

Rinse the condenser and the receiver with a second 5-mL portion of dichloromethane. Transfer the rinsing to the separatory funnel. Repeat the extraction of the aqueous layer.

Drain the second dichloromethane extract from the separatory funnel and combine it with the first one in the 50-mL Erlenmeyer flask. Repeat the rinsing and extraction process with a third 5-mL portion of dichloromethane. Combine the third extract in the same 50-mL Erlenmeyer flask.

C A U T I O N

Anhydrous sodium sulfate (Na_2SO_4) is irritating and hygroscopic. Do not inhale and ingest this compound.

Add approximately 0.5 g of anhydrous Na_2SO_4 to the flask containing the dichloromethane extracts. Stopper the flask. Allow the extracts to dry for 5 min.

Weigh a clean, dry 50-mL round-bottom flask to the nearest 0.001 g and record the mass. Using a Pasteur filter pipet, transfer the dried dichloromethane into the flask, making certain that no Na_2SO_4 is transferred with the

36.049 g

solution. Use three additional 2-mL portions of dichloromethane to rinse the Na_2SO_4 and ensure complete transfer of the clove oil to the beaker.

Assemble a simple distillation apparatus using the 50-mL round-bottom flask as the pot. Add a boiling chip. Use a 40 °C sand bath or a hot-water bath to distill the dichloromethane away from the product.

When all of the dichloromethane has been distilled, cool the flask. Weigh it to the nearest 0.001 g and record the mass. Subtract the mass of the empty flask to obtain the mass of the clove oil.

CAUTION

Methanol is flammable and toxic. Keep away from flames or other heat sources. Prevent eye, skin, and clothing contact. Use a *fume hood*.

Dissolve the clove oil in 10 mL of methanol. Proceed to the Characterizing the Product Section later in this module.

3. Cleaning Up

Place your recovered materials in the appropriate labeled collection containers as directed by your laboratory instructor. Clean your glassware with soap or detergent.

CAUTION

Wash your hands thoroughly with soap or detergent before leaving the laboratory.

MICROSCALE STEAM DISTILLATION

Using Glassware with Elastomeric Connectors

Equipment

25-mL beaker	10-mL graduated cylinder
boiling chip	marking pen
15-mL centrifuge tube, with cap	microburner
copper metal sponge	microspatula
cotton*	mortar and pestle
10-mL Erlenmeyer flask,	3 Pasteur pipets, with latex bulb
with stopper	1.0-mL pipet
125-mL Erlenmeyer flask	sand bath†
glass stirring rod	support ring
glassware,	support stand
with elastomeric connectors	thermometer, −10 to 260 °C,
distilling head/air condenser	with adapter
distilling tube,	2 utility clamps
with syringe port	wire gauze
10-mL round-bottom flask	
1-mL syringe	

* for Pasteur filter pipet
† sand in crystallizing dish on electric hot plate or sand in electric heating well with heat controller

Reagents and Properties

Substance	Quantity	Molar mass (g/mol)	bp (°C)
cloves	0.5 g		
dichloromethane	4mL	84.93	40
eugenol*		164.20	254
ice			
methanol	1 mL	32.04	64.7
sodium chloride, sat. solution	1 mL	58.44	
sodium sulfate, anhydrous	50 mg	142.04	

*product

Preview

- Grind the cloves with a mortar and pestle
- Place the ground cloves and water in the distilling flask
- Assemble the steam distillation apparatus
- Distill the mixture
- Extract the clove oil into dichloromethane
- Dry the dichloromethane layer with anhydrous Na_2SO_4
- Remove the dichloromethane from the clove oil
- Weigh the clove oil

PROCEDURE

Chemical Alert

dichloromethane—*toxic and irritant*

eugenol—*irritant*

methanol—*flammable and toxic*

anhydrous sodium sulfate—*irritant and hygroscopic*

CAUTION

Wear departmentally approved safety goggles at all times while in the chemistry laboratory.

1. Conducting Steam Distillation

Grind 10 whole cloves to a coarse powder, using a small mortar and pestle. Weigh 0.400–0.500 g of the powder and record the mass to the nearest 0.001 g.

Use a microspatula to carefully transfer the ground cloves to a 10-mL round-bottom flask. Add a boiling chip and 4 mL of deionized or distilled water. Mix well with a glass stirring rod. Mark the level of the mixture on the side of the flask.

Add 3 mL of water to a 15-mL centrifuge tube. Mark the level of the water on the side of the tube. Then discard the water from the tube.

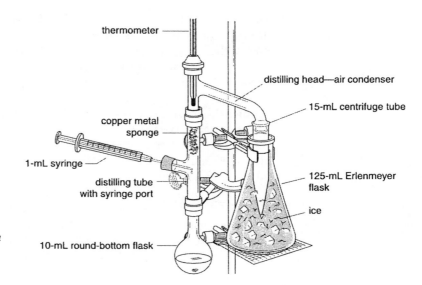

thermometer

distilling head—air condenser

15-mL centrifuge tube

copper metal sponge

1-mL syringe

distilling tube with syringe port

125-mL Erlenmeyer flask

ice

10-mL round-bottom flask

Figure 3

Microscale steam distillation apparatus using elastomeric connectors

Place a small plug of copper metal sponge in the distillation head to help prevent the mixture from foaming over into the centrifuge tube when the distilling flask is heated.

Fill a 125-mL Erlenmeyer flask three-quarters full with crushed ice. Place the centrifuge tube in the flask. Assemble the remainder of the distilling apparatus, as shown in Figure 3. Start the flow of water through the condenser.

Adjust a microburner flame to lessen the hot central cone. Heat the pot by waving the flame back and forth under the pot. Heat the mixture to maintain a distillation rate of approximately one drop every 5 s.

NOTE: Do not heat the mixture too quickly. Rapid heating may cause the mixture to foam violently. A microburner flame can easily be added and withdrawn to control the heating rate.

Draw 1.0 mL of water into the syringe. Add water dropwise to the pot every 5 min to keep the water level to the mark. Refill the syringe with water as needed. Add more ice, as needed, to the Erlenmeyer flask containing the centrifuge tube. Stop the distillation when 3 mL of distillate has been collected in the centrifuge tube.

2. Extracting the Clove Oil

CAUTION

Dichloromethane is toxic and irritating. Use a *fume hood*. Clove oil (eugenol) is irritating. Prevent eye, skin, and clothing contact.

Remove the centrifuge tube from the flask. Add 1 mL of saturated NaCl solution.

Add 1 mL of dichloromethane to the centrifuge tube. Cap the tube and gently mix the layers, being careful to *vent the tube frequently*. After the initial pressure build-up has subsided, shake the centrifuge tube vigorously to mix the layers efficiently.

Swirl the tube. At the same time, gently tap the outside of the centrifuge tube with your index finger to force into the bottom layer any droplets of dichloromethane that are adhering to the sides of the tube.

Using a Pasteur pipet, remove the lower dichloromethane layer containing the clove oil into a 10-mL Erlenmeyer flask. Make certain that no water is transferred to the flask.

Repeat the extraction process two more times using 1-mL portions of dichloromethane. Combine all three dichloromethane extracts in the same 10-mL Erlenmeyer flask.

CAUTION

Anhydrous sodium sulfate (Na_2SO_4) is irritating and hygroscopic. Do not inhale and ingest this compound.

Add approximately 50 mg of anhydrous Na_2SO_4 to the flask containing the dichloromethane extracts. Stopper the flask. Allow the extracts to dry for 5 min.

Weigh a clean, dry 25-mL beaker to the nearest 0.001 g and record the mass. Using a Pasteur filter pipet, transfer the dried dichloromethane into the beaker, making certain that no Na_2SO_4 is transferred with the solution. Use two additional 0.5-mL portions of dichloromethane to rinse the Na_2SO_4 and ensure complete transfer of the clove oil to the beaker.

In a *fume hood*, place the beaker on the *surface* of a 40 °C sand bath to evaporate the dichloromethane. Use a gentle stream of air or nitrogen to speed the evaporation.

NOTE: When evaporating the dichloromethane, use a *gentle* stream of air or nitrogen, one you *barely* feel against your hand. A strong stream of air or nitrogen may blow the solution out of the beaker and product will be lost.

When all of the dichloromethane has been evaporated, weigh the beaker to the nearest 0.001 g and record the mass. Subtract the mass of the empty beaker to obtain the mass of the clove oil.

CAUTION

Methanol is flammable and toxic. Keep away from flames or other heat sources. Prevent eye, skin, and clothing contact. Use a *fume hood*.

Dissolve the clove oil in 1 mL of methanol. Proceed to the Characterizing the Product Section later in this module.

3. Cleaning Up

Place your recovered materials in the appropriate labeled collection containers as directed by your laboratory instructor. Clean your glassware with soap or detergent.

CAUTION

Wash your hands thoroughly with soap or detergent before leaving the laboratory.

MICROSCALE STEAM DISTILLATION

Using the Hickman Still

Equipment

25-mL beaker	marking pen
boiling chip	microburner
5 mL conical vial, with screw cap	microspatula
	mortar and pestle
condenser, with tubing	1-mL pipet[†]
copper metal sponge	4 Pasteur pipets, with latex bulb
cotton*	10-mL round-bottom flask
10-mL Erlenmeyer flask, with stopper	sand bath[‡]
	support ring
glass stirring rod	support stand
10-mL graduated cylinder	2 utility clamps
Hickman still	wire gauze

* for Pasteur filter pipet
† or adjustable micropipet
‡ sand in crystallizing dish on electric hot plate or sand in electric heating well with heat controller

Reagents and Properties

Substance	Quantity	Molar mass (g/mol)	bp (°C)
cloves	0.5 g		
dichloromethane	4 mL	84.93	40
eugenol*		164.20	254
methanol	1 mL	32.04	64.7
sodium chloride, sat. solution	0.5 mL	58.44	
sodium sulfate, anhydrous	50 mg	142.04	

*product

Preview

- Grind the cloves with a mortar and pestle
- Place the ground cloves and water in the distilling flask
- Assemble the steam distillation apparatus
- Distill the mixture
- Extract the clove oil into dichloromethane
- Dry the dichloromethane layer with anhydrous Na_2SO_4
- Remove the dichloromethane from the clove oil
- Weigh the clove oil

PROCEDURE

Chemical Alert

dichloromethane—*toxic and irritant*

eugenol—*irritant*

methanol—*flammable and toxic*

anhydrous sodium sulfate—*irritant and hygroscopic*

CAUTION

Wear departmentally approved safety goggles at all times while in the chemistry laboratory.

---

1. Conducting Steam Distillation

Grind 10 whole cloves to a coarse powder, using a small mortar and pestle. Weigh 0.400–0.500 g of the powder and record the mass to the nearest 0.001 g.

Use a microspatula to carefully transfer the ground cloves to a 10-mL round-bottom flask. Add a boiling chip and 4 mL of deionized or distilled water. Mix well with a glass stirring rod. Mark the level of the mixture on the side of the flask.

Place a small plug of copper metal sponge in the neck of the Hickman still to help prevent the mixture from foaming over as it is heated.

Attach the Hickman still to the round-bottom flask. Assemble the remainder of the apparatus, as shown in Figure 4. Start the flow of water through the condenser.

Adjust a microburner flame to lessen the hot central cone. Heat the pot by waving the flame back and forth under the pot. Heat the mixture to maintain a distillation rate of approximately one drop every 5 s.

NOTE: Do not heat the mixture too rapidly. The clove mixture tends to foam when rapidly heated. The microburner flame can easily be added and withdrawn to control the heating rate.

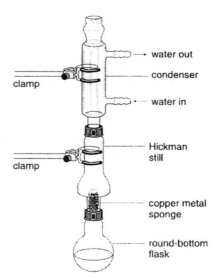

water out

condenser

clamp

water in

Hickman
still

clamp

copper metal
sponge

round-bottom
flask

Figure 4

Microscale steam distillation apparatus using a hickman still

When the bottom portion of the Hickman still is full of distillate, remove the flame. Using a bent-tip Pasteur pipet, carefully remove the distillate from the Hickman still. Place the distillate in a 5-mL conical vial. Cap the vial to avoid spillage.

NOTE: A standard Pasteur pipet can be used in a Hickman still model that has a built-in side port.

Using a clean Pasteur pipet, add water through the top of the condenser to keep the water level at the mark on the round-bottom flask. Again use the flame to distill the mixture. Continue the distillation until 3 mL of distillate has been collected in the 5-mL conical vial.

2. Extracting the Clove Oil

CAUTION

Dichloromethane is toxic and irritating. Use a *fume hood*. Clove oil (eugenol) is irritating. Prevent eye, skin, and clothing contact.

Add 0.5 mL of saturated NaCl solution to the vial. Using a bent-tip Pasteur pipet and a 0.5-mL portion of dichloromethane, carefully wash down the inside walls of the Hickman still to remove residual clove oil that adhered to the glass. Transfer the dichloromethane to the 5-mL conical vial containing the distillate.

Repeat the rinsing with a second 0.5-mL portion of dichloromethane. Transfer the second portion of dichloromethane to the 5-mL conical vial.

Cap the vial tightly and gently mix the layers, being careful to *vent the vial frequently*. After the initial pressure build-up has subsided, shake the vial vigorously to thoroughly mix the layers.

Swirl the vial. At the same time, gently tap the outside of the vial with your index finger to force into the bottom layer any droplets of dichloromethane that are adhering to the sides of the vial.

Using a Pasteur pipet, transfer the lower dichloromethane layer containing the clove oil into a 10-mL Erlenmeyer flask. Make certain that no water is transferred to the flask.

Repeat the extraction process two more times, using 1-mL portions of dichloromethane. Combine all three dichloromethane extracts in the same 10-mL Erlenmeyer flask.

CAUTION

Anhydrous sodium sulfate (Na$_2$SO$_4$) is irritating and hygroscopic. Do not inhale and ingest this compound.

Add approximately 50 mg of anhydrous Na$_2$SO$_4$ to the flask containing the dichloromethane extracts. Allow it to dry for 5 min.

Weigh a clean, dry 25-mL beaker to the nearest 0.001 g and record the mass. Using a Pasteur filter pipet, transfer the dried dichloromethane into the beaker, making certain that no Na$_2$SO$_4$ is transferred with the solution. Use two additional 0.5-mL portions of dichloromethane to rinse the Na$_2$SO$_4$ and ensure complete transfer of the clove oil to the beaker.

In a *fume hood*, place the beaker on the *surface* of a 40 °C sand bath to evaporate the dichloromethane. Use a gentle stream of air or nitrogen to speed the evaporation.

NOTE: When evaporating the dichloromethane, use a *gentle* stream of air or nitrogen, one you *barely* feel against your hand. A strong stream of air or nitrogen may blow the solution out of the beaker and product will be lost.

When all of the dichloromethane has been evaporated, weigh the beaker to the nearest 0.001 g and record the mass. Subtract the mass of the empty beaker to obtain the mass of the clove oil.

C A U T I O N

Methanol is flammable and toxic. Keep away from flames or other heat sources. Prevent eye, skin, and clothing contact. Use a *fume hood*.

Dissolve the clove oil in 1 mL of methanol. Proceed to the Characterizing the Product Section below.

3. Cleaning Up

Place your recovered materials in the appropriate labeled collection containers as directed by your laboratory instructor. Clean your glassware with soap or detergent.

C A U T I O N

Wash your hands thoroughly with soap or detergent before leaving the laboratory.

Characterizing the Product

Equipment

Bunsen burner	4 Pasteur pipets, with latex bulb
developing chamber*	pencil
10-mL graduated cylinder	6 test tubes, 13 × 100-mm
marking pen	3 × 7-cm TLC plate, silica gel,
2 melting point capillary tubes†	with fluorescent indicator
metric ruler	

---

*4-oz jar with lid or 250-mL beaker covered with aluminum foil
†for TLC micropipets

Reagents and Properties

Compound	Quantity	Molar mass (g/mol)	bp (°C)
acetone	0.5 mL	58.08	56
bromine, 1% in dichloromethane	<1 mL		
n-hexane	4.5 mL	86.18	69
iron(III) chloride, 1% aq.	<1 mL	162.21	
methanol	6 mL	32.04	64.7
potassium permanganate, 0.05*M*	<1 mL	158.04	

PROCEDURE

Chemical Alert

acetone—*flammable and irritant*
bromine—*toxic and oxidizer*
dichloromethane—*toxic and irritant*
eugenol—*irritant*
n-hexane—*flammable and irritant*
iodine—*toxic and corrosive*
iron(III) chloride—*toxic and corrosive*
methanol—*flammable and toxic*
potassium permanganate—*corrosive and oxidizer*

1. Analyzing Clove Oil by Chemical Tests

CAUTION

Clove oil (eugenol) is irritating. Methanol is flammable and toxic. Keep away from flames or other heat sources. Prevent eye, skin, and clothing contact. Do not inhale and ingest these compounds. Use a *fume hood*.

Obtain six test tubes and label them 1–6. Label tubes 2, 4, and 6 "control". Add 1 mL of methanol to each of the six tubes.

Using a Pasteur pipet, add 5 drops of the methanol-clove oil solution to test tubes 1 and 3. Add 10 drops of the methanol-clove oil solution to test tube 5. Gently swirl each tube.

Testing with Bromine in Dichloromethane

CAUTION

Bromine (Br_2) is toxic and oxidizing. Dichloromethane is toxic and irritating. Prevent eye, skin, and clothing contact. Do not inhale and ingest these compounds. Use a *fume hood*.

Using a Pasteur pipet, add a 1% Br_2 in dichloromethane solution dropwise to test tube 1. Record your observations after each drop is added. Note how many drops of the dichloromethane-Br_2 solution are needed until pale yellow coloration remains. Repeat this procedure using test tube 2.

NOTE: When all of the clove oil has reacted with Br_2, a pale yellow color will remain.

Testing with Potassium Permanganate

CAUTION

Potassium permanganate ($KMnO_4$) is corrosive and oxidizing. Prevent eye, skin, and clothing contact. Do not inhale or ingest $KMnO_4$.

Using a Pasteur pipet, add three drops of $0.05M$ $KMnO_4$ to test tube 3 and record your observations. Repeat this procedure using test tube 4.

Testing with Iron(III) Chloride

CAUTION

Iron(III) chloride (FeCl₃) is toxic and corrosive. Prevent eye, skin, and clothing contact. Do not inhale or ingest FeCl₃.

Using a Pasteur pipet, add one drop of 1% $FeCl_3$ solution to test tube 5 and one drop to test tube 6. Record your observations.

2. Analyzing Clove Oil by Thin-Layer Chromatography

CAUTION

Acetone and *n*-hexane are flammable and irritating. Keep away from flames or other heat sources. Prevent eye, skin, and clothing contact. Do not inhale and ingest these compounds. Use a *fume hood*.

CAUTION

Clove oil (eugenol) is irritating. Methanol is flammable and toxic. Keep away from flames or other heat sources. Prevent eye, skin, and clothing contact. Do not inhale and ingest these compounds. Use a *fume hood*.

Obtain a 3 × 7-cm silica gel TLC plate from your laboratory instructor. Draw a *very faint* pencil line 1 cm from the bottom to mark the origin. Make two vertical marks that intersect the pencil line 0.5 cm from each edge of the plate and a third mark 1.5 cm from one edge.

Prepare micropipets for spotting the TLC plates by drawing out melting point capillary tubing. Using a micropipet, spot a standard sample of eugenol once on the middle mark, keeping the spot as small as possible. Using a new micropipet, spot your methanol-clove oil sample once on the left-hand mark. Using the same micropipet, spot your sample twice on the right hand mark, allowing the solvent to evaporate between spottings.

Prepare a developing chamber by pouring 4.5 mL of *n*-hexane and 0.5 mL of acetone into a 4-oz jar. Place the TLC plate into the chamber and attach the lid. Allow the eluent to develop the plate.

NOTE: Do not put filter paper or paper towel in the developing chamber. In this case, a better separation occurs without chamber saturation.

CAUTION

Ultraviolet radiation can cause severe eye damage. Wear goggles. Do not look directly into the UV lamp.

Iodine (I₂) is toxic and corrosive. Prevent eye, skin, and clothing contact. Do not inhale and ingest I₂. Use a *fume hood*.

After developing the plate, *immediately* mark the eluent front. Dry the plate in a *fume hood*. Visualize the chromatogram under short-wave UV light or in an I_2 chamber, as directed by your laboratory instructor. Use a pencil to circle the spots on your plate.

Measure the distance from the origin to the eluent front. Measure the distance from the origin to the center of each spot. Record your observations.

NOTE: Eugenol acetate should appear as a minor spot at a higher R_f than that of eugenol.

3. Cleaning Up

Place your recovered materials in the appropriate labeled collection containers as directed by your laboratory instructor. Clean your glassware with soap or detergent.

CAUTION

Wash your hands thoroughly with soap or detergent before leaving the laboratory.

_____   _____   _____
name   *section*   *date*

Post-Laboratory Questions

1. Calculate the percent yield of clove oil based upon the initial mass of the ground cloves.

2. Give your test results for the reaction of your eugenol product with each of the test reagents.

3. Complete the following reactions, giving the correct structure for each organic product.

 (a) eugenol + Br_2 →

 (b) eugenol acetate + $KMnO_4$ →

 (c) eugenol + $FeCl_3$ →

 (d) eugenol acetate + $FeCl_3$ →

4. Complete the following table after performing the TLC analysis on your clove oil sample. Indicate by a yes or no answer whether the spots are visible under UV light or I_2 vapors.

Compound	R_f	UV	I_2
eugenol			
eugenol acetate			
other			

5. Using your R_fs, list the compounds in your clove oil in order of increasing polarity. Briefly explain your answer.

name   section   date

Pre-Laboratory Assignment

1. What precautions must be taken when mixing reagents in a separatory funnel or centrifuge tube?

2. Briefly define the following terms:
   (a) codistillation

   (b) steam distillation

   (c) Raoult's law

   (d) Dalton's law

   (e) essential oil

3. Why is steam distillation preferable to simple distillation for isolating high-boiling natural products?

Properties of Hydrocarbons

Hydrocarbons are those organic compounds composed only of carbon and hydrogen. There are *three main categories of hydrocarbons:* saturated, unsaturated, and aromatic. Saturated hydrocarbons have only carbon–carbon single bonds, whereas unsaturated hydrocarbons have carbon–carbon double or triple bonds. Aromatic hydrocarbons are cyclic compounds whose chemical properties are related to benzene.

Saturated hydrocarbons (alkanes and cycloalkanes) are relatively inert and do not react with common laboratory reagents. Unsaturated hydrocarbons (alkenes and alkynes), however, readily undergo addition reactions and oxidation reactions. Benzene and other aromatic compounds do not readily undergo addition reactions but are characterized by substitution reactions in which another atom or group of atoms replaces a ring hydrogen.

Although alkanes are relatively inert, they do undergo combustion in the presence of air if ignited. The fact that these reactions are highly exothermic and that huge quantities of alkanes are available as petroleum and natural gas has resulted in their extensive use as fuels. While the chemistry of alkanes is relatively straightforward, their economic impact can hardly be overestimated. Consequences resulting from this economic importance include oil spills, air pollution from automobiles, the greenhouse effect, and the threat of war in certain parts of the world.

EXPERIMENTS

Performing the following tests will illustrate general properties of hydrocarbons as well as differences in chemical reactivity due to the type of hydrocarbon (saturated, unsaturated, or aromatic) being considered. Perform all six tests on cyclohexane, cyclohexene, toluene, and two unknowns. One unknown will be an alkane or cycloalkane and a second will be an alkene or alkyne. Using the information that a lack of reactivity is characteristic of saturated hydrocarbons and addition reactions are common for unsaturated hydrocarbons, decide the identity of each unknown as to type of hydrocarbon.

SAFETY NOTE

Concentrated sulfuric acid, concentrated nitric acid, and bromine can cause burns. If any one of these is spilled on the skin, wash immediately with water. Exposure to the vapors of bromine or methylene chloride should be avoided; use these reagents in a hood.

Disposal. Dispose of all waste from these test tube experiments in the appropriate waste containers as directed by your instructor.

PROCEDURE

A. **Solubility**   Place 2 mL of water in a 13 × 100-mm test tube and add 2 or 3 drops of the hydrocarbon to be tested. Shake the mixture to determine whether the hydrocarbon is soluble (a colorless second layer may be hard to see). Record your results and save the mixture for Test B.

B. **Relative Density**   Reexamine the mixtures prepared above and decide in each case whether the hydrocarbon is more dense (sinks) or less dense than water (floats).

C. **Flammability**   Test the flammability of each hydrocarbon by placing 2 or 3 drops on an evaporating dish in the hood and igniting it with a match or microburner. Note the nature of the flame: sooty flames are characteristic of unsaturated compounds.

D. **Addition of Bromine**   Dissolve 3 or 4 drops of the hydrocarbon in 1 mL of methylene chloride (dichloromethane) in a 13 × 100-mm test tube. Add dropwise a 2% solution of bromine dissolved in methylene chloride with shaking. The loss of bromine color is an indication of an unsaturated compound (do not confuse diminution of color due to dilution of the Br_2/CH_2Cl_2 solution with an actual loss of color).

E. **Reaction with Potassium Permanganate**   Dissolve 3 or 4 drops of the hydrocarbon in 1 mL of reagent-grade acetone and then add dropwise a 1% solution of potassium permanganate with shaking. A loss of the purple color of the permanganate solution indicates that a reaction has taken place and that the hydrocarbon is unsaturated.

F. **Reaction with Sulfuric Acid**   Place 1 mL of concentrated sulfuric acid in a 13 × 100-mm test tube and then add 3 or 4 drops of the hydrocarbon one drop at a time. (Caution!) Reaction is indicated not only by the dissolution of the sample but also by changes in color, production of heat, or the formation of insoluble material. If no reaction occurs, warm the mixture (be careful that the hydrocarbon does not evaporate). If the unknown is a simple aromatic hydrocarbon it will react with the warm sulfuric acid to form a sulfonic acid which will dissolve.

At this point, information from Tests D, E, and F should allow you to determine which unknown is an alkane or cycloalkane and which is an alkene or alkyne. Record your conclusions about each unknown.

It should be pointed out that while the reagents in Tests D, E, and F may be used to distinguish saturated and unsaturated hydrocarbons, they will also react with other organic compounds. Potassium permanganate reacts with easily oxidized compounds (alcohols, aldehydes, amines, etc.), while concentrated sulfuric acid reacts with a variety of Lewis bases (such as alcohols and other oxygen-containing compounds and amines). Care should be taken not to use these tests with compounds other than hydrocarbons and then misinterpret the results.

QUESTIONS

1. Considering your results in the solubility tests, what do you conclude about the solubility of hydrocarbons in water? Predict the solubility of gasoline and motor oil in water.
2. Are hydrocarbons less dense or more dense than water? Does this have any practical importance when oil spills occur?
3. Write equations using 1-butene to illustrate the reactions occurring in Tests D, E, and F of the experimental procedure (use your text).
4. Write equations using cyclohexene to illustrate the reactions in Tests D, E, and F.

5. Write a balanced equation for the complete combustion of octane. What other product(s) are produced when incomplete combustion of octanes occurs in an automobile engine?
6. How could one distinguish octane from 1-octene by a simple chemical test; 1-octanol from 1-octene; and toluene from 1-octene?

PRELABORATORY QUESTIONS

1. Draw skeletal (line-bond) structures for cyclohexane, cyclohexene, and toluene.
2. What color is potassium permanganate solution? What is the formula for potassium permanganate?
3. Would you expect a significant difference between the reactivity of hexane and cyclohexane? Explain your answer.
4. The general formula for an alkane is C_nH_{2n+2}. What is the corresponding general formula of a cycloalkene?
5. List four hazardous chemicals that are used in this experiment.

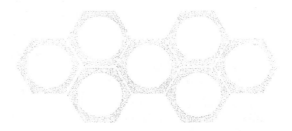

Nucleophilic Substitution of Alkyl Halides

Alkyl halides, alkyl sulfates, and alkyl sulfonates serve as reactants or "substrates" in many nucleophilic substitution reactions. These substitution (or displacement) reactions are useful preparative methods, for example, the Williamson synthesis of ethers. For our purpose the term "nucleophilic" will refer to a reaction in which a nucleophile (HO^-, X^-, S^{2-}, HS^-, etc.) attacks a carbon atom and displaces a "leaving group," another nucleophile. Although these reactions proceed in a continuum of slightly different pathways, they can be viewed as occurring in a combination of two limiting mechanisms:

1. **Substitution: Nucleophilic, Unimolecular (S_N1)**

This mechanism involves more than one step, the first of which is the ionization of the alkyl halide substrate, yielding a carbocation and an anion. The planar carbocation then reacts with a nucleophile, forming the product (in the case of chiral compounds, racemic product generally results). Since the nucleophile is often a solvent molecule, the process is sometimes called **solvolysis.** A typical S_N1 reaction is the solvolysis reaction of *tertiary*-butyl chloride with water to form *tert*-butyl alcohol.

2. **Substitution: Nucleophilic, Bimolecular (S_N2)**

This reaction involves one so-called concerted step in which the nucleophile attacks the carbon atom of the substrate on the side opposite the leaving group. An inversion of configuration of chiral compounds results.

Studies of the mechanisms of these reactions were undertaken in the early 1930s in order to explain the vast differences in the rates of seemingly very similar reactions. Since that time, these findings have been refined to encompass the effects of solvent, ionic strength, added electrolytes, the nature of the alkyl group, and other factors. Some of these factors will be illustrated in this experiment. In addition, the complex methodology of determining the rate of a reaction will be undertaken.

EXPERIMENTS

A. STRUCTURAL EFFECTS ON S_N1 AND S_N2 REACTIVITY

In this experiment the relative reactivities of a series of halides are observed under two sets of conditions, one of which favors the S_N1 mechanism and the other the S_N2. The S_N2 reaction is observed by the displacement of chloride or bromide by an iodide ion in acetone solution. The iodide ion is a good nucleophile for the S_N2 reaction, whereas acetone is a relatively poor ionizing solvent, and S_N1 dissociation is minimized. Sodium iodide is very soluble in acetone, but sodium chloride and sodium bromide have very low solubilities; so the course of the reactions can be followed by the formation of crystalline NaCl or NaBr (Eq. 17.1).

$$R{-}X \ + \ NaI \ \xrightarrow{\text{acetone}} \ R{-}I \ + \ NaX \downarrow \qquad\qquad (17.1)$$

The S_N1 reaction can be observed by treating the alkyl halide with a solution of silver nitrate in aqueous ethanol. Nitrate ion is a very poor nucleophile so there is little opportunity for S_N2 displacement. Dissociation of the alkyl halide by the S_N1 process is followed by the precipitation of the insoluble silver halide (Eq. 17.2); the carbocation is then captured by alcohol or water

$$R{-}X \longrightarrow R^+ + X^- \xrightarrow{\text{AgNO}_3} \ AgX \downarrow \ +NO_3^- \qquad\qquad (17.2)$$

PROCEDURE

SAFETY NOTE

Alkyl halides are toxic and flammable; avoid breathing them or spilling them on the skin. Insure that there is proper ventilation.

Label two series of five clean, thoroughly dry test tubes with numerals 1 to 5. In each series of tubes, place 0.2 mL of the following halides: (1) n-butyl chloride, (2) n-butyl bromide, (3) sec-butyl chloride, (4) tert-butyl chloride, and (5) crotyl chloride [$CH_3CH{=}CHCH_2Cl$]. Keep the tubes stoppered with corks or parafilm and leave them covered at all times, before and after adding reagents. Obtain 15 mL of 15% NaI-acetone solution and 15 mL of 1% ethanolic $AgNO_3$ solution from the side shelf.

Arrange one series of tubes in order, from 1 to 5. Add 2 mL of the NaI solution to tube number 1 and note the time. (Add the solution from a pipet as rapidly as possible—not dropwise.)

After 2 to 3 minutes, add 2 mL of NaI solution to the second tube and again note the time. Continue the addition at 2- to 3-minute intervals with the remaining tubes. After each addition, watch for any rapid reaction and then inspect the other tubes for signs of a precipitate. Note the time as closely as possible when precipitation begins to occur, recording the data in tabular form in your notebook. Cover the tubes and allow them to stand, observing them periodically while the next series is run.

Arrange the second series of tubes, and in the same way add 2-mL portions of the AgNO₃ solution to each tube at 2-minute intervals. Again, watch closely for any that change rapidly and then observe the others periodically. If possible, note the time both for the first appreciable turbidity and also for a definite precipitate. If any tubes in the NaI series are still clear at this point, loosen the covers slightly and place the tubes in a water bath at 50°C; note any changes that occur. Record the data in tabular form with column headings: tube number, time turbidity appears, and time of definite precipitate.

When you have completed these test tube reactions, pour the contents of all of the test tubes into the organic waste container.

B. EFFECTS OF SOLVENT ON S_N1 REACTIVITY

In addition to structural features of the halide, reaction conditions can have a large effect on the rate of nucleophile substitution. For example, the solvent plays a major role in both S_N1 and S_N2 reactions, and in this experiment the effect of solvent on the rate of the S_N1 solvolysis of *tert*-butyl chloride will be studied. For this purpose, the most suitable method for comparing solvolysis rates is based on the fact that a strong acid is liberated in the reaction (Eq. 17.3). To determine the extent to which the reaction has proceeded, enough base is added to the reaction mixture to neutralize a small fraction of the acid produced. The solution becomes acidic after that fraction of the *tert*-butyl chloride has reacted, and the change in pH is detected with phenolphthalein indicator. The time required for neutralization is inversely proportional to the rate constant of the reaction, k_1, as shown in Equation 17.4.

$$t\text{-Bu}\text{—Cl} + ROH \rightarrow t\text{-Bu}\text{—OR} + HCl \qquad (17.3)$$

The rate of formation of HCl by S_N1 solvolysis of an alkyl chloride is equal to the rate of disappearance of alkyl chloride and is proportional to the concentration of the alkyl halide (Eq. 17.4).

$$\frac{d[HCl]}{dt} = k_1[RCl] = \frac{-d[RCl]}{dt} \qquad (17.4)$$

Integration of this equation from 0 to 50% reaction (100 to 50% of the RCl) provides Equation 17.5 where $t_{1/2}$ is the time required for 50% of the alkyl halide to react. If 0.50 equivalents of hydroxide ion were present at the start of the reaction, $t_{1/2}$ will be the time at which the solution becomes acidic.

$$\int_{1.0}^{0.5} \frac{d[RCl]}{[RCl]} = -\int_0^{t_{1/2}} k_1 dt$$

$$2.3 \log 0.5 = -k_1 t_{1/2} \qquad (17.5)$$

$$k_1 = -2.3 \log 0.5 / t_{1/2} = 0.69 / t_{1/2}$$

In the procedure to be used, the amounts of alkyl halide and hydroxide are not accurately measured, since only relative rates are desired. If the alkyl halide used were weighed and the NaOH solution were standardized and accurately dispensed, actual rate constants could be obtained.

Suitable solvent systems for this study are mixtures of water with methanol, ethanol, and acetone. The volume percent compositions indicated below will give conveniently measurable reaction rates, with the exception noted for 70% acetone. The following solutions will be available.

COMPOSITION (SOLVENT: WATER)	
55:45	(all solvents)
60:40	(all solvents)
65:35	(all solvents)
70:30	(not acetone)

PROCEDURE

Select three to five solvent mixtures, using either different ratios of one solvent or the same ratio with the three solvents, and label each of three to five clean, dry 13 × 100-mm test tubes accordingly. To each test tube add 2.0 mL of the solvent system and 3 drops of 0.5 M NaOH solution containing phenolphthalein indicator. Cover the tubes with corks or parafilm, and place them in a bath containing a thermometer and water at 30 ± 1°C. A Styrofoam cup placed in an empty beaker for stability makes a convenient insulated container for the bath. After 4 to 5 minutes in the bath to bring the solvent to bath temperature, add 3 drops of *tert*-butyl chloride to each test tube. Note the time of addition, shake or swirl the test tubes to mix the solutions, and replace them in the bath, swirling intermittently to insure good mixing. Add a few mL of hot water as needed to the bath to maintain the temperature at 30 ± 1°C. Record the time required for the pink (basic) color to disappear in each solvent mixture. Tabulate your results and compare them with those of others in the class to obtain a more complete picture of the solvent effects.

C. EFFECT OF TEMPERATURE ON REACTION RATES

The rate of any reaction increases with increasing temperature because of the greater kinetic energy of the reacting molecules. The effect of temperature on the rate constant of a reaction is generally expressed in terms of the Arrhenius Equation (Eq. 17.6) where E_a is the activation energy, T is the temperature in K, A is a term related to the probability of a reaction occurring if the molecules have sufficient energy, and R is the gas constant (1.99 cal/mole deg). The activation energy can be obtained if the rate constant is known at two or more temperatures. Using the logarithmic form of Equation 17.6 (Eq. 17.7), it is seen that a plot of log k versus $1/T$ gives a straight line with slope equaling $-E_a/2.3R$.

$$k = A \exp\left(-\frac{E_a}{RT}\right) \tag{17.6}$$

$$\log k = \log A - \frac{E_a}{2.3R}\left(\frac{1}{T}\right) \tag{17.7}$$

The effect of temperature on the rate of solvolysis of *tert*-butyl chloride can be studied using the procedure and solvent systems of Part B at different temperatures. To obtain conveniently measurable rates, a solvent should be used that gives an end point at about 10 minutes in Part B. Although numerical values of the rate constants are not obtained by the comparative procedure in Part B, the neutralization times measured are inversely proportional to the rate constants (Eq. 17.5). Thus, a plot of log t values versus $1/T$ gives a straight line with slope $+ E_a/2.3R$ from which the value of E_a can be obtained.

PROCEDURE

From your results in Part B, select the solvent system for which the neutralization time at 30°C is closest to 10 minutes. Obtain two 2-mL mixtures of this solvent composition and add 3 drops of phenolphthalein indicator solution as in Part B. (In this part of the experiment, duplicate samples should be run.)

Adjust the temperature of the water bath to 20 ± 1°C, insert both tubes, and allow 4 to 5 minutes for temperature equilibration. Note the time, add 3 drops of *tert*-butyl chloride to each tube, mix, and measure the time required for the color to disappear. Repeat the procedure with two other samples after adjusting the bath temperature to 40 ± 1°C.

Using the times required for the samples at 20°C and 40°C and the time at 30°C from Part B, make a plot of log t versus $1/T$ (°K), and from the slope, calculate the activation energy for the solvolysis in the solvent used.

D. REACTION OF ETHYL BROMIDE WITH HYDROXIDE ION, AN S_N2 REACTION

This is a variation of the classic experiments of Grant and Hinshelwood involving the reaction of ethyl bromide and hydroxide ion:

$$EtBr + HO^- \rightarrow EtOH + Br^- + \text{other products}$$

If this reaction goes by an S_N2 mechanism, the following equations should apply:

$$\text{rate} = k[EtBr][HO^-]$$

$$\text{if } [EtBr] = [HO^-], \text{ then rate} = k[HO^-]^2$$

$$\frac{1}{[HO^-]} = kt + \frac{1}{[HO^-]_0}$$

A plot of the hydroxide ion concentration versus time then should give a straight line with the slope equal to k (rate constant).

PROCEDURE

Students should work in pairs. For each pair of students, prepare the following solutions:

a. 200 mL of 0.10 M HCl
b. 50 mL of 0.40 M ethyl bromide in ethanol
c. 50 mL of 0.40 M potassium hydroxide (CO_2 free) in ethanol.

Place the stock solutions of ethyl bromide and potassium hydroxide in a water bath at 40°C and allow them to come to temperature equilibrium.

In a 250-mL Erlenmeyer flask, pipet exactly 50 mL of the ethyl bromide solution and exactly 50 mL of the KOH solution. Mix the contents of the flask thoroughly and place it securely in the 40°C water bath (a 1-liter beaker may be used for each pair of students; add ice or hot water as needed). Immediately take a 10-mL aliquot and deliver it into a 250-mL Erlenmeyer flask containing 50 mL of ice water. This will quench the reaction so that a titration can be performed. Take as the starting time when the pipet is half empty. Titrate rapidly with 0.10 M HCl to the phenolphthalein end point. Record the number of mL of acid necessary to allow a faint pink color to remain in the solution and record this as the volume of NaOH at zero time. Repeat, taking aliquots and titrating them at 20-minute intervals up to 2 hours. Record the data in tabular form with these headings: clock, time (minutes), time (seconds), initial buret reading, final buret reading, volume HCl used, $[HO^-]$, and $1/[HO^-]$.

Plot the values of $1/[HO^-]$ versus the time in seconds. The slope of the line is the rate constant (units are liter/mole•sec.). Compare the value obtained with those of others in the class.

QUESTIONS

1. Explain the relative reactivities observed in Part A for butyl chloride, *sec*-butyl chloride, and *tert*-butyl chloride with NaI in acetone in terms of the structure of the transition state.
2. Similarly, explain the relative reactivities of the three butyl chlorides in ethanolic $AgNO_3$.
3. Based on the data obtained by your class in Part B, arrange the following solvents in order of increasing S_N1 solvolytic power: water, acetone, methanol, and ethanol. Explain in terms of the mechanism how the properties of the solvents account for the observed trend.
4. With the procedure used in Part B, would the color change occur sooner, later, or at the same time if: (a) twice as much *tert*-butyl chloride were used; (b) twice as much NaOH-phenolphthalein solution were used?
5. Sketch the reaction coordinate diagram for the solvolysis of *tert*-butyl chloride, labeling the maxima and minima with appropriate structures and indicating the activation energy measured in Part C.

PRELABORATORY QUESTIONS

1. Give structures of the products of the following nucleophilic substitution reactions:
   a. ethyl bromide and KOH (aq.)
   b. butyl chloride and NaI (acetone)
   c. *tert*-butyl iodide and ethanol
2. Illustrate the S_N2 mechanism for the reaction of methyl bromide with iodide ion.
3. How many mL of a 0.10 M solution of HCl are necessary to neutralize 10.00 mL of 0.16 M KOH?
4. Which should have more room for S_N2 attack by a nucleophile: methyl chloride or *tert*-butyl chloride? Explain.

REFERENCES

Grant, G. H.; Hinshelwood. C. N. *J. Chem. Soc.*, 1933, 258.

March, J. *Advanced Organic Chemistry,* 4th ed.; Wiley-Interscience: New York, 1992; Chapter 10.

Moore. J. W.; Pearson. R. G. *Kinetics and Mechanism;* John Wiley and Sons: New York, 1981.

Diphenylacetylene from Stilbene

Background Reading
Material on dehydrohalogenations and alkyne synthesis in your organic textbook.

Timing
(Part **A**: 1.5 h; Part **B**: 2 h; Part **C**:1.5 h)

The addition of bromine to a carbon–carbon double bond is a classic reaction that is stereospecific with anti-addition. Although bromine in an inert solvent such as carbon tetrachloride or methylene chloride can be used as the reagent, a more convenient source of the bromine is pyridinium bromide perbromide, $PyH^+ Br_3^-$ in glacial acetic acid. This reagent is dry solid that can be accurately weighed and is safer to handle than solutions of bromine. The use of this reagent has the advantage of giving greater stereospecificity than bromine solutions.

$$PhCH = CHPh + PyH^+Br_3^- \xrightarrow{\text{HOAc}} PhCHBrCHBrPh + PyH^+Br^-$$

A. *meso*-1,2-Dibromo-1,2-diphenylethane

Weigh 200 mg (1.11 mmol) of (*E*)-stilbene into a tared 10-mL pear-shapedflask, add a very small magnetic stir bar, and introduce about 4 mL of glacial acetic acid from a buret in the hood. Add an air condenser and clamp the flask into a heated sand bath[1] on top of a magnetic stirrer, as shown in Figure E18.1. Stir and heat the suspension to about 100°C to dissolve the stilbene. While the flask is being heated, weigh an amount of pyridinium bromide perbromide (onto glazed weighing paper) that corresponds to a 10 mol % excess relative to the amount of stilbene used.

[1] It works best to preheat the sand bath to about 140°C and then control the temperature in the flask by raising or lowering the flask in the sand.

EXERCISE

1. Check your calculation result with the instructor before you proceed.

Lift the flask out of the sand bath, remove the air condenser, and with a small dry funnel introduce the pyridinium bromide perbromide directly into the flask so as not to let any of the solid get on the glass joint of the flask. Replace the condenser, stir, and continue to heat at 80–100°C for 5–10 min. The initial bromine color will disappear, but there will be persistent yellow after the heating period. Remove the flask and condenser from the sand bath, add 4 mL of water (graduated cylinder) through the condenser, cork the flask, and allow it to stand in an ice bath for about 10–15 min with occasional swirling. (Using a 100–150-mL beaker for the ice bath will eliminate the danger of the flask tipping over.) Collect the product by suction filtration with a Hirsch funnel. Rinse any residual compound in the flask into the funnel with water to remove any residual acetic acid and finally with two portions of about 1 mL each of

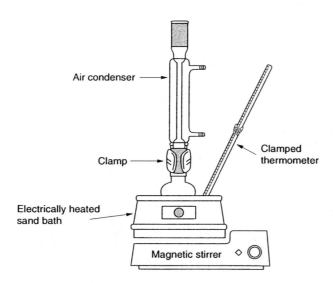

Air condenser

Clamp

Clamped thermometer

Electrically heated sand bath

Magnetic stirrer

Figure E18.1   Apparatus for Part A

methanol. Allow the tiny plate crystals to suck dry for a few minutes, transfer them to a piece of weighed glazed paper, apply gentle heat (heat lamp) until the sample is thoroughly dry, and calculate your yield of *meso*-1,2-dibromo-1,2-diphenylethane. (Yields will normally be greater than 80%; the reported mp is 241°C with decomposition.) A portion of this material can be used to prepare diphenylacetylene, and the remainder submitted to the instructor.

    The elimination of two mols of HBr from a vicinal or geminal dibromide can result in the formation of an alkyne. Although such eliminations sometimes require the use of very strong bases such as sodium amide, the preparation of diphenylacetylene from either *meso*- or (±)-1,2-dibromo-1,2-diphenylethane can be accomplished with potassium hydroxide in triethylene glycol at 190–200°C.

$$\text{PhCHBrCHBrPh} \;+\; 2\text{KOH} \;\xrightarrow[\text{HOCH}_2\text{CH}_2\text{OCH}_2\text{CH}_2\text{OCH}_2\text{CH}_2\text{OH}]{190\text{–}200°\text{C}}\; \text{PhC}\!\equiv\!\text{CPh} \;+\; 2\text{KBr} \;+\; 2\text{HOH}$$

B. Diphenylacetylene from meso-Dibromide

Weigh 200 mg (0.588 mmol) of dry *meso*-1,2-dibromo-1,2-diphenylethane into a 10-mL pear-shaped flask, add 1 mL of triethylene glycol with an automatic pipet, and one small pellet of potassium hydroxide (about 150–200 mg, a large excess; a small oval pellets is about the correct mass.[2] Heat a sand bath containing a thermometer to 185–195°C. Then clamp the flask down in the sand next to the thermometer. Remove the flask when the reaction mixture turns dark (about 1–2 min), swirl it, and replace it in the hot sand for about 5 min. Remove the flask from the sand bath, and allow the dark brown mixture in the flask to cool for a few minutes in the air and then in an ice bath for an additional 5 min (very important). Add 6 mL of water, stir to thoroughly mix in the water, and filter the crude product by suction with a small Hirsch funnel. Residue in the flask can be rinsed into the funnel with water followed by several additional rinses (2–3 mL each) with water to ensure that the crude product is free of excess

2. To avoid using too large an excess of KOH, weigh a pellet to determine that it is in the range stated above and then discard this pellet (because it will pick up too much water) and pick a new one similar in size to use.

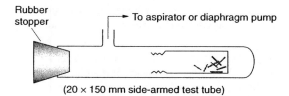

Figure E18.2 Microscale vacuum oven

(20 × 150 mm side-armed test tube)

potassium hydroxide. Allow the diphenylacetylene to suck dry for a few minutes and then air dry to give a dirty, brownish, but largely crystalline crude product.

Recrystallize the product with a microscale procedure from 95% methanol (too much loss occurs with 95% ethanol) A dry sample of 60 mg of crude diphenylacetylene will require at least 1 mL of 95% methanol for the initial part of the recrystallization procedure. Allow the filtrate to cool slowly, then in ice to give off-white (tan) crystals. Transfer the crystals (with the help of a few drops of ice-cold 95% methanol) to a Hirsch funnel, suck the crystals dry, and wash them twice with no more than several drops of ice-cold 95% methanol. Dry the final product carefully in the air or use a vacuum oven (Figure E18.2) with very low heat to avoid melting the product. Determine the yield[3] and melting point. (Reported mps 59–61°C.)

3. The yield of recrystallized product will generally be quite low in this sacrifice to gain purity.

C. (±)-1,2-Dibromo-1,2-diphenylethane

Follow much the same procedure as in the preparation of the *meso*-compound (above), but use an automatic delivery pipet to measure 50 μL (0.280 mmol) of (Z)-stilbene into the reaction flask containing about 1 mL of glacial acetic acid. Add a 10 mol % excess of pyridinium bromide perbromide through a dry funnel into the flask; heat and stir the mixture at 70–90°C for 5–10 min; some yellow color may persist. Add 2 mL of water (graduated cylinder) through the condenser and allow the resulting suspension of product to cool in ice. Collect the crude product on a Hirsch funnel by suction filtration, rinse any residual product from the flask with water, and finally with a small volume of cold 95% methanol. Allow the solid to suck dry for a few minutes and obtain the yield of crude product (typically >60%).

The racemic product will be contaminated with some *meso* product, which has much lower solubility in hot ethanol. Purify the racemic product by recrystallization from 95% ethanol with a Craig tube or with the Pasteur pipet method and check the mp. (Reported mp is 113–114°C.) In that recrystallization, use about 0.2 mL of 95% ethanol for each 15 mg of crude product to be recrystallized. Any *meso*-1,2-dibromo-1,2-diphenylethane that is present will remain essentially undissolved under these conditions. After suction filtration on a Hirsch funnel, wash the crystals with a small volume of cold 95% ethanol. Check the mp of the dry crystalline product. Record both the crude yield (racemic + *meso*) and the purified yield of the racemic compound.

EXERCISES

2. Show a step-by-step mechanism to rationalize the formation of *meso*- and of (±)-1,2-dibromo-1,2-diphenylethane from *E*- and (Z)-stilbene, respectively. Draw "sawhorse" and Newman projection formulas for the two diasteriomeric vicinal dibromides.

3. If the observed mp for (±)-1,2-dibromo-1,2-diphenylethane represents the behavior of a mixture at its eutectic point, what experiment could you do to prove it?

4. From your knowledge that the E2 reaction is most favored when the leaving groups are anti- and coplanar, predict the stereochemistry of the bromoalkene that would result from the loss of one mol of HBr from *meso*- and from (±)-1,2-dibromo-1,2-diphenylethane. Which reaction should be slower? Why?

5. Suggest a possible reason why the reaction of pyridinium bromide perbromide with pure (Z)-stilbene gave some *meso*-dibromide in addition to the expected (±)-dibromide. What change in the usual mechanism for bromination of an alkene would explain this result?

Dehydration of Alcohols

Alcohols may be dehydrated under acid-catalyzed conditions to form alkenes. In the presence of Bronsted acids, such as sulfuric or phosphoric acid, dehydrations involve the initial protonation of the hydroxyl group (Eq. 20.1), converting it to an excellent leaving group. Loss of water then normally takes place by a unimolecular process, resulting in a highly reactive carbocation that can stabilize itself by the elimination of a proton from an adjacent carbon to give the alkene.

$$
\underset{\text{alcohol}}{-\overset{\overset{\displaystyle H}{|}}{C}-\overset{\overset{\displaystyle OH}{|}}{C}-} \xrightarrow{H^+} -\overset{\overset{\displaystyle H}{|}}{C}-\overset{\overset{\displaystyle \overset{+}{O}H_2}{|}}{C}- \xrightarrow{-H_2O}
$$

$$
\underset{\text{carbocation}}{-\overset{\overset{\displaystyle H}{|}}{C}-\overset{+}{C}-} \xrightarrow{-H^+} ^{\diagup}_{\diagdown}C=C^{\diagup}_{\diagdown}
$$

(20.1)

Carbocations can also rearrange, by alkyl and/or hydride shifts, to form more stable cationic species that then yield other alkenes. A typical example of such a multiple-product reaction is shown in Equation 20.2.

$$
\underset{\underset{\displaystyle CH_3}{|}}{\overset{\overset{\displaystyle CH_3}{|}}{CH_3-C}}-\underset{\underset{\displaystyle OH}{|}}{CH}-CH_3 \xrightarrow[-H_2O]{H^+} \underset{\underset{\displaystyle CH_3}{|}}{\overset{\overset{\displaystyle CH_3}{|}}{CH_3-C}}-CH=CH_2
$$

0.4%

$$
+ \underset{\underset{\displaystyle 80.0\%}{}}{CH_3-\overset{\overset{\displaystyle CH_3}{|}}{C}=\overset{\overset{\displaystyle CH_3}{|}}{C}-CH_3} + \underset{\underset{\displaystyle 19.6\%}{}}{CH_3-\overset{\overset{\displaystyle CH_3}{|}}{CH}-\overset{\overset{\displaystyle CH_3}{|}}{C}=CH_2}
$$

(20.2)

The ratios and types of alkenes formed depend on the catalyst used and the reaction conditions. Many types of catalysts other than Bronsted acids have been used in alcohol dehydrations.

These include iodine, alumina, molecular sieves, and ion exchange resins. Dehydrating agents such as $POCl_3$ and acetic anhydride have also been used, in which case the elimination usually proceeds via the corresponding ester intermediate.

With secondary and tertiary alcohols, direct Bronsted acid–catalyzed dehydration is often a simple and convenient procedure. If the elimination product is sensitive to further reaction with acid, as may be the case if the alcohol contains other functional groups, procedures that avoid strong acids must be used.

Dehydration of alcohols using Bronsted acids is illustrated in the following experiments. The procedures described use phosphoric acid; sulfuric acid can cause charring and can give off sulfur dioxide fumes.

EXPERIMENTS

SAFETY NOTE

The dehydration products formed in these reactions are highly flammable. If a burner is used in the distillation, take care that vapors of the product are not exposed to the flame. Handle phosphoric acid with care. Should phosphoric acid be spilled on your skin. wash it off with copious amounts of water. If droplets of phosphoric acid are splashed in your eyes, use the eyewash fountain to properly wash them.

Disposal. Dispose of all waste products from these experiments in the appropriate waste containers as directed by your instructor.

A.   PREPARATION OF CYCLOHEXENE

(Macroscale)

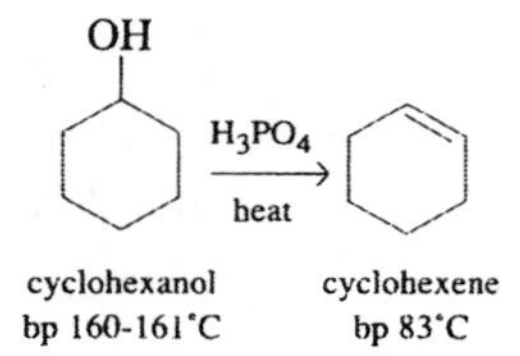

cyclohexanol 　　　 cyclohexene
bp 160-161°C 　　　 bp 83°C

PROCEDURE

Weigh 10.0 grams of cyclohexanol into a 25-mL round-bottom flask. Carefully add 5 mL of 85% phosphoric acid. then a boiling stone, and mount the flask for fractional distillation (see Fig. 5.7; either use no column packing or a low hold-up packing). Slowly heat the mixture until it comes to a gentle boil. After 10 minutes of gentle boiling, increase the heat sufficiently to cause distillation (the temperature of the distilling vapor should not exceed 100°C) and collect the distillate in a cooled receiver.

To the distillate, add 2 mL of 10% sodium carbonate solution to neutralize any traces of acid that may have been carried over. Transfer the liquids to a separatory funnel, add 10 mL of cold water, swirl the mixture gently, and drain off the lower aqueous layer. Pour the cyclohexene into a small, dry Erlenmeyer flask and dry it over anhydrous sodium sulfate for 10 to 15 minutes.

Decant the dried cyclohexene into a small dry distilling flask, add a boiling stone, attach the flask to a simple distillation assembly, and distill carefully. Collect the material distilling at 80 to 85°C. Determine the weight of the product and calculate the percentage yield.

Test the reactions of the product with bromine and with potassium permanganate (see Chapter 16, Procedure Tests D and E). Also examine the purity of product by use of vapor phase chromatography, IR, or NMR as designated by your instructor. Submit the product in an appropriately labeled container to your instructor.

B.   DEHYDRATION OF 2-METHYLCYCLOHEXANOL

(Macroscale)

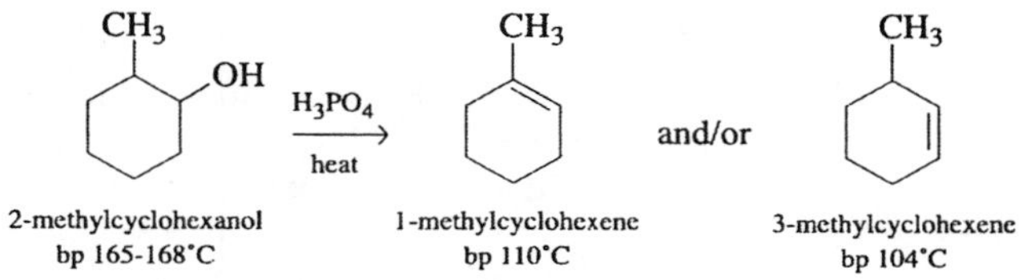

2-methylcyclohexanol
bp 165-168°C

1-methylcyclohexene
bp 110°C

and/or

3-methylcyclohexene
bp 104°C

The dehydration of 2-methylcyclohexanol can occur in two directions, giving rise to 1-methylcyclohexene or 3-methylcyclohexene. In this experiment, gas chromatography (GC) will be used to determine the product composition. A disadvantage of using sulfuric acid in this experiment is that it is a sufficiently strong acid to reprotonate the double bond of the initial product and cause isomerization to other alkenes; therefore, phosphoric acid is used. In addition to the reactants it may be advantageous to use a "chaser" such as bromobenzene or decalin. These relatively high-boiling substances are inert under the reaction conditions and allow a more complete distillation of the product.

PROCEDURE

To a 25-mL round-bottom flask, add 6 mL of 2-methylcyclohexanol, 5 mL of 85% phosphoric acid, and a boiling stone. Attach the flask to a fractional distillation assembly (see Fig. 5.7; either use no column packing or a low hold-up packing). Slowly heat the contents of the flask to boiling and distill out the product. The distillation temperature should be kept below 96°C by regulating the rate of heating. Continue the distillation until 4 to 6 mL of liquid have been collected (a test tube or distillation receiver [centrifuge tube] is a convenient collection vessel).

Separate the product from the water layer by using a Pasteur pipet. Transfer the product to a clean, dry test tube and dry it over Na_2SO_4 for 10 minutes.

Inject 0.5 μL of the dried liquid onto a nonpolar gas chromatograph column. Before doing so, be sure to fill and empty the syringe several times, discarding the sample each time, to clean out the previous contents. Draw approximately 1 μL of air into the syringe after the liquid when you are ready to analyze the sample. Insert the needle as far as possible into the injection port before injecting the sample to insure placing the sample directly onto the column.

Mark the point of injection on the recorder chart paper and measure accurately the distance (or time) from this point to the olefin peak(s). By comparing the results with the retention times of 1-methylcyclohexene and 3-methylcyclohexene, determine the identity of the dehydration product(s). If both are present, determine the approximate composition by triangulation of peak areas (see Fig. 6.4). Explain your results. If additional peaks are present, attempt to identify these as well.

If GC analysis is unavailable, measure the refractive index of the product and assume a linear relationship between the molar concentration and the refractive index. Refractive index values for 1-methylcyclohexene and 3-methylcyclohexene are 1.4503 and 1.4414, respectively.

C.   DEHYDRATION OF 2-METHYLCYCLOHEXANOL

(Microscale)

See the previous discussion in Experiment B. In the following procedure, phosphoric acid is used as a catalyst; however, the quantity used also allows it to function as a "chaser." Because of the relatively high ratio of phosphoric acid, a separate water phase may not be seen in the distillate.

PROCEDURE

To a 5-mL round-bottom flask, add 1 mL of 2-methylcyclohexanol, 2 mL of 85% phosphoric acid, and a boiling stone. Mount the flask for simple distillation (see Fig. 5.6), slowly heat the contents of the flask to boiling, and distill out the product keeping the distillation temperature below 96°C. Continue the distillation until 0.5 to 0.7 mL of product is collected (a small test tube or centrifuge tube is a convenient receiver). Dry the product for 10 minutes over anhydrous Na_2SO_4, then transfer the dried liquid to a clean test tube so as not to get Na_2SO_4 in the syringe. Examine the dried liquid by gas chromatography as described in Experiment B.

QUESTIONS

1. What alkene(s) will be produced when each of the following alcohols is dehydrated:
   a.   cyclohexanol
   b.   2-methylcyclopentanol
   c.   3-methylcyclopentanol
   d.   2,3-dimethyl-2-butanol
2. Illustrate the mechanism for the acid-catalyzed dehydration of cyclohexanol.
3. Illustrate the mechanism for the acid-catalyzed dehydration of 2-methylcyclohexanol. How many products are possible?
4. Give equations to show how sulfuric acid can convert 4-methylcyclohexene into a mixture of four isomeric C_7H_{12} compounds (including starting material). Predict the relative amounts of each isomer.
5. Explain how the methylcyclohexene(s) can be distilled from the reaction mixture if the distillation temperature is kept well below 100°C.
6. The 2-methylcyclohexanol used in Experiments B and C is actually a mixture of two isomers. What are they? Is it likely that this makes a difference in the product composition? Explain your answer.
7. Write equations to illustrate the reaction of cyclohexene with $KMnO_4$.
8. Given the following data, calculate the theoretical yield and percentage yield of cyclohexene:
   Cyclohexanol used: 20.0 mL
   Cyclohexene obtained: 12.0 g

PRELABORATORY QUESTIONS

1. What alkene(s) will be produced when each of the following alcohols is dehydrated?
   a.   2-propanol
   b.   2-butanol

2. Why is phosphoric acid preferred over sulfuric acid for dehydration of alcohols?
3. What measures should be taken if droplets of phosphoric acid are splashed in the eyes?
4. Give an example of a skeletal rearrangement during a dehydration experiment.
5. What is the purpose of adding anhydrous sodium sulfate to the dehydration product in Experiment B?

REFERENCES

Banthrope, D. V. *Elimination Reactions;* Elsevier: New York, 1963.

Taber, R. L.; Champion, W. C. *J. Chem. Ed.,* 1967, *44*, 620.

Taber, R. L.; Grantham, G. D.: Champion, W. C. *J. Chem. Ed.,* 1969, *46*, 849.

Triphenylcarbinol—Addition of a Grignard Reagent to a Ketone

Background Reading
The Grignard reaction in any organic textbook

Timing
(4–5 h)

Developed by Victor Grignard, who received the Nobel Prize for his efforts in 1912, the reaction between an alkyl (or aryl) halide and magnesium in ether, known as the **Grignard reaction**, produces an alkylmagnesium (or arylmagnesium) halide, one of the most versatile synthetic reagents available to the organic chemist. The general reaction is written

$$RX + Mg \xrightarrow{\text{Et}_2\text{O}} RMgX$$

Grignard reagent

Diethyl ether, the usual solvent for such reactions, is more than a mere solvent; it is essential to the success of the reaction. Lone pairs of electrons on the oxygen atoms of two molecules of ether apparently coordinate with the magnesium atom in the alkylmagnesium halide to form a relatively stable dietherate complex, which is frequently not shown in the equations describing the reactions of Grignard reagents.

EXERCISES

1. Evidence has been found that RMgR is also present in ether solutions prepared from an alkyl halide and magnesium. Suggest a reaction for its formation.
2. The reaction of 1,2-dibromoethane with magnesium produces a gas! What is it? Write a balanced equation for its formation.

Grignard reagents are readily formed from primary, secondary, or tertiary alkyl chlorides, bromides, and iodides, and from aryl bromides and iodides, but only with great difficulty from aryl, vinyl, and cyclopropyl chlorides. Kept out of contact with oxygen and moisture, Grignard reagents can be stored for long periods of time as ether solutions; however, it is common practice to utilize Grignard reagents immediately after their preparation.

Of crucial importance to the successful production of Grignard reagents is the absence of moisture, which can inhibit the union of the organic halide and the magnesium by forming an impervious layer of oxide and hydroxide on the magnesium surface. The reaction flask to be used is often dried in an oven or heated with a burner to drive moisture from the pores of the glass. The alkyl halide, which may contain traces of hydrogen halide as well as moisture, can be conveniently purified and dried by passage through a short column containing activated aluminum oxide (alumina). The ether can be purchased dry or can be dried by allowing it to stand over anhydrous calcium chloride for a few hours, but if the Grignard reaction is of a type that is particularly sensitive to moisture, the ether should be distilled from lithium aluminum hydride and stored over activated molecular sieves.

Under the most ideal circumstances, Grignard reactions should be carried out in an atmosphere of dry, inert gas, such as argon or nitrogen, so as to exclude the moisture or oxygen of the air from the reaction vessel. However, many reactions can be done successfully by simply attaching a drying tube containing anhydrous calcium chloride or calcium sulfate (Drierite™) to the top of the condenser. Because of the ether vapor in the flask, most of the oxygen that might otherwise be a problem is excluded and there is no need for a blanket of inert gas.

> **NOTE**
>
> Certain grades of commercial diethyl ether are contaminated with ethyl alcohol, which can only be removed by treatment with lithium aluminum hydride.

EXERCISE

3. Once formed, Grignard reagents react with water and with oxygen followed by water to produce hydrocarbons and alcohols, respectively. Write balanced equations for these two reactions.

In the following experiment, bromobenzene is converted to phenylmagnesium bromide, which then reacts with benzophenone to give triphenylcarbinol.

$$PhBr \ + \ Mg \ \longrightarrow \ PhMgBr$$

$$PhMgBr \ + \ PhCOPh \ \longrightarrow \ Ph_3COMgBr$$

$$Ph_3COMgBr \ + \ HOH \ \longrightarrow \ Ph_3COH \ + \ MgBrOH$$

A. Preparation of Apparatus

Warm a dry 10-mL pear-shaped flask, magnetic stir bar, and dry condenser in the oven (in a labeled beaker) or with a heat lamp for about 15 min. Prepare a drying tube from an eye dropper containing a small amount of anhydrous $CaCl_2$ between two cotton plugs. Except for the plastic syringe, assemble the warm apparatus as shown in Figure E22.1. Try the magnetic stirrer to make certain the stirring bar is small enough that it turns freely. Do not use grease on the joints. You will need a dry filter pipet calibrated by making several marks at 4-mm intervals (about 0.1 mL between marks) to handle dry diethyl ether. (This works better than a Pasteur pipet for transfer of liquids with a high vapor pressure.)

> **CAUTION!**
>
> Diethyl ether is extremely flammable. Avoid open flames or sparks.

B. Phenylmagnesium Bromide

Lightly sand some magnesium ribbon, cut off about 3 cm. and weigh it to the nearest mg. You need a minimum of 23 mg (0.95 mmol), but avoid an amount in excess of 27 mg. Always handle the ribbon by the edge or with forceps. Disconnect the flask, clamp it, and insert a small dry funnel. With a calibrated filter pipet add about 800 μL of commercial dry diethyl ether (from a freshly opened container). Then cut the Mg with scissors into 2- to 3-mm-long pieces so that they fall through the funnel into the flask.

Gently turn on the water in the condenser. begin magnetic stirring, and heat the ether to reflux. With an automatic pipet, deliver exactly 94 μL (141 mg, 0.90 mmol) of bromobenzene (previously purified by passage through a short column of activated

> **NOTE**
>
> Be certain to recap the ether container immediately to keep it dry.

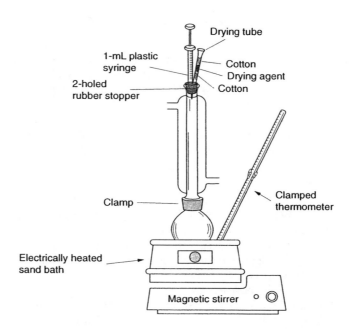

Figure E22.1   Apparatus for Grignard reaction (stirring bar not visible)

Al_2O_3 in the hood) to a small *dry* vial, and then add about 500 μL of dry ether (a freshly opened containers is preferred) with the calibrated filter pipet. Draw this solution carefully (*slowly*) into the 1-mL plastic syringe and place the needle through the second hole in the rubber stopper. Add 5–8 drops of the bromobenzene solution with the syringe dropping funnel. Continue to apply gentle heat to help the reaction start (as evidenced by a cloudy appearance; you may have to turn down the heat after the reaction starts because it is exothermic.) A few more drops of the bromobenzene may be needed. When the reaction has started, add the remainder of the bromobenzene solution slowly (15–20 min). Continue to heat the reaction mixture gently for 15 min with stirring. Only a small amount of the original Mg should remain. Remove the sand bath, but leave the apparatus on the magnetic stirrer. Allow the Grignard solution to cool.

NOTE

Although it is unlikely they will be needed, other techniques that have been used to start Grignard reactions include the following: (1) Add a very small crystal of iodine to the ether (light red-brown color); (2) crush some of the magnesium turnings (under the ether) with a stirring rod against the inside of the flask.

EXERCISE

4. Iodine, which reacts with magnesium to form magnesium iodide, has sometimes been used to treat the magnesium first. What is the likely reason why the iodine helps to start the Grignard reaction? Why would the use of 1,2-dibromoethane or crushing magnesium under the surface of the ether be effective?

C. Triphenylcarbinol

Tare a small *dry* vial to the nearest mg, and weigh 124 mg (0.68 mmol; based on an assumed yield of Grignard reagent of at least 75%) of benzophenone (finely powdered) into it. Add about 500 μL of dry ether (with the calibrated filter pipet) cap the vial, and carefully swirl the solution until the benzophenone has dissolved. Draw the solution into the plastic syringe. Magnetically stir the Grignard solution (without heating) and add the benzophenone slowly (30 sec). The magnesium salt of the triphenylcarbinol will precipitate, and the reaction mixture may solidify

D. Product Isolation

With the reaction mixture at about room temperature, slowly add 3M HCl (stir with a spatula) until two layers are formed and the lower aqueous layer is distinctly acid to pH paper. Allow any unused Mg to dissolve. With a Pasteur pipet carefully transfer the lower aqueous layer to a 1-dram vial and extract the layer with three 0.5-mL portions of diethyl ether (*not the special dry ether*).

After each extraction, transfer the lower layer with a Pasteur pipet to a second vial and combine the ether layer with the original ether layer by means of a filter pipet. The combined ether layer is then washed with 0.5 mL of water, which is removed and discarded. The ether solution should then be dried with about 300 mg of anhydrous Na_2SO_4 for 10 min and then rinsed carefully into a clean, tared 1-dram vial in small amounts followed by careful evaporation of the ether (boiling stick) with a sand bath to give a solid residue of the product mixed with biphenyl, a reaction by-product.

Cold ligroin (bp 30–60°C) or petroleum ether (0.5 mL) is then added to the crude product to selectively dissolve the biphenyl. Scrape and stir the suspension for a few minutes followed by removal of the solvent with a filter pipet. Rinse the crude triphenylcarbinol with an additional 0.5 mL of the solvent, and allow it to dry before determining the crude yield or taking a mp.

EXERCISE

5. Indicate with a balanced equation how biphenyl arises in the formation of phenylmagnesium bromide.

E. Optional Laboratory Exercise

To determine the yield of biphenyl, transfer the two portions of solvent to a tared, 1-dram vial, label it, and place it in the back of a designated hood to evaporate until the next laboratory period.

F. Recrystallization (Optional)

(Directions are given for the Pasteur pipet method.) Pure triphenylcarbinol can be obtained by recrystallizing the solid on a microscale from a mixture of ethyl acetate and Skelly B (or hexane). In the microscale recrystallization procedure, dissolve the sample in warm ethyl acetate (about 40 μL of solvent for each 10 mg of crude product) and carry out the hot filtration into the small vial. Concentrate the solvent to

NOTE

The pink color commonly observed is due to very small amounts of a radical anion formed by transfer of an electron to benzophenone. Such radical anions are known as ketyls.

NOTE

Always place the vials in a small beaker so they cannot be tipped over accidentally.

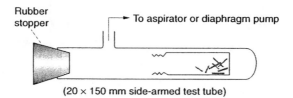

Figure E22.2 Microscale vacuum oven

(20 × 150 mm side-armed test tube)

about 1/3 of the original volume and slowly add warm Skelly B (or hexane) equivalent to about twice the volume of the concentrated ethyl acetate solution. Cap the vial and allow the solution to cool to room temperature for several min, and then in ice for about 15 min. Remove the solvent with a filter pipet and wash the crystals with a small amount of cold Skelly B (or hexane), and dry them carefully in the microscale vacuum oven shown in Figure E22.2. Obtain the mp. Calculate the yield of purified material.

EXERCISE

6. What side reaction might occur if the recrystallization were attempted from ethanol with a trace of acid present? (*Hint: Triphenylcarbinol and acid initially forms a stabilized carbocation.*)

Identifying an Unknown Alcohol

Prepared by Jan William Simek, California Polytechnic State University

PURPOSE OF THE EXPERIMENT

Identify an unknown liquid alcohol by qualitative chemical tests and by comparison of a derivative melting point to literature values.

BACKGROUND REQUIRED

You should be familiar with melting point measurement, boiling point measurement, refractive index measurement, recrystallization, and vacuum filtration.

BACKGROUND INFORMATION

Organic qualitative analysis is an exercise in spectroscopy. Nuclear magnetic resonance spectroscopy and infrared spectroscopy are the major spectroscopic techniques used by organic chemists. However, much insight can be gained from using simple qualitative tests to determine the identity of unknowns. Structures of unknown compounds can be determined by comparing physical properties, performing functional group tests, and checking melting points of derivatives against those of known compounds reported in the literature. Solubility properties and chemical reactivity become apparent during these qualitative tests.

Classification Tests

Qualitative tests are called **classification tests** because they support or refute the presence of certain structural features of a molecule. For example, certain classification tests indicate the presence of a particular functional group, such as an aldehyde or an alcohol. Other tests indicate a functional group that easily undergoes oxidation. Still other tests show the presence of an acidic hydrogen or other specific feature. A feature common to all classification tests is that the results of a test are readily visible. For example, the color may change, a precipitate may form, a gas may evolve, or a separate layer may form.

There are two inviolable rules when performing classification tests. First, perform the test exactly as described. If the procedure says add 3 drops, do not add 4 or 5. Second, always perform tests on a known compound that will result in a positive test (**known positive**); perform the tests on a known compound that will result in a negative test (**known negative**); and perform the tests on the unknown compound. This direct visual comparison of the results of testing the unknown against a known positive test and a known negative test confirms that the reagents are good and you are performing the test properly.

The following classification tests are performed in this experiment and are among those tests commonly performed when an unknown is thought to be an alcohol. In these cases, the control reactions (known positive and known negative) are primary, secondary, and tertiary alcohols.

Lucas Test

Hydrochloric acid (HCl) can be used to replace the –OH group of alcohols with Cl^-. The rate of this S_N1 reaction depends on the stability of the carbocation formed at the carbon bonded to the –OH group. In general, tertiary alcohols react fastest and primary alcohols react slowest. Alcohols such as allyl alcohol and benzyl alcohol, which can produce resonance-stabilized carbocations, will react just as fast as tertiary alcohols.

The Lucas reagent is a solution of zinc chloride ($ZnCl_2$) in concentrated HCl. $ZnCl_2$ is a Lewis acid that increases the acidity of the solution. A positive test occurs when the nonpolar alkyl halide formed in the reaction begins to separate from the aqueous solution to form a second layer. The solution will appear cloudy. For the Lucas test to work, the alcohol must be soluble in the aqueous $ZnCl_2$ solution. In practice, only alcohols containing no more than seven or eight carbon atoms will dissolve in the Lucas reagent.

For the simple alcohols, reaction times are reproducible and characteristic of the type of alcohol. As shown in Equation 1, tertiary alcohols and alcohols that form resonance-stabilized carbocations react to form a cloudy mixture in less than 30 seconds at room temperature. Secondary alcohols react similarly in one to three minutes, as shown in Equation 2. Primary alcohols require more than an hour to react, as shown in Equation 3.

3° alcohol: *reacts within 30 s also applies to ROH form-ing resonance-stabilized carbocations*

$$R-\underset{\underset{R}{|}}{\overset{\overset{R}{|}}{C}}-OH + HCl \xrightarrow{ZnCl_2} R-\underset{\underset{R}{|}}{\overset{\overset{R}{|}}{C}}-Cl + H_2O \qquad (Eq. 1)$$

soluble in water   *insoluble in water*

2° alcohol: *reacts within 1–3 min*

$$R-\underset{\underset{R}{|}}{\overset{\overset{H}{|}}{C}}-OH + HCl \xrightarrow{ZnCl_2} R-\underset{\underset{R}{|}}{\overset{\overset{H}{|}}{C}}-Cl + H_2O \qquad (Eq. 2)$$

soluble in water   *insoluble in water*

1° alcohol: *no reaction in 60 min*

$$R-\underset{\underset{H}{|}}{\overset{\overset{H}{|}}{C}}-OH + HCl \xrightarrow{ZnCl_2} R-\underset{\underset{H}{|}}{\overset{\overset{H}{|}}{C}}-Cl + H_2O \qquad (Eq. 3)$$

soluble in water   *insoluble in water*

TCICA Test

1,3,5-Trichloroisocyanuric acid (TCICA) is a common source of chlorine used to disinfect swimming pools. TCICA is also found in some kitchen cleansers. Commercial products list TCICA as *s*-trichlorotriazinetrione.

In acid solution, TCICA slowly releases chlorine, which is an oxidizing agent. The reaction is rapid in the presence of an oxidizable compound like a primary or secondary alcohol, as shown in Equation 4. The product is isocyanuric acid, which is very soluble in water but precipitates from the solvent acetonitrile. The time it takes for isocyanuric acid precipitate to appear is characteristic of the type of alcohol. Secondary alcohols react fastest, within 15–30 seconds; primary alcohols produce a precipitate usually within 3–7 minutes, although some can take up to 20 minutes; tertiary alcohols are not oxidizable at room temperature and produce no precipitate within an hour.

$$3 \; \text{alcohol} \; + \; \text{TCICA} \; \xrightarrow[\text{CH}_3\text{CN}]{\begin{array}{c}\text{1 drop}\\\text{HCl (aq)}\end{array}} \; 3 \; \text{carbonyl compound} \; + \; \text{isocyanuric acid precipitate} \; + \; 3 \; \text{HCl} \qquad \text{(Eq. 4)}$$

Derivatives

Unknown compounds can be reacted with various reagents to give new compounds called **derivatives**. Stable, crystalline derivatives can be used to help identify unknowns by comparing the derivative melting point with literature values. For any derivative, purity is more important than yield. Only a small amount of derivative is needed for a melting point, but it must be pure to give accurate results.

Several derivatives can be made to confirm an unknown alcohol. Alcohols are only mildly nucleophilic, however, so a reactive electrophile is needed to form a solid derivative in a relatively short time period. Tertiary alcohols have significant steric hindrance that slows their rate of reaction. Also, alcohols can dehydrate under strongly acidic conditions.

The alcohol derivative that best balances these considerations is the 3,5-dinitrobenzoate ester. The ester is formed by reaction of the alcohol and 3,5-dinitrobenzoyl chloride, as shown in Equation 5.

$$\text{ROH} + \text{3,5-dinitrobenzoyl chloride, (DNB-Cl)} \longrightarrow \text{3,5-dinitrobenzoate ester} + \text{HCl} \qquad \text{(Eq. 5)}$$

For alcohols that are slow to react, particularly tertiary alcohols, a catalyst can be added. 4-Dimethylaminopyridine (DMAP) is an excellent acylation catalyst. The reaction is shown in Equation 6 on the next page. DMAP has the added advantage of being a base, thereby removing the HCl as it is formed, preventing the acid-catalyzed dehydration of the alcohol.

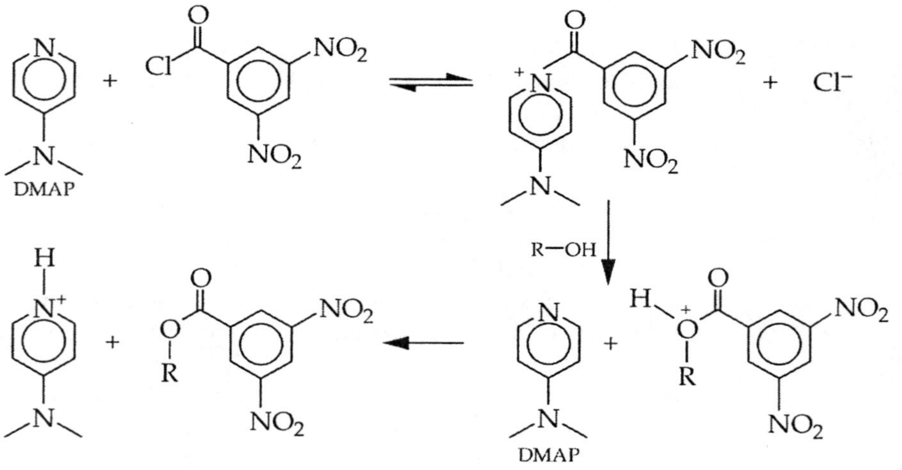

(Eq. 6)

In this experiment, you will analyze an unknown alcohol by performing qualitative tests, by measuring the refractive index, by measuring the boiling point, and by preparing a derivative and measuring its melting point. You will identify your unknown by comparing its data with the data shown in Table 1.

Equipment

250-mL beaker
400-mL beaker
boiling chip
Büchner funnel, with adapter*
125-mL filter flask, with
　vacuum tubing
filter paper
glass stirring rod
*or Hirsch funnel

10-mL graduated cylinder
marker
melting point capillary tube
Pasteur pipet, with latex bulb
1.0-mL pipet
spatula
12 test tubes, 13 × 100-mm

Table 1 *Physical properties of alcohols*

name	type	bp (°C)	n_D^{20}	3,5-dinitrobenzoate mp (°C)
2-methyl-2-propanol	3°	83	1.3870	142
2-butanol	2°	99	1.3970	76
2-methyl-1-propanol	1°	108	1.3960	87
3-pentanol	2°	116	1.4103	101
1-butanol	1°	118	1.3990	64
3-methyl-3-pentanol	3°	123	1.4190	96
2-methyl-1-butanol	1°	129	1.4107	70
1-pentanol	1°	138	1.4099	46
cyclopentanol	2°	141	1.4530	115
1-hexanol	1°	158	1.4178	61
cyclohexanol	2°	160	1.4650	112
4-methylcyclohexanol	2°	174	1.4580	142
cyclohexylmethanol	1°	181	1.4650	96
benzyl alcohol	1°	206	1.5396	106
2-phenylethanol	1°	219	1.5302	97

Reagents and Properties

substance	quantity	molar mass (g/mol)	mp (°C)	bp (°C)
acetone	5 mL	58.1		56
4-dimethylaminopyridine	0.12 g	122.2	114	
3,5-dinitrobenzoyl chloride	0.23 g	230.6	71	
ethanol, 95%	7 mL	46.0		78
hydrochloric acid, 1M	0.25 mL	36.5		
Lucas reagent ($ZnCl_2$ in HCl)	8 mL			
2-methyl-2-propanol	0.5 mL	74.1	26	83
1-propanol	0.5 mL	60.1		97
2-propanol	0.5 mL	60.1		82
sodium carbonate, 2%	5 mL	106.0		
TCICA in acetonitrile, 3%	2 mL	232.4		

Preview

- Prepare and crystallize a 3,5-dinitrobenzoate derivative of the unknown
- Filter the derivative and allow it to dry
- Perform a Lucas test on a primary, a secondary, a tertiary alcohol, and the unknown
- Perform a TCICA test on a primary, a secondary, a tertiary alcohol, and the unknown
- Measure the refractive index of the unknown
- Measure the boiling point of the unknown
- Measure the melting point of the 3,5-dinitrobenzoate derivative
- Compare your data with the data in Table 1 to deduce the identity of the unknown

PROCEDURE

CAUTION

Wear departmentally approved safety goggles at all times while in the chemistry laboratory.

Always use caution in the laboratory. Many chemicals are potentially harmful. Follow safety precautions given for all reagents used in this experiment. Prevent contact with your eyes, skin, and clothing. Avoid ingesting any of the reagents.

1. Preparing a 3,5-Dinitrobenzoate Derivative [NOTE 1]

NOTE 1: For efficient use of laboratory time, begin by forming the derivative. Perform other tests while waiting for the derivative to crystallize and dry.

CAUTION

3,5-Dinitrobenzoyl chloride is corrosive and a lachrymator. 4-Dimethylaminopyridine is toxic and corrosive. Acetone is flammable and irritating. 95% Ethanol is flammable and toxic. Keep flammable reagents away from flames or other heat sources.

2,572 + .872

5.9
7.6
5.028

Prepare a hot-water bath by heating 100 mL water in a 250-mL beaker to near boiling.

Prepare an ice-water bath in a 400-mL beaker. Place 2 mL of 95% ethanol in a test tube. Chill the ethanol in the ice-water bath for later use.

Procedure A Place 0.23 g of 3,5-dinitrobenzoyl chloride into a test tube. Use
[NOTE 2] a dropper to add 8 drops of unknown alcohol to the test tube.

Place the test tube in the hot-water bath for 10–15 min. Observe to see if bubbles are evolved.

Allow the tube to cool until the reaction mixture has solidified. If the mixture is still liquid after 5 min, place it in an ice-water bath for 5 min. If no crystals form in the ice-water bath, begin again following Procedure B. If crystals form, skip Procedure B.

NOTE 2: Try Procedure A first. Use Procedure B only if Procedure A does not give a product.

Procedure B Place 0.23 g of 3,5-dinitrobenzoyl chloride into a test tube.
[NOTE 3] Add 0.12 g of 4-dimethylaminopyridine to the test tube.

Add 1 mL of acetone. Use a dropper to add 8 drops of unknown alcohol to the test tube.

Place the test tube in the hot-water bath until the acetone boils. Stir the contents of the tube frequently. Be careful not to boil off the acetone.

Allow the tube to cool to room temperature. Then place the tube into the ice-water bath for 5 min.

NOTE 3: Follow procedure B if Procedure A did not give satisfactory results.

Using a spatula or glass stirring rod, break up the derivative until no large chunks remain. Add 5 mL of 2% sodium carbonate. Stir vigorously for 30 s. Using a Büchner funnel, vacuum filter the derivative. Rinse the derivative in the funnel with 4–5 mL of distilled or deionized water.

To recrystallize, transfer the derivative to a test tube. Add 2 mL of 95% ethanol and a boiling chip. Heat the solution in the hot-water bath until the derivative dissolves. Be careful not to boil away the ethanol.

If any of the derivative remains undissolved in 2 mL of 95% ethanol, add 1 mL more. Continue heating. If any of the derivative remains undissolved, continue adding 1 mL amounts of 95% ethanol, with heating, until the derivative dissolves. Do not exceed a 5-mL total volume of ethanol.

If the cooling solution turns cloudy and the compound starts coming out of solution as a liquid instead of a solid, quickly put the test tube in an ice-water bath and rapidly swirl the tube until a solid is visible. Then remove the tube from the ice-water bath and allow the recrystallization to continue at room temperature.

When the derivative has crystallized completely, vacuum filter the derivative. Rinse the derivative with the 2 mL of chilled 95% ethanol.

Spread the derivative on a filter paper. Allow the derivative to dry for 30 min.

Measure the melting point of the derivative. Compare the melting point with the melting points in Table 1.

2. Performing the Lucas Test

CAUTION   ⚠

Lucas reagent (zinc chloride in concentrated hydrochloric acid) is toxic and corrosive. 1-Propanol, 2-propanol, and 2-methyl-2-propanol are flammable and irritating. Keep away from flames or other heat sources.

Label 4 test tubes "Lucas" 1–4, respectively. Add 2 mL of Lucas reagent to each test tube. Add 4 drops of 1-propanol to tube 1. Mix well. Observe for 1 hr for any sign of cloudiness. Record the result.

Add 4 drops of 2-propanol to tube 2. Mix well. Note and record the time until the cloudiness appears.

Add 4 drops of 2-methyl-2-propanol (*tert*-butyl alcohol) to tube 3. Mix well. Measure and record the time until cloudiness appears.

Add 4 drops of your unknown to tube 4. Mix well. Measure and record the time until cloudiness appears. If there is no visible change within 5 min, assume no reaction.

3. Performing the TCICA Test

CAUTION

1,3,5-Trichloroisocyanuric acid (TCICA) is corrosive and oxidizing. Acetonitrile is toxic. 5% Hydrochloric acid (HCl) is toxic and corrosive.

Label 4 test tubes "TCICA" 1–4, respectively. Put 0.5 mL of the TCICA test solution into each test tube. Add 1 drop of 1M HCl to each tube. Shake each tube to mix.

Add 1 drop of 1-propanol to tube 1. Shake the tube to mix. Note and record the time for a precipitate to appear.

NOTE 4: The refractive index at 20 °C is calculated by using the following equation, where T is the ambient temperature in degrees Celsius and n_D^T is the refractive index measured at ambient temperature.

$$n_D^{20} = n_D^T + 0.00066\,(T - 20\,^\circ\text{C})$$

Add 1 drop of 2-propanol to tube 2. Shake the tube to mix. Note and record the time for a precipitate to appear.

Add 1 drop of 2-methyl-2-propanol to tube 3. Observe for 20 min. If no precipitate forms within 20 min, record no reaction.

Add 1 drop of the unknown to tube 4. Shake the tube to mix. Note and record the time for a precipitate to appear.

4. Measuring the Refractive Index

Measure the refractive index of your unknown. Note and record the laboratory temperature. Correct the refractive index to 20 °C, if necessary. [NOTE 4]

5. Measuring the Boiling Point

Measure the boiling point of your unknown. Use either distillation or the capillary tube method, as directed by your laboratory instructor.

6. Cleaning Up

Use the labeled collection containers provided by your laboratory instructor. Turn in any remaining unknown to your laboratory instructor. Clean your glassware with soap or detergent.

CAUTION

Wash your hands with soap or detergent before leaving the laboratory.

Name _____   Section _____   Date _____

Post-Laboratory Questions

1. Discuss the results of your classification tests and 3,5-dinitrobenzoate derivative formation. What is your unknown? How do your data exclude other possibilities?

2. In making the 3,5-dinitrobenzoate ester derivative, what compounds could be present besides the ester? Indicate any step in the procedure that is intended to remove a possible impurity.

3. How is it possible for the Lucas test to give a false positive? That is, if you see a second layer of insoluble organic liquid, what could the unknown be in addition to a tertiary alcohol?

4. Most alcohols are soluble in methanol or ethanol. Explain why these compounds are not used as solvents in the TCICA test.

5. Briefly explain why it is necessary to run the TCICA test in acetonitrile instead of water.

Name _____   Section _____   Date _____

Pre-Laboratory Assignment

1. What special precautions should be used when performing the Lucas test?

2. Why are primary and secondary alcohols relatively easy to oxidize, but tertiary alcohols resist oxidation?

3. What are the disadvantages of not performing the qualitative tests on known alcohols?

4. Why is it advisable to correct the measured refractive index for temperature?

5. Procedure B for the preparation of a 3,5-dinitrobenzoate ester uses DMAP. What are the two functions of DMAP?

6. One of the unknowns from Table 1 gave the following results. Identify the unknown.

Lucas test: cloudy in 2.5 min;
TCICA test: precipitate in 20 s;
3,5-dinitrobenzoate melting point: 113–114 °C;
refractive index (corrected to 20 °C): 1.4535.

18

Borohydride Reduction of 9-Fluorenone

Background Reading
Material on the reduction of ketones to alcohols

Timing
(3 h)

Although the reduction of a ketone (or aldehyde) to the corresponding alcohol can be accomplished with a variety of reagents, the use of sodium borohydride ($NaBH_4$) is one of the most convenient and safest procedures. All four hydrides are available for reduction, and ketones and aldehydes can be selectively reduced in the presence of the less reactive carbonyl groups of esters and amides. Shown below is the reduction illustrated in this experiment. The reaction is easy to follow because the starting ketone is bright yellow, while the product alcohol is colorless (a white solid).

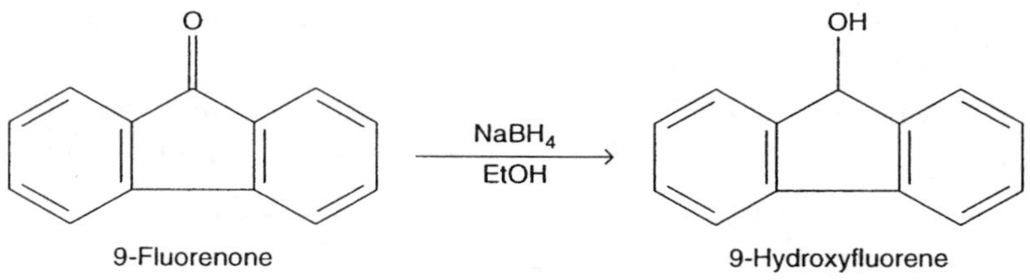

9-Fluorenone $\xrightarrow[\text{EtOH}]{NaBH_4}$ 9-Hydroxyfluorene

EXERCISE

1. Write a balanced equation for the reduction of 9-fluorenone to 9-hydroxyfluorene by sodium borohydride. What is the limiting reagent in the following procedure?

A. 9-Hydroxyfluorene

Dissolve 200 mg (1.11 mmol) of 9-fluorenone in 2.5 mL of absolute ethanol in a 25-mL pear-shaped flask. To speed up dissolution, warm the ethanol in a sand bath and swirl. Then add a stir bar and stir the solution with a magnetic stirrer at room temperature while you introduce 50 mg (1.32 mmol) of sodium borohydride. Continue to stir the solution for about 2–3 min or until the initial yellow solution becomes colorless. Add 2 mL of distilled or deionized water, remove the flask from the magnetic stirrer, and mix the thick white suspension of product with a microspatula. Add an additional 2 mL of water, and stir with the microspatula as you add 2–3 drops (Pasteur pipet) at a time of 3 M HCl with stirring (microspatula) until hydrogen evolution from destruction of the excess borohydride no longer occurs.

Isolate the product by vacuum filtration on a Hirsch funnel. Use water at room temperature to aid in the transfer to the funnel and to rinse the product. After the solid has sucked dry for a few minutes, rinse it with 2 mL of ice-cold methanol, allow it to remain under vacuum for at least 5 min, and transfer it to glazed weighing paper to dry overnight.[1] Take a mp and compare it with the reported value of 153–154°C. If your mp is much lower and has a wide range, it may not be dry enough.

Transfer the dry 9-hydroxyfluorene to a weighed vial by scraping the sides of the flask with a spatula and tapping the powder onto glazed paper first. Determine the yield of dry, white crystalline product; it should be above 75%. Take an IR spectrum as a solid dispersed on Teflon tape.

1. More rapid drying can be accomplished by use of a drying oven, shown in Figure 5.11, with gentle heating from a heat lamp.

NOTE

A fine nichrome wire may be required to help get the sample to the bottom of the mp capillary.

EXERCISES

2. From information in your lecture textbook, suggest at least two reagents other than sodium borohydride that could be used to carry out the reduction in this experiment.

3. Sodium borohydride reacts very slowly with ethanol to evolve a gas. Write a balanced equation for this reaction.

4. (Optional; Spectroscopic) Suggest at least one characteristic absorption each in the IR spectra of 9-fluorenone and 9-hydroxyfluorene that could be used to distinguish between these two compounds.

5. (Optional; Spectroscopic) What characteristic ^{1}H NMR absorptions would be expected in the aliphatic region for 9-hydroxyfluorene?

6. (Optional; Spectroscopic) How could a ^{13}C NMR spectrum be used to distinguish between the structures for 9-fluorenone and 9-hydroxyfluorene?

19

Photoreduction of Aromatic Ketones[1]

Background Reading
Sections 12.1 and 13.8 of this text

Timing
(Part **A**: allow 20 min to begin the reaction in one laboratory period and 30 min to isolate the product in a second laboratory period. Part **B**: allow 20 min to begin the reaction in one laboratory period and 1 h to isolate and purify the product in a second laboratory period.)

The absorption of a photon of light by many aromatic ketones results in one of the nonbonded electrons on oxygen being promoted into an antibonding π-molecular orbital. Because the electrons in the **ground state** (designated S_0) are all paired, the quantum-mechanically allowed process requires that they also be paired in the resulting **excited state**. For this reason, this excited state is called a **singlet excited state** (all electrons paired) and is designated in Figure E35.1 below as S_1. Once formed, the singlet excited state can either drop to the ground state with the emission of a photon (a process known as **fluorescence**) or can undergo what is normally a "forbidden" process known as **intersystem crossing** (abbreviated ISC) to a **triplet excited state** shown as T_1. Because there is an overlap between the energies of some of the vibrational levels within S_1 with those within T_1 in many aromatic ketones, intersystem crossing occurs more rapidly than fluorescence and is the dominant process.

Once formed, the triplet excited state can either drop to the ground state, S_0, with the emission of a photon (known as **phosphorescence**), can drop to the ground state with the liberation of heat (known as a **radiationless transition**), or can undergo chemical reactions. It is the latter possibility that we exploit in the current experiment.

Triplet excited states often behave like free radicals in chemical reactions. For example, the photolysis of benzophenone in isopropyl alcohol results in the formation of a 1,2-diol (or **pinacol**) known as benzopinacol. The final product is the result

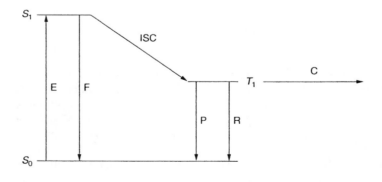

Figure E35.1 Important Photochemical Processes
(E = excitation; F = fluorescence;
ISC = intersystem crossing;
P = phosphorescence;
R = radiationless transition;
C = chemical reactions)

1. Part **B** should be selected if the study of "Aryl Migratory Aptitudes in Carbocation Rearrangements" (Experiment 37) will be done as the next experiment.

of the dimerization of two radicals derived from the abstraction of a hydrogen atom
from isopropyl alcohol by the triplet state of benzophenone.

$$Ph_2C\!=\!O \xrightarrow{h\nu} Ph_2C\!=\!O\ (S_1) \xrightarrow[\text{fast}]{\text{ISC}} Ph_2\overset{\bullet}{C}\!-\!\overset{\bullet}{O}\ (T_1)$$
$$\qquad\qquad\qquad \text{excited singlet} \qquad\qquad\qquad \text{excited triplet}$$

$$2\ Ph_2\overset{\bullet}{C}\!-\!OH \longrightarrow$$

Benzopinacol

<hr>

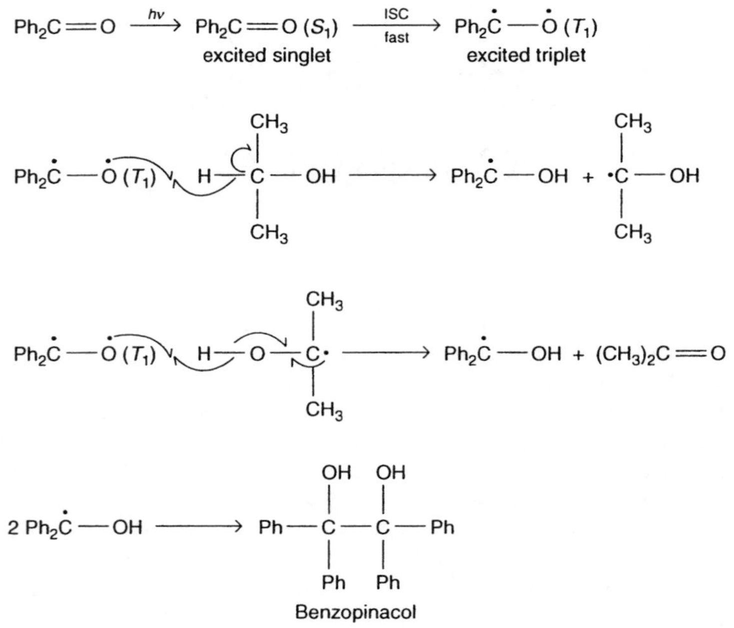

EXERCISES

1. Write the structures of the products expected from the photoreduction of
   acetophenone in 2-butanol.

2. Photolysis of *o*-hydroxybenzophenone gives only the product shown rather
   than the pinacol. Write a stepwise mechanism to explain this result.

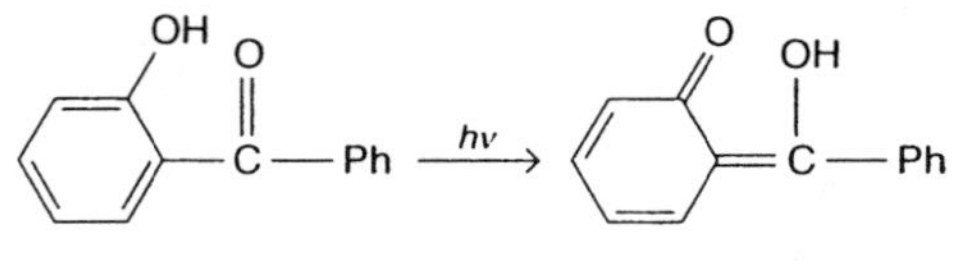

Part A of the following experiment is an opportunity to photoreduce benzophenone to benzopinacol and to test the effects of naphthalene, a photochemical
quencher on this process. The first triplet state of benzophenone, T_1, is 69 kcal/mol
(289 kJ/mol) above the ground state while naphthalene has a triplet state just 61 kcal/mol
(255 kJ/mol) above its ground state. In contrast to benzophenone, naphthalene will not
absorb any of the wavelengths of light transmitted through the Pyrex™ walls of a reaction vessel. However, when benzophenone and naphthalene are present together, the
benzophenone triplet transfers its energy to the naphthalene, raising the latter to its
triplet state and lowering itself to the ground state. Thus, the naphthalene quenches
the normal photoreduction of the benzophenone by greatly reducing the lifetime of
the benzophenone triplet.

3. The first triplet states for benzene, acetophenone, and fluorene are 85, 74, and 68 kcal/mol, respectively. Would benzene or fluorene be a suitable quencher for the triplet of acetophenone? Explain.

In Part **B** of this experiment a photoreduction of 4-methylbenzophenone is carried out to give a pinacol that can be used to study aryl migratory aptitudes in carbocation rearrangements in a separate experiment.

4,4′-Dimethylbenzopinacol

4. What is the missing organic product in the above equation?

A. Photoreduction of Benzophenone

Place 1.0 g (5.49 mmol) of benzophenone in a labeled, 15×125 mm test tube, add a few mL of isopropyl alcohol, and heat the solvent briefly with a heat lamp, steam bath, or sand bath to effect solution. Add 1 drop of glacial acetic acid, fill most of the remaining volume of the tube with isopropyl alcohol, and fit it with a rubber stopper. Turn the test tube end over end to ensure thorough mixing.

Prepare a second test tube exactly the same but with 100 mg (0.78 mmol) of naphthalene also present.

Place the tubes about 15 cm in front of a shielded, GE 275-watt sun lamp for at least 3–4 hours or in direct sunlight on a window sill or on the roof of a building (in warm weather) for at least one week. Note the results in each tube.

The product will crystallize from solution. Cool the suspension of crystals to room temperature if necessary and collect the product by suction filtration. Determine the mp and yield (keep the stoichiometry in mind). The reported mp is 184–186°C; the yield after a few hours in front of a sunlamp should be at least 30% and with an extended period of irradiation can exceed 90%.

CAUTION!

Exposure to UV light can cause serious eye injuries. The sunlamp must be carefully shielded from anyone's vision.

NOTE

The benzopinacol product can be used as the starting material in Experiment 36.

5. In the presence of base (such as hydroxide), benzopinacol reacts to form benzophenone and benzhydrol (diphenylcarbinol). Show a step-by-step mechanism to explain this result. (The glacial acetic acid used in the reaction helps prevent base derived from the glass from causing this undesired side reaction.)

B. Photoreduction of 4-Methylbenzophenone

Place 4.0 g (20 mmol) of 4-methylbenzophenone, 25 mL of isopropyl alcohol, and 2 drops of glacial acetic acid into a labeled, 24 mm × 200 mm test tube and warm the mixture to effect complete solution. Dimerization is readily accomplished by exposing the test tube to a shielded GE 275-watt sunlamp (with occasional turning) for 3 days. Several test tubes can be arranged at a distance of about 15 cm from the lamp. An alternative is to place the tubes in direct sunlight on a window sill or on the roof of a building (during warm weather) for one to two weeks.

At the end of the reaction time, cool the mixture in ice, filter the yellow to white solid, and dissolve it in 50 mL of propyl alcohol at reflux. Add water until cloudiness persists, and allow the solution to cool slowly so as to form a white amorphous product, mp 162–164°C. The yield should be approximately 60%.

CAUTION!

Exposure to UV light can cause serious eye injuries. The sunlamp must be carefully shielded from anyone's vision.

WASTE DISPOSAL NOTE

Isopropyl alcohol containing some acetic acid should be diluted and flushed. These are biodegradable compounds.

NOTE

The 4,4′-benzopinacol product can be used as the starting material in Experiment 37.

EXERCISE

6. How many stereoisomers of 4,4′-dimethylbenzopinacol are formed in this experiment? What are the stereochemical relationships between the various isomers?

20

Carbocation Rearrangements— Benzopinacolone

Background Reading
Material on the pinacol–pinacolone rearrangement in your lecture text

Timing
(30 min at beginning of period to isolate the benzopinacol prepared in Part **A** of Experiment 35; 1 h for the preparation of benzopinacolone)

A variety of organic reactions involve generation of carbocations followed by rearrangement (migration of a group) and the eventual formation of products with structures substantially different from those of the starting materials. An example is the rearrangement of benzopinacol to benzopinacolone.

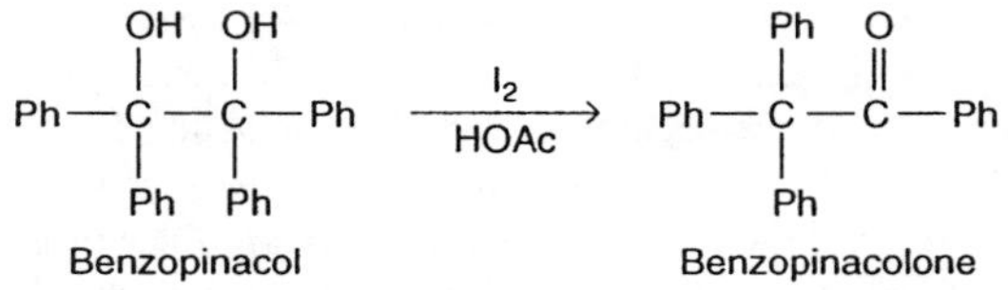

The reaction proceeds by initial formation of a carbocation, followed by rearrangement of a phenyl group and loss of a proton to give the product. Evidence suggests that as the phenyl migrates, it forms a bridged intermediate called a **phenonium ion**.

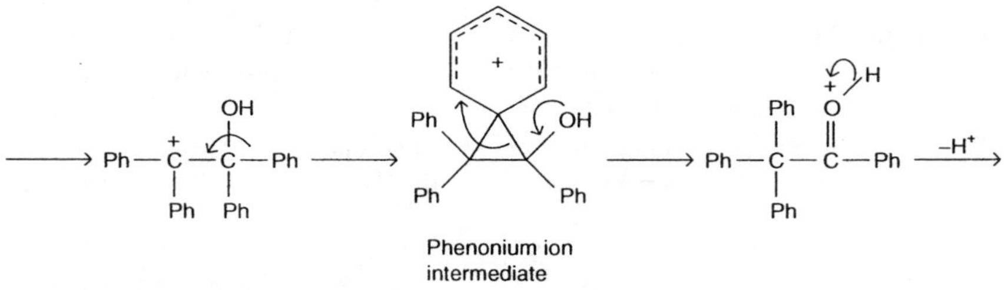

Phenonium ion intermediate

EXERCISES

1. Add one or two steps to the beginning of the above mechanism to show the function of the I_2 in the rearrangement of benzopinacol. Can you suggest any other reagent that might be used to effect the rearrangement?

2. Draw individual resonance-contributing structures showing positions to which the charge is delocalized in the phenonium ion.

3. Predict how the stability of the phenonium ion would change if it contained a p-CH_3O substituent; a p-NO_2 substituent.

CAUTION!

Glacial acetic acid is corrosive. Plastic gloves are recommended.

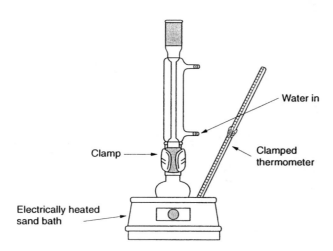

Water in

Clamp

Clamped
thermometer

Electrically heated
sand bath

Figure E36.1 Apparatus for
preparation of benzopinacolone

A. Benzopinacolone

Charge a small pear-shaped flask with 200 mg (0.546 mmol) of benzopinacol,[1] 1 mL   1. Either the commercial material or that
of glacial acetic acid, and a tiny crystal (about 5 mg) of iodine. Attach a condenser   prepared in Experiment 35A can be
and heat to reflux using a sand-bath (Figure E 36.1) for about 5 min. Allow the solu-   used.
tion to cool. Benzopinacolone separates from solution. Add a little ethanol, mix thoroughly, and isolate the product by suction filtration on a small Hirsch funnel. Use
additional ethanol to rinse the flask and to remove any iodine color from the product.
Suck the benzopinacolone dry for a few minutes, weight it, and determine the yield
and mp. The reported mp is 182–184°C. The yield should exceed 70%.

EXERCISES

4. Because benzopinacol and benzopinacolone have nearly identical melting
    points, describe (without using spectroscopic methods) how you might prove
    that samples of the two compounds are different.

5. (Optional; Spectroscopic) Describe any important differences between
    benzopinacol and benzopinacolone in the IR, ^{1}H NMR and ^{13}C NMR spectra.

Oxidizing Methoxybenzyl Alcohol to Methoxybenzaldehyde Using Phase-Transfer Catalysis

Prepared by Joseph W. LeFevre, SUNY Oswego

PURPOSE OF THE EXPERIMENT

Oxidize methoxybenzyl alcohol to methoxybenzaldehyde, using sodium hypochlorite as the oxidizing agent and tetrabutylammonium hydrogen sulfate as the phase-transfer catalyst. Monitor the progress of the reaction by thin-layer chromatography. Characterize the product by infrared spectroscopy.

EXPERIMENTAL OPTIONS

Semi-Microscale Oxidation
Microscale Oxidation

BACKGROUND REQUIRED

You should be familiar with extraction, distillation, evaporation, infrared spectroscopy, and thin-layer chromatography techniques.

BACKGROUND INFORMATION

In organic chemistry, oxidation occurs when oxygen is added to, or hydrogen is lost from, an organic molecule. Many different types of oxidizing agents exist. Chromium in the +6 oxidation state, Cr(VI), is often used. Examples of reagents containing Cr(VI) are chromate, CrO_4^{2-}, dichromate, $Cr_2O_7^{2-}$, and chromium trioxide, CrO_3. Chromate and $Cr_2O_7^{2-}$ are normally used under acidic, aqueous conditions. These agents are used to oxidize primary alcohols to carboxylic acids, as shown in Equation 1 on the next page.

2   *Oxidizing Methoxybenzyl Alcohol to Methoxybenzaldehyde Using Phase-Transfer Catalysis*

$$CH_3CH_2CH_2CH_2CH_2OH \xrightarrow[\substack{aqueous \\ H_2SO_4}]{K_2CrO_4} CH_3CH_2CH_2CH_2\overset{\overset{\displaystyle O}{\|}}{C}OH \qquad \text{(Eq. 1)}$$

primary alcohol   carboxylic acid

Initially, aldehydes are formed; however, under these reaction conditions, the aldehydes are further oxidized to carboxylic acids. The Cr(VI) agents also oxidize secondary alcohols to ketones, as shown in Equation 2.

$$CH_3CH_2CH_2\underset{\underset{\displaystyle OH}{|}}{C}HCH_3 \xrightarrow[\substack{aqueous \\ H_2SO_4}]{Na_2Cr_2O_7} CH_3CH_2CH_2\overset{\overset{\displaystyle O}{\|}}{C}CH_3 \qquad \text{(Eq. 2)}$$

secondary alcohol   ketone

Chromium trioxide is often used in the presence of pyridine to form Collin's reagent, which is used with methylene chloride (CH_2Cl_2) as the solvent. Collin's reagent is a toxic complex composed of one molecule of CrO_3 and two molecules of pyridine (CrO_3-pyridine$_2$). Because this reagent contains no water, it can be used to oxidize a primary alcohol to an aldehyde without further oxidation to a carboxylic acid, as shown in Equation 3.

$$CH_3CH_2CH_2CH_2CH_2OH \xrightarrow[CH_2Cl_2]{CrO_3\text{-pyridine}_2} CH_3CH_2CH_2CH_2\overset{\overset{\displaystyle O}{\|}}{C}H \qquad \text{(Eq. 3)}$$

primary alcohol   aldehyde

In all cases, the Cr(VI) is reduced to Cr(III) in the course of the reaction. Normally, tertiary alcohols are not oxidized with these reagents. All Cr(VI) reagents are toxic.

Potassium permanganate ($KMnO_4$) is another useful oxidizing agent. It is used in basic solution to oxidize primary alcohols to potassium carboxylate salts. A carboxylic acid is then obtained after addition of a strong acid such as dilute HCl. The permanganate ion (MnO_4^-) contains Mn in the +7 oxidation state. The Mn(VII) is reduced to Mn(IV) in the form of manganese dioxide (MnO_2), a muddy, brown precipitate. Because $KMnO_4$ also reacts with carbon-carbon double or triple bonds, it is not used to oxidize an alcohol that contains a double or triple bond. Also, $KMnO_4$ is normally not used to oxidize secondary alcohols to ketones because many ketones react further with $KMnO_4$.

One of the most convenient and inexpensive oxidizing agents is sodium hypochlorite (NaOCl). A readily available source of NaOCl is commercial bleach, a 5.25% aqueous NaOCl solution. Sodium hypochlorite oxidizes aromatic and aliphatic secondary alcohols to ketones and primary aromatic alcohols to aldehydes, as shown in Equation 4.

primary alcohol   aldehyde

Thus, NaOCl is a substitute for the toxic Cr(VI) Collin's reagent.

Primary aliphatic alcohols oxidize very slowly with NaOCl. Therefore, NaOCl selectively oxidizes secondary alcohols in the presence of primary alcohols, as shown in Equation 5.

$$\underset{\overset{\displaystyle |}{\underset{\displaystyle OH}{}}\quad\overset{\displaystyle |}{\underset{\displaystyle OH}{}}}{\overset{\overset{\displaystyle CH_3}{\displaystyle |}}{CH_2CHCHCH_2CH_3}} \xrightarrow{NaOCl} \underset{\overset{\displaystyle |}{\underset{\displaystyle OH}{}}\quad\overset{\displaystyle ||}{\underset{\displaystyle O}{}}}{\overset{\overset{\displaystyle CH_3}{\displaystyle |}}{CH_2CHCCH_2CH_3}} \qquad \text{(Eq. 5)}$$

primary alcohol and ketone

The mechanism of an NaOCl oxidation is not known in detail, but it presumably involves the formation of an alkyl hypochlorite intermediate. Equation 6 shows this intermediate in the oxidation of benzhydrol to benzophenone. A simple E2 elimination involving water leads to the products.

$$\text{(Eq. 6)}$$

Sodium hypochlorite will be used in this experiment to prepare an aromatic aldehyde from the corresponding primary alcohol. One problem that must be overcome in this reaction is that the starting alcohol is soluble in organic solvents such as dichloromethane or ethyl acetate, but is not soluble in water. On the other hand, NaOCl is soluble in water, but not in organic solvents. Therefore, a way must be devised to bring the water-soluble NaOCl and the ethyl acetate-soluble alcohol into contact so they can react. A **phase-transfer catalyst** such as tetrabutyl-ammonium hydrogen sulfate (TBAS)

$$HSO_4^- \overset{+}{N}(CH_2CH_2CH_2CH_3)_4$$

can be used to bring the two reactants together.

TBAS is a quaternary ammonium salt containing four alkyl groups. The alkyl groups render TBAS soluble in ethyl acetate. At the same time, TBAS is a salt, which makes it water-soluble. Therefore, TBAS acts as a shuttle, moving back and forth between the aqueous layer and the organic layer. TBAS can exchange its HSO_4^- counter ion for ClO^-, forming

$$ClO^- \overset{+}{N}(CH_2CH_2CH_2CH_3)_4$$

In this way, TBAS transfers the ClO^- into the ethyl acetate layer, where ClO^- can react with the alcohol. Figure 1(a) shows that no appreciable reaction occurs without the catalyst. Figure 1(b) shows how the reaction functions in the presence of the catalyst.

In this experiment, you will use NaOCl to oxidize methoxybenzyl alcohol to the corresponding aldehyde. Because the alcohol is a disubstituted

4   *Oxidizing Methoxybenzyl Alcohol to Methoxybenzaldehyde Using Phase-Transfer Catalysis*

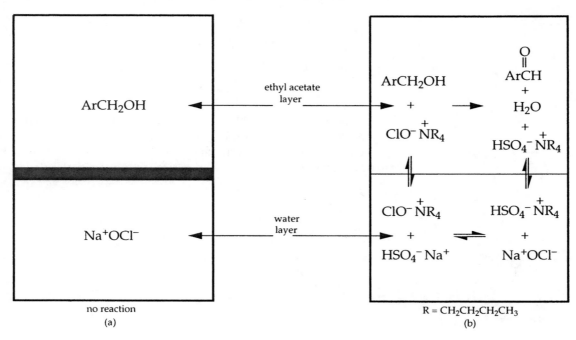

Figure 1
Oxidation of an aromatic alcohol using (a) no phase-transfer catalyst; (b) a phase-transfer catalyst

aromatic compound, there are three possible isomers, which are designated *ortho* (*o*), *meta* (*m*), and *para* (*p*), as shown in Figure 2.

The possible oxidation products are *o-*, *m-*, or *p*-methoxybenzaldehyde, all of which are liquids with similar boiling points.

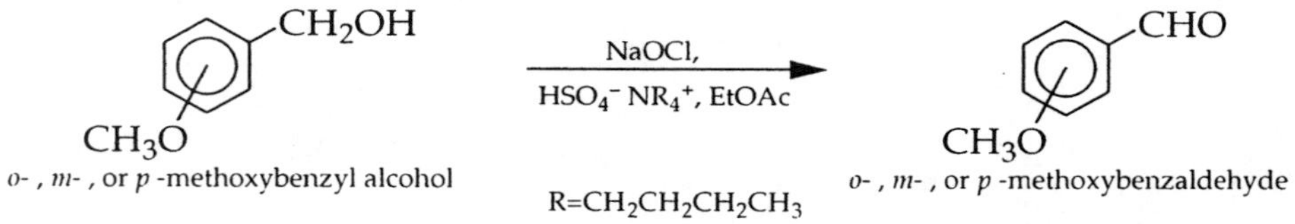

The product can be identified as *o-*, *m-*, or *p*-methoxybenzaldehyde by IR spectroscopy. Each of these isomers shows characteristic absorption bands, as shown in Table 1.

You will use TLC to monitor the course of the reaction. You should observe the disappearance over time of the alcohol at a lower R_f and the appearance of the aldehyde at a higher R_f.

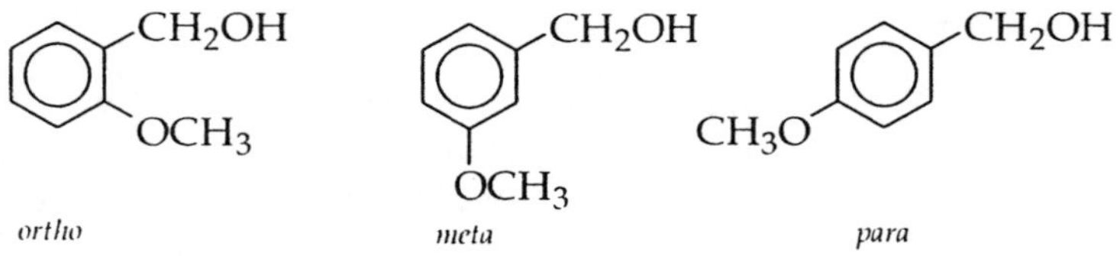

Figure 2
The three possible methoxybenzyl alcohols

Table 1 *Characteristic IR absorption bands of* o, m, *and* p-*disubstituted aromatics*

substitution pattern	frequency range (cm^{-1})	intensity
ortho	735–770	strong
meta	680–725 and	very strong
	750–810	very strong
para	800–840	very strong

SEMI-MICROSCALE OXIDATION OF METHOXYBENZYL ALCOHOL

Equipment

AgCl plates*, with sample holder
2 beakers, 100-mL
250-mL beaker
burner, Bunsen
8–10 capillary tubes, open-ended[†]
condenser, with tubing
distilling head
125-mL Erlenmeyer flask
12-cm filter paper, cut to fit the
 developing chamber
10-mL graduated cylinder
50-mL graduated cylinder
magnetic stir bar
magnetic stirrer
12 Pasteur pipets, with latex bulb
pencil

product vial
2 round-bottom flasks, 100-mL, with
 glass stoppers
250-mL round-bottom flask
ruler, mm
sand bath[‡]
3 screw–cap jars, 4-oz[§]
125-mL separatory funnel
spatula
starch–liodide paper
support stand
thermometer, −10 to 260 °C
4 TLC plates, silica gel, 3.5 × 8-cm
 with fluorescent indicator
utility clamp

*or NaCl or KBr
[†]for preparing micropipets
[‡]sand in crystallizing dish on electric hot plate or sand in electric heating well with heat controller
[§]or 250-mL beakers with aluminum foil for developing chambers

Reagents and Properties

substance	quantity	molar mass (g/mol)	bp (°C)
bleach (NaOCl)	20 mL		
dichloromethane	18 mL	84.93	40
ethyl acetate	40 mL	88.11	76–77
magnesium sulfate, anhydrous	1 g	120.37	
methoxybenzaldehyde*		136.15	
methoxybenzyl alcohol	1.5 g	138.15	
sodium chloride, saturated solution	20–30 mL		
sodium hydroxide, 5%	20 mL		
tetrabutylammonium hydrogen sulfate	0.15–0.2 g	339.54	

* product

6   *Oxidizing Methoxybenzyl Alcohol to Methoxybenzaldehyde Using Phase-Transfer Catalysis*

Preview

- Prepare TLC micropipets, plates, and developing chambers
- Weigh methoxybenzyl alcohol and dissolve it in ethyl acetate
- Weigh tetrabutylammonium hydrogen sulfate and add it to the methoxybenzyl alcohol solution
- Measure bleach and add it with stirring to the methoxybenzyl alcohol solution
- Monitor the reaction by TLC until completion
- Transfer the two-layer reaction solution to a separatory funnel, add saturated sodium chloride, and shake
- Separate the layers and extract the lower aqueous layer with ethyl acetate
- Combine the two ethyl acetate layers and extract with 5% sodium hydroxide followed by distilled or deionized water
- Dry the ethyl acetate layer with anhydrous magnesium sulfate
- Distill the ethyl acetate
- Measure the mass of the product
- Characterize the product using IR spectroscopy

PROCEDURE

CAUTION

Wear departmentally approved safety goggles at all times while in the chemistry laboratory.

Always use caution in the laboratory. Many chemicals are potentially harmful. Prevent contact with your eyes, skin, and clothing. Avoid inhaling vapors and ingesting any of the reagents.

1. Setting Up the Chromatography System

Using open-ended capillary tubing and a Bunsen burner, prepare 8–10 micropipets for TLC spotting. Make each micropipet approximately 20 cm long. Alternatively, draw out the stems of long-stem Pasteur pipets to prepare 8–10 micropipets.

Obtain three 3.5 × 8-cm silica gel TLC plates. Using a ruler as a straightedge, draw a *very faint* horizontal pencil line across the plates, 1 cm from the bottom. Make five small vertical lines that intersect the horizontal line at 6, 12, 18, 24, and 30 mm from the left side of each plate. Using a pencil, label the first plate from left to right below the vertical lines with Alc, 5, 10, 15, and Ald.

In a similar way, label the second plate Alc, 20, 25, 30, and Ald. Label the third plate Alc, 35, 40, 45, and Ald.

Methoxybenzyl alcohol and methoxybenzaldehyde are irritating.

Obtain standard samples of methoxybenzyl alcohol and methoxybenzaldehyde from your laboratory instructor. Using a micropipet, spot methoxybenzyl alcohol at the position labeled Alc on each plate. Discard the micropipet. Using a new micropipet, spot the methoxybenzaldehyde at the position marked Ald on each plate. Discard the micropipet.

CAUTION

Dichloromethane is toxic and irritating.

Prepare three developing chambers by adding 6 mL of dichloromethane to each chamber. Add filter paper to each chamber to act as a wick. Cover the chambers and set them aside in a *fume hood*.

2. Using NaOCl to Oxidize Methoxybenzyl Alcohol to Methoxybenzaldehyde

---

CAUTION

Bleach (NaOCl) is corrosive and an oxidant. Tetrabutylammonium hydrogen sulfate is irritating. Ethyl acetate is flammable and irritating. Do not use near flames or other heat sources.

Place a 100-mL round-bottom flask into a 250-mL beaker. Tare the flask and beaker on a balance.

Using a Pasteur pipet, dispense approximately 1.5 g of methoxybenzyl alcohol into the flask. Record the mass to the nearest 0.01 g.

Add 20 mL of ethyl acetate and a stir bar. Weigh 0.15–0.20 g of tetrabutylammonium hydrogen sulfate. Using a spatula, transfer the solid to the flask. Stopper the flask.

Attach a clamp to the neck of the flask and fasten the clamp to a support stand. Adjust the height so that the bottom of the flask rests in the center of the magnetic stirrer.

Place 20 mL of bleach in a 50-mL graduated cylinder. Remove the stopper from the round-bottom flask. Using a new Pasteur pipet, add the bleach at the rate of 1 mL every 5 s. Stir vigorously during the addition.

When all of the bleach has been added, reinsert the stopper and begin timing the reaction. [NOTE 1]

NOTE 1: Efficient stirring is necessary for the reaction to go to completion within 30 min.

After 5 min, turn off the magnetic stirrer and remove the stopper. After the turbulence subsides, note that there are two layers in the round-bottom flask.

Insert the tip of a new micropipet just below the surface of the top ethyl acetate layer. *Work quickly to remove samples so the stirrer can be restarted without delay*. Spot the solution once on the first TLC plate at the position labeled "5".

CAUTION

Ultraviolet radiation can cause severe damage to the eyes. Wear goggles. Do not look directly into the UV lamp.

View the TLC plate under a short-wave UV lamp to make sure that you see a dark spot at the origin. If you see no UV-absorbing spot, re-spot the sample until you do.

Moisten a strip of starch–iodide paper with distilled or deionized water. Place your finger over the top of a Pasteur pipet. Insert the tip of the pipet into the *bottom* aqueous layer. Remove your finger to allow liquid to enter the pipet. Place your finger over the end again and remove the pipet from the flask. Spot the solution on the starch-iodide paper. Note the blue-black color indicating excess NaOCl.

Reinsert the stopper and turn on the magnetic stirrer to continue the reaction. Spot the solution and test for excess NaOCl at 5-min intervals. If at any point an excess of NaOCl is not observed, add more bleach dropwise to the round-bottom flask until an excess of NaOCl is detected.

To assess the progress of the reaction, develop the first TLC plate after spotting the 15-min sample. *Keep the oxidation reaction going while developing the first TLC plate.* After the eluent reaches 1 cm from the top of the plate, remove the plate and mark the eluent front before the dichloromethane evaporates. View the plate under short-wave UV light and circle the spots with a pencil.

Develop the second TLC plate after spotting the 30-min sample. *Keep the oxidation reaction going while developing the second TLC plate.*

If a significant amount of methoxybenzyl alcohol is still present after 30 min, continue spotting the third TLC plate.

Develop the third plate after spotting the 45-min sample. If methoxybenzyl alcohol is still present, prepare a fourth TLC plate with Alc and Ald standards and a spot for a 60-min sample. Do not continue the reaction longer than 60 min. [NOTE 2]

NOTE 2: Prolonged reaction times must be avoided to prevent overoxidation.

3. Isolating Methoxybenzaldehyde

CAUTION

5% Sodium hydroxide is toxic and corrosive.

When the reaction is complete, remove the magnetic stir bar. Decant both layers into a 125-mL separatory funnel. Rinse the round-bottom flask with 5 mL of ethyl acetate and transfer the rinse to the separatory funnel.

Add 20 mL of saturated NaCl solution. Stopper the separatory funnel and shake it vigorously for 10–15 s. Allow the layers to separate.

Drain the lower aqueous layer into a labeled 100-mL beaker. Pour the ethyl acetate layer into a labeled 125-mL Erlenmeyer flask. [NOTE 3]. Pour the aqueous layer back into the separatory funnel.

NOTE 3: The product will be located in the upper ethyl acetate layer throughout all of the extractions.

Extract the aqueous layer with 10 mL of ethyl acetate. Transfer the lower aqueous layer to the labeled 100-mL beaker.

Combine the two ethyl acetate layers and extract with 20 mL of 5% NaOH. If an emulsion forms, add 10 mL of saturated NaCl solution and shake gently. Transfer the lower aqueous layer to the labeled 100-mL beaker.

Extract the ethyl acetate layer with 20 mL of distilled or deionized water. Remove the lower aqueous layer. Transfer the ethyl acetate layer to the 125-mL Erlenmeyer flask.

Dry the ethyl acetate layer by adding approximately 1 g of anhydrous $MgSO_4$. Let the solution stand for 5–10 min.

While the ethyl acetate layer is drying, assemble a simple distillation apparatus, using a 250-mL round-bottom flask as the receiver. Weigh a clean, dry 100-mL round-bottom flask to serve as the distilling pot. Record the mass of the flask to the nearest 0.01 g.

Decant the dried ethyl acetate layer from the 125-mL Erlenmeyer flask to the preweighed 100-mL flask. Avoid transferring any of the solid $MgSO_4$. Rinse the Erlenmeyer flask with 5 mL of ethyl acetate and add the rinse to the dried ethyl acetate layer in the 100-mL flask.

Add a boiling chip. Attach the 100-mL flask to the distillation apparatus. Distill the ethyl acetate away from the product.

When the volume in the pot reaches approximately 2 mL, stop the distillation. [NOTE 4]

NOTE 4: Prolonged heating will cause some loss of liquid product from the distillation flask.

Let the 100-mL flask containing the product cool to the touch. Disassemble the distillation apparatus.

Place the round-bottom flask in a sand bath under a *fume hood*. Use a gentle stream of air or nitrogen to evaporate the remaining ethyl acetate, leaving the liquid product in the flask.

Allow the flask to cool to room temperature. Reweigh the flask and record the mass of your product to the nearest 0.01 g. Put the product into a labeled product vial.

4. Characterizing the Methoxybenzaldehyde by IR Spectroscopy

Place one drop of your product between two salt plates and record the IR spectrum. Using Table 1 as a guide, determine the substitution position of your product.

5. Cleaning Up

Place your recovered materials in the appropriate labeled collection containers as directed by your laboratory instructor. Clean your glassware with soap or detergent.

CAUTION

Wash your hands thoroughly with soap or detergent before leaving the laboratory.

MICROSCALE OXIDATION OF METHOXYBENZYL ALCOHOL

Equipment

AgCl plates*, with sample holder
2 beakers, 10-mL
50-mL beaker
8–10 capillary tubes, open-ended†
2 centrifuge tubes, 15-mL, with caps
10-mL Erlenmeyer flask
2 filter papers, 12-cm, cut to fit the developing chambers
10-mL graduated cylinder
magnetic stir bar
magnetic stirrer
microburner
microspatula
5 Pasteur pipets, with latex bulb

pencil
product vial
10-mL round-bottom flask, with stopper
ruler, mm
sand bath‡
3 screw-cap jars, 4-oz§
starch-iodide paper
support stand
thermometer, −10 to 260 °C
utility clamp
4 TLC plates, silica gel, 3.5 × 8-cm, with fluorescent indicator

*or NaCl or KBr
†for preparing micropipets
‡sand in crystallizing dish on electric hot plate or sand in electric heating well with heat controller
§or 250-mL beakers with aluminum foil for developing chambers

10   *Oxidizing Methoxybenzyl Alcohol to Methoxybenzaldehyde Using Phase-Transfer Catalysis*

Reagents and Properties

substance	quantity	molar mass (g/mol)	bp (°C)
bleach (NaOCl)	2 mL		
dichloromethane	18 mL	84.93	40
ethyl acetate	6 mL	88.11	76–77
magnesium sulfate, anhydrous	50–100 mg	120.37	
methoxybenzaldehyde*		136.15	
methoxybenzyl alcohol	200 mg	138.15	
sodium chloride, saturated solution	2–3 mL		
sodium hydroxide, 5%	2 mL		
tetrabutylammonium hydrogen sulfate	15–20 mg	339.54	

* product

Preview

- Prepare TLC micropipets, plates, and developing chambers
- Weigh methoxybenzyl alcohol and dissolve it in ethyl acetate
- Weigh tetrabutylammonium hydrogen sulfate and add it to the methoxybenzyl alcohol solution
- Measure bleach and add it with stirring to the methoxybenzyl alcohol solution
- Monitor the reaction by TLC until completion
- Transfer the two-layer reaction solution to a centrifuge tube, add saturated sodium chloride, and shake
- Separate the layers and extract the lower aqueous layer with ethyl acetate
- Combine the two ethyl acetate layers and extract with 5% sodium hydroxide followed by distilled or deionized water
- Dry the ethyl acetate layer with anhydrous magnesium sulfate
- Transfer the dried ethyl acetate to a beaker
- Evaporate the ethyl acetate using a warm sand bath
- Determine the mass of the product
- Characterize the product using IR spectroscopy

PROCEDURE

Wear departmentally approved safety goggles at all times while in the chemistry laboratory.

Always use caution in the laboratory. Many chemicals are potentially harmful. Prevent contact with your eyes, skin, and clothing. Avoid inhaling vapors and ingesting any of the reagents.

1. Setting Up the Chromatography System

Using open-ended capillary tubing and a microburner, prepare 8–10 micropipets for TLC spotting.

Obtain three 3.5 × 8-cm silica gel TLC plates. Using a ruler as a straightedge, draw a *very faint* horizontal pencil line across the plates, 1 cm from the bottom. Make five small vertical lines that intersect the horizontal line at 6, 12, 18, 24, and 30 mm from the left side of each plate. Using a pencil, label the first plate from left to right below the vertical lines with Alc, 5, 10, 15, and Ald.

In a similar way, label the second plate Alc, 20, 25, 30, and Ald. Label the third plate Alc, 35, 40, 45, and Ald.

CAUTION

Methoxybenzyl alcohol and methoxybenzaldehyde are irritating.

Obtain standard samples of methoxybenzyl alcohol and methoxybenzaldehyde from your laboratory instructor. Using a micropipet, spot methoxybenzyl alcohol at the position labeled Alc on each plate. Discard the micropipet. Using a new micropipet, spot the methoxybenzaldehyde at the position marked Ald on each plate. Discard the micropipet.

CAUTION

Dichloromethane is toxic and irritating.

Prepare three developing chambers by adding 6 mL of dichloromethane to each chamber. Add filter paper to each chamber to act as a wick. Cover the chambers and set them aside in a *fume hood*.

2. Using NaOCl to Oxidize Methoxybenzyl Alcohol to Methoxybenzaldehyde

CAUTION

Bleach (NaOCl) is corrosive and an oxidant. Tetrabutylammonium hydrogen sulfate is irritating. Ethyl acetate is flammable and irritating. Do not use near flames or other heat sources.

Place a 10-mL round-bottom flask into a 50-mL beaker. Tare the flask and beaker on a balance. Using a Pasteur pipet, dispense 200 mg of methoxybenzyl alcohol into the flask. Record the mass to the nearest mg.

Add 2 mL of ethyl acetate and a stir bar. Weigh 15–20 mg of tetrabutylammonium hydrogen sulfate. Using a microspatula, transfer the solid to the flask.

Attach a clamp to the neck of the flask and stopper the flask. Fasten the clamp to a support stand. Adjust the height so that the bottom of the flask rests in the center of the magnetic stirrer.

Place 2 mL of bleach in a 10-mL graduated cylinder. Remove the stopper from the round-bottom flask. Using a new Pasteur pipet, add the bleach dropwise at the rate of one drop every 1–2 s. Stir vigorously during the addition. When all of the bleach has been added, reinsert the stopper and begin timing the reaction. [NOTE 1]

NOTE 1: Efficient stirring is necessary for the reaction to go to completion within 30 min.

© 1999 Cengage Learning

12   *Oxidizing Methoxybenzyl Alcohol to Methoxybenzaldehyde Using Phase-Transfer Catalysis*

After 5 min, turn off the magnetic stirrer and remove the stopper. After the turbulence subsides, note that there are two layers in the round-bottom flask.

Insert the tip of a new micropipet just below the surface of the *top* ethyl acetate layer. *Work quickly to remove samples so the stirrer can be restarted without delay.* Spot the solution once on the first TLC plate at the position labeled "5".

CAUTION

Ultraviolet radiation can cause severe damage to the eyes. Wear goggles. Do not look directly into the UV lamp.

View the TLC plate under a short-wave UV lamp to make sure that you see a dark spot at the origin. If you see no UV-absorbing spot, re-spot the sample until you do.

Moisten a strip of starch-iodide paper with distilled or deionized water. Insert the tip of the micropipet into the *bottom* aqueous layer and spot the solution on the starch-iodide paper. Note the blue-black color indicating excess NaOCl. Discard the micropipet.

Reinsert the stopper and turn on the magnetic stirrer to continue the reaction. Spot the solution and test for excess NaOCl at 5-min intervals. If at any point an excess of NaOCl is not observed, add more bleach dropwise to the round-bottom flask until an excess of NaOCl is detected.

To assess the progress of the reaction, develop the first TLC plate after spotting the 15-min sample. *Keep the oxidation reaction going while developing the first TLC plate.* After the eluent reaches 1 cm from the top of the plate, remove the plate and mark the eluent front before the dichloromethane evaporates. View the plate under short-wave UV light and circle the spots with a pencil.

Develop the second TLC plate after spotting the 30-min sample. *Keep the oxidation reaction going while developing the second TLC plate.*

If a significant amount of methoxybenzyl alcohol is still present after 30 min, continue spotting the third TLC plate.

Develop the third plate after spotting the 45-min sample. If methoxybenzyl alcohol is still present, prepare a fourth TLC plate with Alc and Ald standards and a spot for a 60-min sample. Do not continue the reaction longer than 60 min. [NOTE 2]

NOTE 2: Prolonged reaction times must be avoided to prevent over-oxidation.

3. Isolating Methoxybenzaldehyde

CAUTION

5% Sodium hydroxide is toxic and corrosive.

When the reaction is complete, remove the magnetic stir bar. Using a Pasteur pipet, transfer both layers to a 15-mL centrifuge tube. Rinse the round-bottom flask with 1 mL of ethyl acetate and transfer the rinse to the centrifuge tube.

Add 2 mL of saturated NaCl solution. Cap the tube and shake it vigorously for 10–15 s. Allow the layers to separate.

Use a Pasteur pipet to remove the lower aqueous layer and place the aqueous layer into a second 15-mL centrifuge tube. [NOTE 3]. Extract the

NOTE 3: The product will be located in the upper ethyl acetate layer throughout all of the extractions.

aqueous layer with 2 mL of ethyl acetate. Transfer the lower aqueous layer to a labeled 10-mL beaker.

Combine the two ethyl acetate layers and extract with 2 mL of 5% NaOH. If an emulsion forms, add 1 mL of saturated NaCl solution and shake gently. Transfer the lower aqueous layer to a labeled 10-mL beaker.

Extract the ethyl acetate layer with 2 mL of distilled or deionized water. Discard the lower aqueous layer. Using a Pasteur pipet, transfer the ethyl acetate layer to a 10-mL Erlenmeyer flask.

Dry the ethyl acetate layer by adding approximately 50–100 mg of anhydrous $MgSO_4$. Let the solution stand for 5–10 min.

While the ethyl acetate layer is drying, preheat a sand bath in the fume hood to 55–60 °C. Place the thermometer bulb just beneath the surface of the sand when recording the temperature.

Weigh a clean, dry, 50-mL beaker and record the mass to the nearest mg. Using a *clean* Pasteur pipet, transfer the dried ethyl acetate layer from the centrifuge tube to the preweighed 50-mL beaker. Avoid transferring any of the solid $MgSO_4$.

Rinse the centrifuge tube with 1 mL of ethyl acetate and add the rinse to the dried ethyl acetate in the 50-mL beaker. Place the bottom of the beaker just beneath the surface of the sand in the warm sand bath. Use a gentle stream of air or nitrogen to evaporate the ethyl acetate, leaving the liquid product in the beaker.

Continue the evaporation for 6–7 min. Do not exceed this time or you will begin to evaporate your product. Reweigh the beaker and record the mass of your product. Place the product into a labeled product vial.

4. Characterizing the Methoxybenzaldehyde by IR Spectroscopy

Place one drop of your product between two salt plates and record the IR spectrum. Using Table 1 as a guide, determine the substitution position of your product.

5. Cleaning Up

Place your recovered materials in the appropriate labeled collection containers as directed by your laboratory instructor. Clean your glassware with soap or detergent.

CAUTION

Wash your hands thoroughly with soap or detergent before leaving the laboratory.

14   *Oxidizing Methoxybenzyl Alcohol to Methoxybenzaldehyde Using Phase-Transfer Catalysis*

POST-LABORATORY QUESTIONS

1. Calculate the percent yield for your product. [Note: if the amount of methoxybenzyl alcohol you used differs from the amount listed in the Reagents and Properties section, calculate the theoretical yield using the amount you used.]

2. Draw the structure of your product. Explain how your IR spectrum supports your proposed structure.

3. Compare the IR spectrum of your product with the spectrum of the starting alcohol provided by your laboratory instructor to answer the following questions:

   (a) Which major peak in the aldehyde is absent in the alcohol?

   (b) Which major peak in the alcohol is absent in the aldehyde?

4. Draw a mechanism similar to that in Equation 6 for the conversion of methoxybenzyl alcohol to methoxybenzaldehyde.

5. Calculate the R_fs for methoxybenzyl alcohol and methoxybenzaldehyde using the 10-min spotting time. Explain why the alcohol has a lower R_f than the aldehyde.

6. The ethyl acetate layer was extracted with $0.2M$ NaOH to remove traces of methoxybenzoic acid that result from additional oxidation of the aldehyde to the carboxylic acid.

   (a) Write a balanced equation for this reaction.

   (b) Explain how crystals of methoxybenzoic acid could be isolated from the NaOH solution.

7. Explain how TLC could be used to monitor the reduction of methoxybenzaldehyde to methoxybenzyl alcohol using $NaBH_4$ as a reducing agent.

Name _____   Section _____   Date _____

Pre-Laboratory Assignment

1. What safety precautions must be observed when using

    (a) ethyl acetate?

    (b) dichloromethane?

2. Using the data in the *Reagents and Properties* table, calculate the theoretical yield of methoxybenzaldehyde. Record the calculations here and in your laboratory notebook.

3. In its IR spectrum, a disubstituted aromatic compound showed a strong absorption at 740 cm^{-1}. Was the compound *ortho-*, *meta-*, or *para*-substituted? Briefly explain.

4. Draw the structure of the expected organic product for each of the reactions shown below:

    (a)

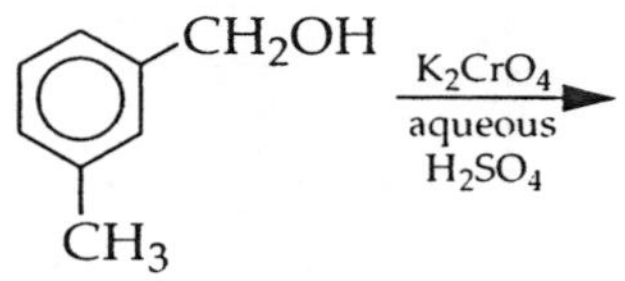

    (b)

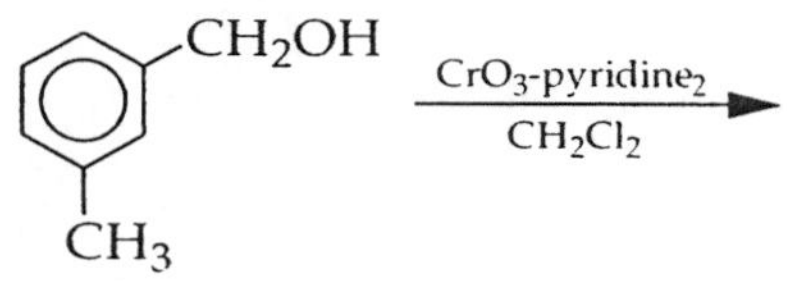

232   SYNT0725: Oxidizing Methoxybenzyl Alcohol to Methoxybenzaldehyde Using Phase-Transfer Catalysis

16   *Oxidizing Methoxybenzyl Alcohol to Methoxybenzaldehyde Using Phase-Transfer Catalysis*

(c)

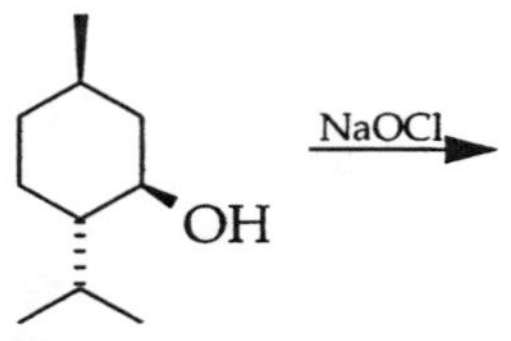

(d)

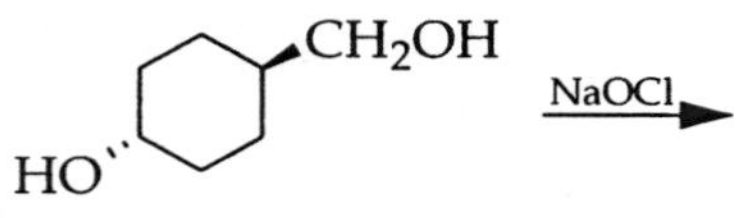

5. Explain why a phase-transfer catalyst is used when oxidizing methoxybenzyl alcohol using NaOCl.

Two Methods for the Synthesis of Phenacetin

Prepared by Jerry Manion, University of Central Arkansas

PURPOSE OF THE EXPERIMENT

Synthesize phenacetin by formation of an ether functional group and/or an amide functional group. Compare the products by mixture melting point, IR spectroscopy, and NMR spectroscopy.

EXPERIMENTAL OPTIONS

Williamson Ether Synthesis of Phenacetin
  Semi-Microscale Synthesis
  Microscale Synthesis
Amide Synthesis of Phenacetin
  Semi-Microscale Synthesis
  Microscale Synthesis

BACKGROUND REQUIRED

You should be familiar with recrystallization, reflux, melting point and mixture melting point measurements, IR spectroscopy, and NMR spectroscopy.

BACKGROUND INFORMATION

Phenacetin is an active constituent of APC tablets, along with aspirin and caffeine. These tablets were used for years as an analgesic to relieve pain and as an antipyretic to reduce fever. They were removed from the market after long-term studies suggested phenacetin is carcinogenic when ingested over long time periods.

Aspirin and phenacetin are synthesized chemically. Caffeine is obtained as a by-product from the production of caffeine-free coffee. These constituents are mixed with binders and inert ingredients to create the tablets.

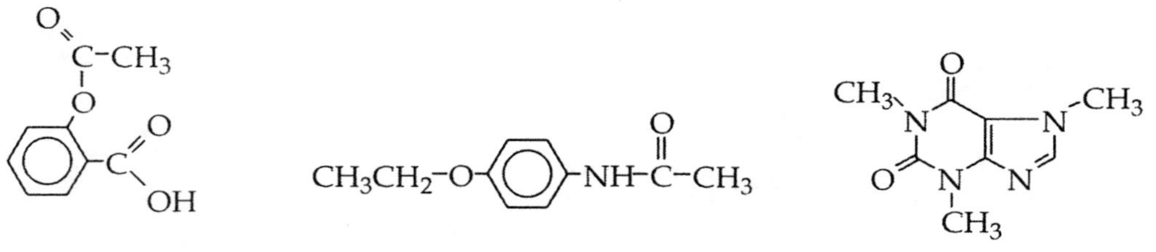

Figure 1
Active constituents in APC analgesic tablets

     As shown in Figure 1, each organic compound contains more than one functional group. Therefore, more than one method can be used to synthesize each compound.

     Phenacetin, *p*-ethoxyacetanilide, contains both an ether group and an amide group substituted *para* on a benzene ring. Either of these functional groups might be produced as the final step in a synthesis of phenacetin.

Williamson Ether Synthesis

     Equation 1 shows the formation of the ether functional group in phenacetin. The formation of an ether by reaction of an alkyl halide with the conjugate base of an alcohol or phenol is called a **Williamson ether synthesis**. The reactant, acetaminophen (*p*-acetamidophenol), is the active ingredient in Tylenol®.

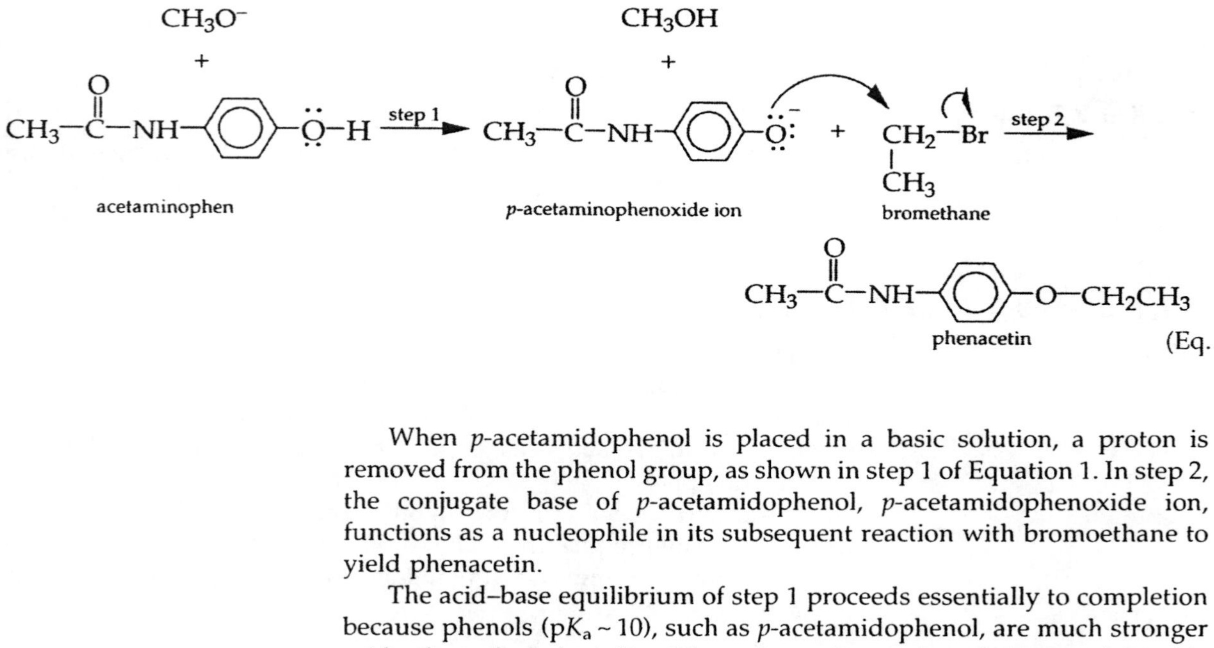

(Eq. 1)

     When *p*-acetamidophenol is placed in a basic solution, a proton is removed from the phenol group, as shown in step 1 of Equation 1. In step 2, the conjugate base of *p*-acetamidophenol, *p*-acetamidophenoxide ion, functions as a nucleophile in its subsequent reaction with bromoethane to yield phenacetin.

     The acid–base equilibrium of step 1 proceeds essentially to completion because phenols ($pK_a \sim 10$), such as *p*-acetamidophenol, are much stronger acids than alcohols ($pK_a \sim 16$), such as the methanol produced in this reaction.

     The number of moles of methoxide ion that are added to the reaction flask must exactly equal the number of moles of *p*-acetamidophenol. If insufficient methoxide ion is used, some of the *p*-acetamidophenol will not be converted to its conjugate base and will not be reactive toward the bromoethane. If excess methoxide ion is used, methoxide ion will compete as a nucleophile with the *p*-acetamidophenoxide ion, also reducing the yield of phenacetin.

The second step in the overall process is an S_N2 nucleophilic substitution reaction. S_N2 reactions occur in one step with the leaving group departing simultaneously. An important factor in determining the rate of S_N2 reactions is the degree of crowding at the reaction site in the alkyl halide. For this reason, the reaction proceeds best when relatively uncrowded primary alkyl halides are used.

In practice, this reaction works equally well with most primary halides and might be used to produce a series of phenacetin analogs with different alkoxy groups. Synthesizing compounds that are related in structure to known beneficial agents is a common method used to search for more effective drugs.

Amide Synthesis

Equation 2 shows the synthesis of phenacetin by formation of an amide functional group. In step 1, acetic anhydride is protonated to increase its reactivity. In step 2, *p*-phenetidine (*p*-ethoxyaniline) acts as a nucleophile and attacks the carbonyl carbon of acetic anhydride to form a tetrahedral intermediate.

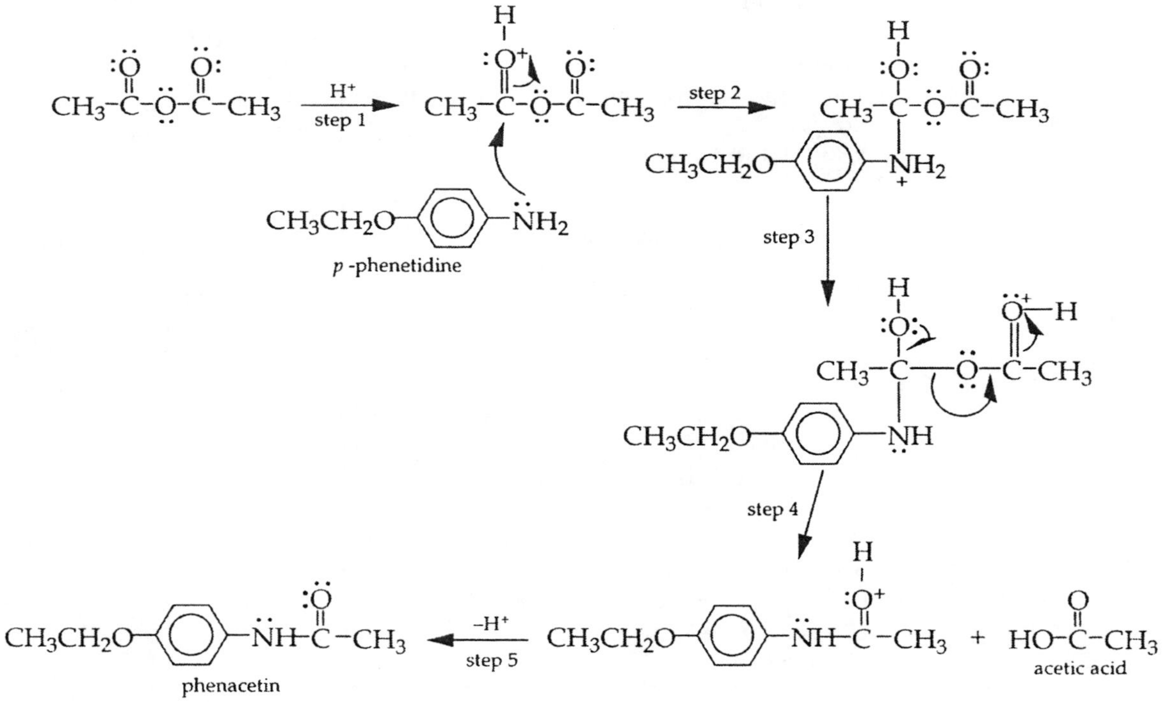

(Eq. 2)

In step 3, a proton shifxt occurs. In step 4, acetic acid leaves to form protonated phenacetin. Finally, in step 5, the proton is removed.

Control of the solution acidity is important in maximizing the product yield. Protonation activates the acetic anhydride toward nucleophilic attack; however, if the pH of the solution is too low, *p*-phenetidine is converted to its conjugate acid and is unavailable for the reaction. A buffer solution consisting of acetic acid and its conjugate base sodium acetate is used to control the pH.

A fundamental principle in chemistry is that the properties of a substance do not depend upon its source. Consequently, samples of phenacetin synthesized by either of the methods described above should be identical.

In this experiment, you will prepare phenacetin by the Williamson ether synthesis and by the amide synthesis. You will compare the products by melting point measurement, infrared spectroscopy, and/or nuclear magnetic resonance spectroscopy.

WILLIAMSON ETHER SYNTHESIS OF PHENACETIN

Semi-Microscale Synthesis

Equipment

2 beakers, 100-mL
250-mL beaker
boiling chip
Büchner funnel, with adapter
125-mL filter flask,
  with vacuum tubing
filter paper
10-mL graduated cylinder
hot plate*
*or electric flask heater, with regulator

melting point capillary tubes
2 Pasteur pipets, with latex bulb
spatula
standard taper glassware
  condenser, with tubing 25-mL
  round-bottom flask
support stand
16 × 150-mm test tube
2 utility clamps

Reagents and Properties

substance	quantity	molar mass (g/mol)	mp (°C)	bp (°C)
p-acetamidophenol	1.51 g	151.17	169–172	
bromoethane	1.64 g	108.97		37–40
deutero-chloroform*	1 mL	120		61
ethanol, 100%	4 mL	46.07		78
ethanol, 95%	6 mL			
phenacetin⁺		179	134–136	
potassium bromide‡	100 mg			
25% sodium methoxide in methanol	2.5 mL			

* for NMR
⁺ product
‡ for IR

Preview

- Place sodium methoxide solution, 100% ethanol, and *p*-acetamidophenol in a reaction flask

- Assemble the reflux apparatus

- Add bromoethane
- Reflux the mixture for 45 min
- Add water to the hot reaction mixture and cool it in ice to crystallize the product
- Isolate the crude product by vacuum filtration
- Purify the product by recrystallization from an ethanol–water mixture
- Isolate the purified phenacetin by vacuum filtration; dry and weigh the crystals
- Characterize the product by melting point and infrared and/or NMR spectroscopy

PROCEDURE

CAUTION

Wear departmentally approved safety goggles at all times while in the chemistry laboratory.

   Always use caution in the laboratory. Many chemicals are potentially harmful. Prevent contact with your eyes, skin, and clothing. Avoid ingesting any of the reagents.

1. Refluxing the Reaction Mixture

CAUTION

***p*-Acetamidophenol is toxic and irritating. Ethanol is flammable and irritating. 25% Sodium methoxide in methanol is flammable, toxic, and corrosive. Keep away from flames or other heat sources.**

Place 2.5 mL of 25% sodium methoxide in methanol, 4 mL of 100% ethanol, and 1.51 g of *p*-acetamidophenol in a 25-mL round-bottom flask. Add a boiling chip.

CAUTION

Bromoethane is flammable and irritating. Keep away from flames or other heat sources.

   Use this flask to set up the reflux apparatus shown in Figure 2 on the next page. Immediately before joining the flask to the condenser, add 1.64 g (1.12 mL) of bromoethane to the flask. Turn on the water to the condenser. Adjust the flask heater to produce moderate boiling. Reflux the mixture for 45 min.

   Prepare an ice bath in a 250-mL beaker.

   When the reflux time is completed, remove the heater. While the reaction mixture is still hot, slowly add 12 mL of distilled or deionized water through the top of the condenser. Allow the reaction mixture to cool to room temperature.

   Turn off the water and remove the reflux condenser.

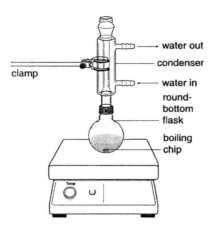

Figure 2
Semi-microscale reflux apparatus

Pour the reaction mixture into a 100-mL beaker. Rinse the round-bottom flask with 3 mL of water and add the rinse to the beaker.

Cool the beaker in the ice bath to crystallize the product. Collect the product by vacuum filtration using a Büchner funnel.

2. Recrystallizing the Crude Phenacetin

NOTE 1: Food and drug substances undergo a much higher scrutiny than do most other chemicals. Use normal precautions when working with phenacetin.

NOTE 2: Phenacetin is very soluble in ethanol and quite insoluble in water. Because ethanol and water are miscible liquids, a mixture of the two solvents can be used for recrystallization. *Take great care with the recrystallization or low product yields will result.*

> **CAUTION**
>
> **Phenacetin is a suspected carcinogen. [NOTE 1]**

Purify the product by recrystallization from an ethanol–water mixture as follows: [NOTE 2] Place the impure phenacetin in a 100-mL beaker. Put 6 mL of 95% ethanol into a test tube and heat to boiling. Maintain the temperature of the ethanol close to the boiling point, but do not allow the ethanol to boil away.

Add hot ethanol to the phenacetin until the solid just dissolves. Once the solid has dissolved, use a Pasteur pipet to add water dropwise to decrease the solubility of the phenacetin *while maintaining the solution at a temperature close to its boiling point*. Once the solution becomes cloudy, add hot ethanol dropwise to bring the product back into solution. Then set it aside to cool slowly. If the solution appears milky or if an oil appears, add more ethanol and heat to redissolve. Then cool the solution again.

Isolate the purified phenacetin by vacuum filtration using a Büchner funnel. Pull air through the funnel for 5 min to dry the product. Alternatively, dry the product in a 110 °C drying oven. Weigh the product and record its mass.

3. Characterizing the Product

Measure the melting point of your product. If product is available from the amide synthesis, conduct a mixture melting point. Thoroughly mix equal amounts of phenacetin from each procedure. Take the melting point of the mixture.

Obtain an infrared spectrum of your product by preparing a KBr pellet or as indicated by your laboratory instructor.

Dissolve a small amount of the product in *deutero*-chloroform. Place the solution in a NMR sample tube. Obtain a NMR spectrum as directed by your laboratory instructor.

4. Cleaning Up

Place your recovered materials in the appropriate labeled collection containers as directed by your laboratory instructor. Clean your glassware with soap or detergent.

WILLIAMSON ETHER SYNTHESIS OF PHENACETIN

Microscale Synthesis

Equipment

25-mL beaker
100-mL beaker
conical vial reflux apparatus*
    condenser, with tubing
    5.0-mL conical vial
    magnetic spin vane
    thermometer, −10 to 260 °C
elastomeric connector
    reflux apparatus*
        condenser, with tubing
        elastomeric connector
        magnetic stir bar
        5.0-mL round-bottom flask

25-mL filter flask,
    with vacuum tubing
filter paper
graduated pipet or syringe
Hirsch funnel, with adapter
hot plate
melting point capillary tubes
microspatula
2 Pasteur pipets, with latex bulb
sand bath†
support stand
2 test tubes, 13 × 100-mm
2 utility clamps

*use reflux apparatus indicated by your laboratory instructor
†stirring hot plate with crystallizing dish filled with sand or magnetic stirrer and electric flask heater filled with sand

Reagents and Properties

substance	quantity	molar mass (g/mol)	mp (°C)	bp (°C)
p-acetamidophenol	0.151 g	151.17	169–172	
bromoethane	0.17 g	108.97		37–40
deutero-chloroform*	1 mL	120		61
ethanol, 100%	1.0 mL	46.07		78
ethanol, 95%	1.5 mL			
phenacetin†		179	134–136	
potassium bromide‡	100 mg			
25% sodium methoxide in methanol	0.25 mL			

* for NMR
† product
‡ for IR

Preview

- Place sodium methoxide solution, ethanol, and p-acetamidophenol in a reaction flask or vial
- Assemble the reflux apparatus
- Add bromoethane through the condenser
- Reflux the mixture for 45 min
- Add water to the hot reaction mixture and cool it in ice to crystallize the product
- Isolate the crude product by vacuum filtration
- Purify the product by recrystallization from an ethanol–water mixture
- Isolate the purified phenacetin by vacuum filtration; dry and weigh the crystals
- Characterize the product by melting point and infrared and/or NMR spectroscopy

PROCEDURE

CAUTION

Wear departmentally approved safety goggles at all times while in the chemistry laboratory.

Always use caution in the laboratory. Many chemicals are potentially harmful. Prevent contact with your eyes, skin, and clothing. Avoid ingesting any of the reagents.

1. Refluxing the Reaction Mixture

Place exactly 0.25 mL of 25% sodium methoxide in methanol, 1.0 mL of 100% ethanol, and 0.151 g of *p*-acetamidophenol in a 5-mL conical vial or 5-mL round-bottom flask. Add a magnetic spin vane or stir bar. If a magnetic stirrer is not available, add a boiling chip. Use this vial(flask) to set up the reflux apparatus shown in Figure 3.

Carefully add 0.17 g (0.12 mL) of bromoethane through the top of the condenser. Turn on the water to the condenser. Adjust the sand bath to produce moderate boiling. Reflux the mixture for 45 min.

Prepare an ice bath in a 100-mL beaker.

When the reflux time is completed, remove the heater. While the reaction mixture is still hot, slowly add 1.0 mL of distilled or deionized water through the top of the condenser. Allow the reaction mixture to cool to room temperature.

Turn off the water and remove the reflux condenser.

Pour the reaction mixture into a 25-mL beaker. Rinse the vial (flask) with 0.5 mL of water and add the rinse to the beaker.

Cool the beaker in the ice bath to crystallize the product. Collect the product by vacuum filtration using a Hirsch funnel.

2. Recrystallizing the Crude Phenacetin

NOTE 1: Food and drug substances undergo a much higher scrutiny than do most other chemicals. Use normal precautions when working with phenacetin.

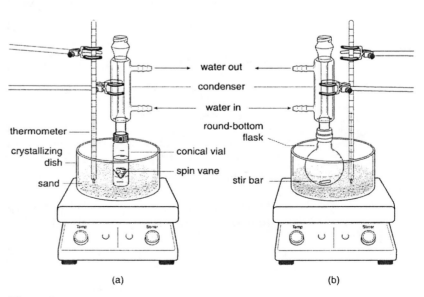

(a)   (b)

Figure 3
Microscale reflux apparatus with (a) conical vial or (b) round-bottom flask and elastomeric connectors

NOTE 2: Phenacetin is very soluble in ethanol and quite insoluble in water. Because ethanol and water are miscible liquids, a mixture of the two solvents can be used for recrystallization. *Take great care with the recrystallization or low-product yields will result.*

Purify the product by recrystallization from an ethanol–water mixture as follows: [NOTE 2] Place the impure phenacetin in a 13 × 100-mm test tube. Add 1 mL of 95% ethanol to a second test tube. Use a sand bath to heat the ethanol to boiling. Maintain the temperature of the ethanol close to the boiling point, but do not allow the ethanol to boil away.

Using a Pasteur pipet, add the hot ethanol dropwise to just dissolve the phenacetin. Place this mixture on a sand bath and heat to the boiling point.

Once the solid has dissolved, use a Pasteur pipet to add water dropwise to decrease the solubility of the phenacetin *while maintaining the solution at a temperature close to its boiling point.* Once the solution becomes cloudy, add ethanol dropwise to bring the product back into solution. Then set it aside to cool slowly. If the solution appears milky or if an oil appears, add more ethanol and heat to redissolve, then cool the solution again.

Isolate the purified phenacetin by vacuum filtration using a Hirsch funnel. Pull air through the funnel for 5 min to dry the product. Alternatively, dry the product in a 110 °C drying oven. Weigh the product and record its mass.

3. Characterizing the Product

Measure the melting point of your product. If product is available from the amide synthesis, conduct a mixture melting point. Thoroughly mix equal amounts of phenacetin from each procedure. Take the melting point of the mixture.

CAUTION

Potassium bromide (KBr) is irritating and hygroscopic.

Obtain an infrared spectrum of your product by preparing a KBr pellet or as indicated by your laboratory instructor.

CAUTION

***deutero*-Chloroform is toxic and a suspected carcinogen. Dispense in a *fume hood* or glove box. Wear protective gloves.**

Dissolve a small amount of the product in *deutero*-chloroform. Place the solution in a NMR sample tube. Obtain a NMR spectrum as directed by your laboratory instructor.

4. Cleaning Up

Place your recovered materials in the appropriate labeled collection containers as directed by your laboratory instructor. Clean your glassware with soap or detergent.

CAUTION

Wash your hands thoroughly with soap or detergent before leaving the laboratory.

AMIDE SYNTHESIS OF PHENACETIN

Semi-Microscale Synthesis

Equipment

100-mL beaker	glass stirring rod
250-mL beaker	25-mL graduated cylinder
400-mL beaker	hot plate
Büchner funnel, with adapter	melting point capillary tubes
25-mL Erlenmeyer flask	spatula
125-mL Erlenmeyer flask	support ring or funnel support
125-mL filter flask,	support stand
with vacuum tubing	16×150-mm test tube
filter papers	thermometer, -10 to 260 °C
funnel, general-purpose	

Reagents and Properties

substance	quantity	molar mass (g/mol)	mp (°C)	bp (°C)
acetic anhydride	1.2 mL	102.09		138–140
activated carbon	0.4 g			
deutero-chloroform*	1 mL	120		61
ethanol, 95%	6 mL			
hydrochloric acid, concentrated	1.0 mL			
phenacetin[†]		179	134–136	
p-phenetidine	1.38 g	137.18	4	250
potassium bromide[‡]	100 mg			
sodium acetate	2.0 g	82.03		

* for NMR
[†] product
[‡] for IR

Preview

- Decolorize the *p*-phenetidine
- Combine the solution of *p*-phenetidine with acetic anhydride and sodium acetate
- Isolate the crude product by vacuum filtration
- Purify the product by recrystallization from an ethanol–water mixture
- Isolate the purified phenacetin by vacuum filtration; dry and weigh the crystals
- Characterize the product by melting point and infrared and/or NMR spectroscopy

PROCEDURE

1. Conducting the Reaction

In a 250 mL-beaker, add 1.0 mL of conc. HCl to 25 mL of distilled or deionized water. Dissolve 1.38 g (1.3 mL) of *p*-phenetidine (*p*-ethoxyaniline) in the solution.

Decolorize the solution by stirring it with 0.4 g of activated carbon for 1–2 min. Remove the carbon by gravity filtration.

Place the decolorized *p*-phenetidine solution in a 125-mL Erlenmeyer flask. Warm it on a hot plate to 50 °C.

Using a 25-mL Erlenmeyer flask, dissolve 2 g of sodium acetate in 6 mL of water. Warm it on a hot plate to 50 °C.

Add 1.2 mL of acetic anhydride to the *p*-phenetidine solution and swirl to mix. Add, all at once, the sodium acetate solution to the *p*-phenetidine solution and swirl to mix. Allow the reaction mixture to stand for 15 min, maintaining the temperature at 50 °C.

Prepare an ice bath using a 400-mL beaker. Cool the reaction mixture in the ice bath.

Stir vigorously during the crystallization of the product. Collect the crystals by vacuum filtration using a Büchner funnel.

2. Recrystallizing the Crude Phenacetin

NOTE 1: Food and drug substances undergo a much higher scrutiny than do most other chemicals. Use normal precautions when working with phenacetin.

NOTE 2: Phenacetin is very soluble in ethanol and quite insoluble in water. Because ethanol and water are miscible liquids, a mixture of the two solvents can be used for recrystallization. *Take great care with the recrystallization or low product yields will result.*

Purify the product by recrystallization from an ethanol–water mixture as follows: [NOTE 2] Place the impure phenacetin in a 100-mL beaker. Put 6 mL of 95% ethanol into a test tube and heat to boiling. Maintain the temperature of the ethanol close to the boiling point, but do not allow the ethanol to boil away.

Add hot ethanol to the phenacetin until the solid just dissolves. Once the solid has dissolved, use a Pasteur pipet to add water dropwise to decrease the solubility of the phenacetin *while maintaining the solution at a temperature close to its boiling point*. Once the solution becomes cloudy, add hot ethanol dropwise to bring the product back into solution. Then set it aside to cool slowly. If the solution appears milky or if an oil appears, add more ethanol and heat to redissolve. Then cool the solution again.

Isolate the purified phenacetin by vacuum filtration using a Büchner funnel. Pull air through the funnel for 5 min to dry the product. Alternatively, dry the product in a 110 °C drying oven. Weigh the product and record its mass.

3. Characterizing the Product

Measure the melting point of your product. If product is available from the Williamson ether synthesis, conduct a mixture melting point. Thoroughly mix equal amounts of phenacetin from each procedure. Take the melting point of the mixture.

CAUTION

Potassium bromide (KBr) is irritating and hygroscopic.

Obtain an infrared spectrum of your product by preparing a KBr pellet or as indicated by your laboratory instructor.

CAUTION

***deutero*-Chloroform is toxic and a suspected carcinogen. Dispense in a *fume hood* or glove box. Wear protective gloves.**

Dissolve a small amount of the product in *deutero*-chloroform. Place the solution in a NMR sample tube. Obtain a NMR spectrum as directed by your laboratory instructor.

4. Cleaning Up

Place your recovered materials in the appropriate labeled collection containers as directed by your laboratory instructor. Clean your glassware with soap or detergent.

CAUTION

Wash your hands thoroughly with soap or detergent before leaving the laboratory.

AMIDE SYNTHESIS OF PHENACETIN

Microscale Synthesis

Equipment

50-mL beaker	Hirsch funnel, with adapter
100-mL beaker	hot plate
2 Erlenmeyer flasks, 25-mL	melting point capillary tubes
25-mL filter flask,	microspatula
with vacuum tubing	2 Pasteur pipets, with latex bulb
filter papers	sand bath*
funnel, general-purpose	support ring or funnel support
glass stirring rod	support stand
10-mL graduated cylinder	2 test tubes, 13 × 100-mm
1.0-mL graduated pipet or syringe	thermometer, −10 to 260 °C

*stirring hot plate with crystallizing dish filled with sand or magnetic stirrer and electric flask heater filled with sand

Reagents and Properties

substance	quantity	molar mass (g/mol)	mp (°C)	bp (°C)
acetic anhydride	0.25 mL	102.09		138–140
activated carbon	0.1 g			
deutero-chloroform*	1 mL	120		61
ethanol, 95%	1.5 mL			
hydrochloric acid, concentrated	0.2 mL			
phenacetin†		179	134–136	
p-phenetidine	0.266 g	137.18	4	250
potassium bromide‡	100 mg			
sodium acetate	0.42 g	82.03		

* for NMR
† product
‡ for IR

Preview

- Decolorize the *p*-phenetidine
- Combine the solution of *p*-phenetidine with acetic anhydride and sodium acetate
- Isolate the crude product by vacuum filtration
- Purify the product by recrystallization from an ethanol–water mixture
- Isolate the purified phenacetin by vacuum filtration; dry and weigh the crystals
- Characterize the product by melting point and infrared and/or NMR spectroscopy

PROCEDURE

CAUTION

Wear departmentally approved safety goggles at all times while in the chemistry laboratory.

Always use caution in the laboratory. Many chemicals are potentially harmful. Prevent contact with your eyes, skin, and clothing. Avoid ingesting any of the reagents.

1. Conducting the Reaction

CAUTION

Activated carbon and *p*-phenetidine are irritating.

Concentrated hydrochloric acid (HCl) is toxic and corrosive. It can cause severe burns. Use a *fume hood* when working with concentrated HCl.

In a 50 mL-beaker, add 0.2 mL of conc. HCl to 5 mL of distilled or deionized water. Dissolve 0.266 g (0.25 mL) of *p*-phenetidine (*p*-ethoxyaniline) in the solution.

Decolorize the solution by stirring it with 0.1 g of activated carbon for 1–2 min. Remove the carbon by gravity filtration.

Place the decolorized *p*-phenetidine solution in a 25-mL Erlenmeyer flask. Warm it on a hot plate to 50 °C.

Using a 25-mL Erlenmeyer flask, dissolve 0.42 g of sodium acetate in 1.5 mL of water. Warm it on a hot plate to 50 °C.

Add 0.25 mL of acetic anhydride to the *p*-phenetidine solution and swirl to mix. Add, all at once, the sodium acetate solution to the *p*-phenetidine solution and swirl to mix. Allow the reaction mixture to stand for 15 min, maintaining the temperature at 50 °C.

Prepare an ice bath using a 100-mL beaker. Cool the reaction mixture in the ice bath.

Stir vigorously during the crystallization of the product. Collect the crystals by vacuum filtration using a Hirsch funnel.

2. Recrystallizing the Crude Phenacetin

NOTE 1: Food and drug substances undergo a much higher scrutiny than do most other chemicals. Use normal precautions when working with phenacetin.

NOTE 2: Phenacetin is very soluble in ethanol and quite insoluble in water. Because ethanol and water are miscible liquids, a mixture of the two solvents can be used for recrystallization. *Take great care with the recrystallization or low product yields will result.*

CAUTION ⚠

Phenacetin is a suspected carcinogen. [NOTE 1] Ethanol is flammable and irritating. Keep away from flames or other heat sources.

Purify the product by recrystallization from an ethanol–water mixture as follows: [NOTE 2] Place the impure phenacetin in a 13 × 100-mm test tube. Add 1 mL of 95% ethanol to a second test tube. Use a sand bath to heat the ethanol to boiling. Maintain the temperature of the ethanol close to the boiling point, but do not allow the ethanol to boil away.

Using a Pasteur pipet, add the hot ethanol dropwise to just dissolve the phenacetin. Place this mixture on a sand bath and heat to the boiling point.

Once the solid has dissolved, use a Pasteur pipet to add water dropwise to decrease the solubility of the phenacetin *while maintaining the solution at a temperature close to its boiling point*. Once the solution becomes cloudy, add ethanol dropwise to bring the product back into solution. Then set it aside to cool slowly. If the solution appears milky or if an oil appears, add more ethanol and heat to redissolve, then cool the solution again.

Isolate the purified phenacetin by vacuum filtration using a Hirsch funnel. Pull air through the funnel for 5 min to dry the product. Alternatively, dry the product in a 110 °C drying oven. Weigh the product and record its mass.

3. Characterizing the Product

Measure the melting point of your product. If product is available from the Williamson ether synthesis, conduct a mixture melting point. Thoroughly mix equal amounts of phenacetin from each procedure. Take the melting point of the mixture.

CAUTION ⚠

Potassium bromide (KBr) is irritating and hygroscopic.

Obtain an infrared spectrum of your product by preparing a KBr pellet or as indicated by your laboratory instructor.

> **CAUTION**
>
> **deutero-Chloroform is toxic and a suspected carcinogen. Dispense in a fume hood or glove box. Wear protective gloves.**

Dissolve a small amount of the product in *deutero*-chloroform. Place the solution in a NMR sample tube. Obtain a NMR spectrum as directed by your laboratory instructor.

4. Cleaning Up

Place your recovered materials in the appropriate labeled collection containers as directed by your laboratory instructor. Clean your glassware with soap or detergent.

> **CAUTION**
>
> **Wash your hands thoroughly with soap or detergent before leaving the laboratory.**

POST-LABORATORY QUESTIONS

1. Calculate the percent yield of phenacetin obtained in both the Williamson ether synthesis and the amide synthesis.

2. Does the melting point obtained for your product indicate that the sample is indeed phenacetin? What additional evidence can you cite that your product is phenacetin?

3. Comment on the value of finding the mixture melting point of the products from the two procedures in this module. What does this value indicate about the identities of the two products?

4. The infrared spectrum of phenacetin shows absorption bands at the following positions. Match each absorption band with the structural characteristic indicated by that absorption band.

_____ (a) 3300 cm^{-1}	(1) C–O–C
_____ (b) 1653 cm^{-1}	(2) C = O
_____ (c) 1244 and 1047 cm^{-1}	(3) *para* disubstituted benzene
_____ (d) 837 cm^{-1}	(4) N–H

5. The aromatic region (7–8 ppm) of the proton NMR spectrum of compounds with *para* disubstituted benzene rings such as phenacetin is often referred to as an AB pattern. This pattern has two doublet signals coupled to each other. Explain the origin of this AB pattern.

Name _____   Section _____   Date _____

Pre-Laboratory Assignment

1. What precautions should one use when working with phenacetin?

2. Calculate the theoretical yield in grams for the Williamson ether synthesis of phenacetin. Repeat the calculation for the amide synthesis of phenacetin. (The density of *p*-phenetidine is 1.065 g/mL.)

3. Why is it important that the number of moles of methoxide ion be the same as the number of moles of *p*-acetamidophenol used for Williamson synthesis of phenacetin?

4. If phenacetin "oils out" of solution during a recrystallization, what remedial action should be taken?

5. What role does the sodium acetate play in the synthesis of the amide functional group of phenacetin?

The Diels–Alder Reaction of Anthracene with Maleic Anhydride

Prepared by L. G. Wade, Jr., Whitman College

PURPOSE OF THE EXPERIMENT

Use the Diels–Alder reaction to form a bridged polycyclic anhydride. Recrystallize the product and characterize it by using melting point and infrared spectroscopy.

BACKGROUND REQUIRED

You should be familiar with reflux techniques, vacuum filtration, recrystallization, melting point measurement, and infrared spectroscopy.

EXPERIMENTAL OPTIONS

Semi-Microscale Diels–Alder Reaction
Microscale Diels–Alder Reaction

BACKGROUND INFORMATION

Otto Diels, Professor of Chemistry at the University of Kiel, Germany, and his student Kurt Alder published a paper in 1928 on additions of electron-poor alkenes and alkynes to electron-rich dienes to form cyclohexenes and cyclohexadienes. These [4 + 2] cycloadditions came to be known as Diels–Alder reactions. Diels and Alder received the 1950 Nobel Prize in chemistry for this work.

The Diels–Alder reaction is one of the most useful synthetic reactions in organic chemistry. In one step the reaction forms a six-membered ring with one or two double bonds from an open-chain compound, as shown in Equations 1 and 2 on the next page. A **diene** is the 4-π-electron component. It is electron-rich, like a nucleophile in a Lewis acid-base reaction. Simple dienes like 1,3-butadiene are sufficiently electron-rich to react, but electron-releasing groups such as alkyl groups (–R) or alkoxy groups (–OR) enhance a diene's reactivity.

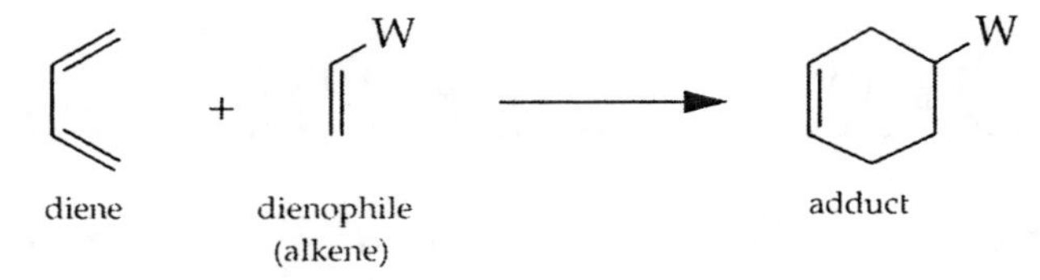

(Eq. 1)

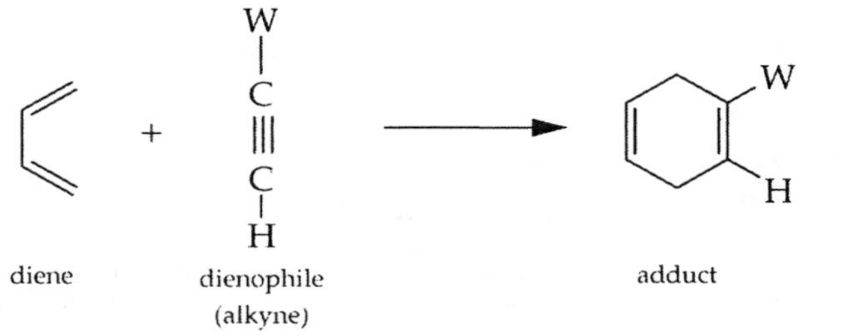

diene   dienophile (alkene)   adduct

(Eq. 2)

diene   dienophile (alkyne)   adduct

The 2-π-electron component is called a **dienophile** ("lover of dienes"). Good dienophiles contain relatively electron-poor double bonds or triple bonds; at least one strongly electron-withdrawing group (W) is needed. Therefore, ethylene and acetylene are not good dienophiles.

Because the reaction is concerted—that is, bond breaking and bond forming take place in the same step—the stereochemistry of the reactants and the symmetry of their molecular orbitals control the stereochemistry of the products. Using well-chosen reactants, a chemist can control the stereochemistry of a Diels–Alder product at up to four carbon atoms, as shown in Figure 1.

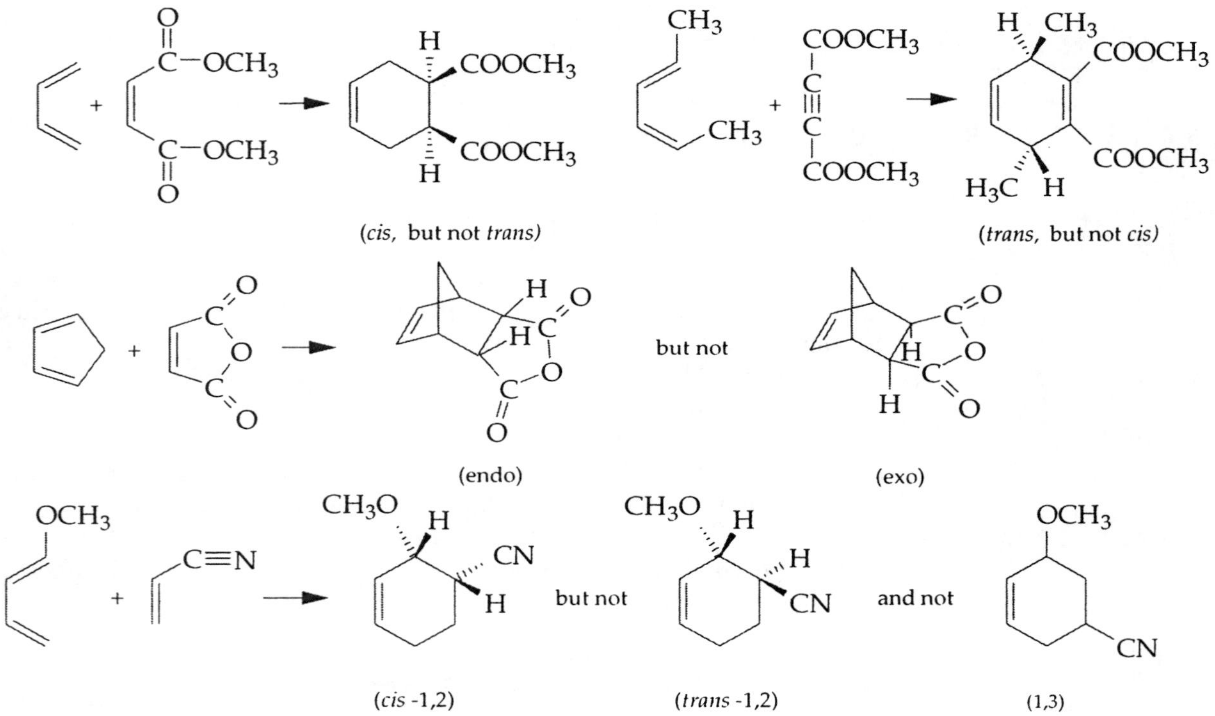

(cis, but not trans)   (trans, but not cis)

but not

(endo)   (exo)

but not   and not

(cis -1,2)   (trans -1,2)   (1,3)

Figure 1
Stereochemical patterns of Diels–Alder reactions

In this experiment, maleic anhydride is used as the dienophile. Maleic anhydride is an excellent dienophile because two strongly electron-withdrawing groups are attached to the double bond.

The diene is anthracene, which is commonly thought of as an aromatic compound, and not as a diene. However, in polynuclear aromatic compounds like anthracene, each individual ring may not be as well stabilized as an isolated benzene ring. Anthracene has only 14 π electrons, compared with 18 needed for three fully independent aromatic rings. When anthracene's center ring reacts as a diene, the product has two fully aromatic rings, each with six pi electrons, as shown in Equation 3.

anthracene
(diene)

maleic anhydride
(dienophile)

(adduct)

(Eq. 3)

The reaction is carried out in xylene, which is actually a mixture of the three dimethylbenzenes, for three reasons. First, the 140 °C boiling point provides a good reaction temperature. Second, the xylene mixture does not freeze when it is cooled in ice water. Third, the reactants are more soluble in xylene than is the product, which crystallizes.

The product is a relatively stable anhydride. Although anhydrides react with water in air, this one reacts slowly and is easily isolated and characterized before much hydrolysis occurs. There are several possible ways to name the product, but 9,10-dihydroanthracene-9,10-α,β-succinic anhydride is probably the simplest.

SEMI-MICROSCALE DIELS–ALDER REACTION

Equipment

250-mL beaker*
boiling chip
Büchner funnel, with adapter
condenser, with tubing
electric flask heater
50-mL Erlenmeyer flask
125-mL filter flask,
   with vacuum tubing
filter paper
glass stirring rod
*for ice bath

10-mL graduated cylinder
hot plate
2 melting point capillary tubes
microspatula
25-mL round-bottom flask
support stand
13 × 100-mm test tube
2 utility clamps
3-mL product vial
watch glass

Reagents and Properties

substance	quantity	molar mass (g/mol)	mp (°C)	bp (°C)
anthracene	0.5 g	178.23	216–218	
9,10-dihydroanthracene-9, 10-α,β-succinic anhydride*		276.29	262–264	
maleic anhydride	0.25 g	98.06	54–56	200
potassium bromide	100 mg			
xylene	27 mL	106.17		137–144

* product

Preview

- Weigh anthracene and maleic anhydride
- Place weighed reagents in flask; add xylene
- Assemble a reflux apparatus
- Heat anthracene and maleic anhydride at reflux for 30 min
- Cool the reaction mixture in an ice bath
- Use vacuum filtration to collect crude product
- Weigh the crude product
- Recrystallize the product from xylene
- Use vacuum filtration to collect purified product
- Dry and weigh the product on a watch glass
- Measure the melting points of both crude and purified product
- Take an IR spectrum of the product

PROCEDURE

CHEMICAL ALERT

anthracene—*irritant*
maleic anhydride—*toxic and corrosive*
potassium bromide—*irritant and hygroscopic*
xylene—*flammable and irritant*

CAUTION

Wear departmentally approved safety goggles at all times while in the chemistry laboratory.

1. Reacting Anthracene with Maleic Anhydride

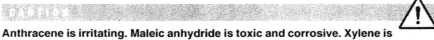

Anthracene is irritating. Maleic anhydride is toxic and corrosive. Xylene is flammable and irritating. Keep away from flames or other heat sources. Use a *fume hood.* Prevent eye, skin, and clothing contact. Avoid inhaling and ingesting these compounds.

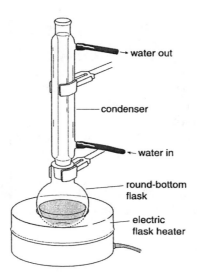

Figure 2
Reflux apparatus for semi-microscale glassware

Weigh 0.5 g of anthracene and 0.25 g of maleic anhydride. Place them in a 25-mL round-bottom flask. Add 6 mL of xylene. Add a boiling chip. Use the round-bottom flask to assemble the reflux apparatus shown in Figure 2.

Turn on the water to the condenser. Heat the mixture at reflux for 30 min, boiling vigorously for good mixing. [NOTE 1]

NOTE 1: The reactants do not dissolve completely at first. They gradually dissolve as the reaction takes place.

Cool the mixture to room temperature. Prepare an ice bath, using a 250-mL beaker. Then cool the mixture in the ice bath for 5 min. At the same time, pour 6 mL of xylene into a test tube and chill the xylene in the ice bath.

Collect the crystallized solid by vacuum filtration, using a Büchner funnel. Rinse the crystals with 3 mL of ice-cold xylene.

Weigh the crude product. Set aside a small sample to dry for a melting point measurement.

2. Purifying the Product

For recrystallization, place the product in a 50-mL Erlenmeyer flask. Add 5–10 mL of xylene. Heat the mixture gently on a hot plate until the xylene boils. Gradually add more xylene until all the product dissolves or until no more appears to be dissolving. Do not exceed 15 mL total volume of xylene to dissolve the crystals.

Allow the solution to cool to room temperature. Then cool the solution in an ice bath for 5 min. If necessary, scratch the bottom of the flask with a glass rod to induce crystallization.

Collect the crystallized solid by vacuum filtration, using a Büchner funnel. Rinse the crystals with 3 mL of ice-cold xylene.

Spread the product crystals thinly over a clean watch glass. Allow the crystals to dry for about half an hour, with occasional stirring.

Weigh the product and record the mass. Place the product in a labeled product vial.

3. Characterizing the Product

CAUTION

Potassium bromide (KBr) is irritating. Prevent eye, skin, and clothing contact. Avoid inhaling dust and ingesting KBr.

Measure the melting points for both the crude product and the recrystal-lized product.

Make a KBr pellet or a mineral-oil mull. Take an IR spectrum of the product. Compare the product spectrum with the spectra of maleic anhydride and anthracene, provided by your laboratory instructor.

4. Cleaning Up

Place your recovered materials in the appropriate labeled collection containers, as directed by your laboratory instructor. Clean your glassware with soap or detergent.

> **CAUTION**
>
> **Wash your hands thoroughly with soap or detergent before leaving the laboratory.**

MICROSCALE DIELS—ALDER REACTION

Equipment

150-mL beaker*	microspatula
boiling chip	Pasteur pipet, with latex bulb
condenser, with tubing†	1-mL pipet§
5-mL conical vial‡	sand bath¶
2 Erlenmeyer flasks, 10-mL	support stand
25-mL filter flask,	13 × 100-mm test tube
with vacuum tubing	thermometer, −10 to 260 °C
filter paper	3-mL product vial
glass stirring rod	2 utility clamps
Hirsch funnel, with adapter	watch glass
2 melting point capillary tubes	

*for ice bath
†or distilling column with elastomeric connector and pipe cleaner
‡or 10 × 100-mm reaction tube
§or 1-mL micropipet
¶sand in crystallizing dish on electric hot plate or sand in electric heating well with heat controller

Reagents and Properties

substance	quantity	molar mass (g/mol)	mp (°C)	bp (°C)
anthracene	100 mg	178.23	216–218	
9,10-dihydroanthracene-9,10-α,β-succinic anhydride*		276.29	262–264	
maleic anhydride	55 mg	98.06	54–56	200
potassium bromide	100 mg			
xylene	6 mL	106.17		137–144

* product

Preview

- Weigh anthracene and maleic anhydride
- Place weighed reagents in conical vial; add xylene

- Assemble a reflux apparatus
- Heat anthracene and maleic anhydride at reflux for 30 min
- Cool the reaction mixture in an ice bath
- Use vacuum filtration to collect crude product
- Weigh the crude product
- Recrystallize the product from xylene
- Use vacuum filtration to collect purified product
- Dry the purified product on a watch glass
- Weigh the purified product
- Measure the melting points of both crude and purified product
- Take an IR spectrum of the product

PROCEDURE

CHEMICAL ALERT

anthracene—*irritant*
maleic anhydride—*toxic and corrosive*
potassium bromide—*irritant and hygroscopic*
xylene—*flammable and irritant*

CAUTION

Wear departmentally approved safety goggles at all times while in the chemistry laboratory.

1. Reacting Anthracene with Maleic Anhydride

CAUTION

Anthracene is irritating. Maleic anhydride is toxic and corrosive. Xylene is flammable and irritating. Keep away from flames or other heat sources. Use a *fume hood*. Prevent eye, skin, and clothing contact. Avoid inhaling and ingesting these compounds.

Tare a 5-mL conical vial (or 10×100-mm reaction tube) and record the mass. Weigh 100 mg of anthracene and 55 mg of maleic anhydride and place them in the vial (reaction tube). Add 1.0 mL of xylene. Add a boiling chip. Fit the vial (tube) with a condenser, as shown in Figure 3 on the next page.

Turn on the water to the condenser (or add a wet pipe cleaner around the reaction tube). Use a 200 ° C sand bath to heat the mixture at reflux for 30 min, boiling vigorously for good mixing. [NOTE 2]

NOTE 2: The reactants do not dissolve completely at first. They gradually dissolve as the reaction takes place.

Cool the mixture to room temperature. Prepare an ice bath, using a 150-mL beaker. Then cool the mixture in the ice bath for 5 min. At the same time, pour 2 mL of xylene into a test tube and chill the xylene in the ice bath.

Collect the crystallized solid by vacuum filtration, using a Hirsch funnel. Rinse the crystals with 1 mL of ice-cold xylene.

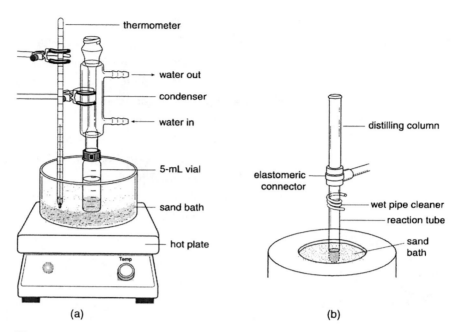

Figure 3
Reflux apparatus for (a) vial, or (b) reaction tube

Weigh the crude product. Set aside a small sample to dry for a melting point measurement.

2. Purifying the Product

For recrystallization, place the product in a 10-mL Erlenmeyer flask. Add 1–2 mL of xylene. Heat the mixture gently in a sand bath until the xylene boils. Gradually add more xylene until all the product dissolves or until no more appears to be dissolving. Do not exceed 3 mL total volume of xylene. If solid impurities remain, use a Pasteur pipet to transfer the solution to another 10-mL Erlenmeyer flask.

Allow the solution to cool to room temperature. Then cool the solution in an ice bath for 5 min. If necessary, scratch the bottom of the flask with a glass rod to induce crystallization.

Collect the crystallized solid by vacuum filtration, using a Hirsch funnel. Rinse the crystals with 1 mL of ice-cold xylene.

Spread the product crystals thinly over a clean watch glass. Allow the crystals to dry for about 15 min. Weigh the product and record the mass. Place the product in a labeled product vial.

3. Characterizing the Product

CAUTION

Potassium bromide (KBr) is irritating. Prevent eye, skin, and clothing contact. Avoid inhaling dust and ingesting KBr.

Measure the melting points for both the crude product and the recrystallized product.

Make a KBr pellet or a mineral-oil mull. Take an IR spectrum of the product and compare it with the spectra of maleic anhydride and anthracene, provided by your laboratory instructor.

4. Cleaning Up

Place your recovered materials in the appropriate labeled collection containers, as directed by your laboratory instructor. Clean your glassware with soap or detergent.

CAUTION

Wash your hands thoroughly with soap or detergent before leaving the laboratory.

POST LABORATORY QUESTIONS

1. Calculate the percent yield for your product, before and after recrystallization.

2. Calculate the percent recovery from the recrystallization.

3. The product of this reaction can be hydrolyzed by water. Show the product of hydrolysis.

4. Recrystallizing an anhydride (such as the product of this reaction) from water or from an alcohol is rarely a good idea. Explain why.

5. (a) Compare the carbonyl region of your IR spectrum with that of maleic anhydride. What are the similarities? What are the differences?

   (b) Does your IR spectrum allow you to confirm that the structure of the product is a combination of the two reactants? Briefly explain.

Name   Section   Date

Pre-Laboratory Assignment

1. Briefly describe the hazards associated with xylene, anthracene, and maleic anhydride.

2. Calculate the theoretical yield for your product. Show the calculation here and in your laboratory notebook.

3. List three reasons why xylene is often used in Diels–Alder reactions.

4. Write the equation for each of the following Diels–Alder reactions.

5. Draw the structures for the diene and dienophile you would use to synthesize each of the following:

Nitrating Acetanilide or Methyl Benzoate: Electrophilic Aromatic Substitution

Prepared by Carl T. Wigal, Lebanon Valley College

PURPOSE OF THE EXPERIMENT

Demonstrate the regiochemistry of electrophilic aromatic substitution reactions for monosubstituted aromatic compounds.

EXPERIMENTAL OPTIONS

Nitrating Acetanilide
Nitrating Methyl Benzoate

BACKGROUND REQUIRED

You should be familiar with vacuum filtration, melting point measurement, and recrystallization techniques.

BACKGROUND INFORMATION

Most substitution reactions at aliphatic carbon atoms are nucleophilic. However, aromatic substitution reactions are generally electrophilic, due to the high electron density of the benzene ring. The species reacting with the aromatic ring is usually a positive ion or the positive end of a dipole. This electron-deficient species, or **electrophile**, may be produced in various ways, but the reaction between the electrophile and the aromatic ring is essentially the same in all cases. The most common electrophilic aromatic substitution mechanism is the **arenium ion mechanism** shown in Figure 1.

In the first step of the reaction, benzene donates an electron pair to the electrophilic species, designated E^+. A carbocation intermediate is formed, called an **arenium ion** or **sigma complex**. This arenium ion can be written in

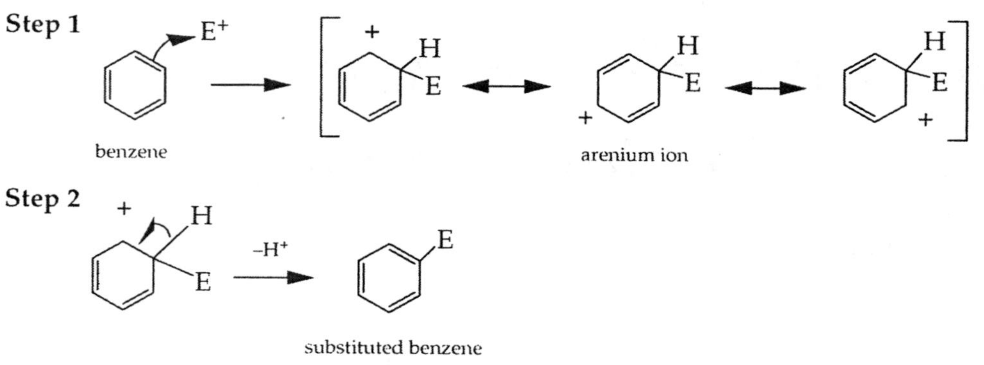

Step 1

Step 2

Figure 1
The arenium ion mechanism for electrophilic aromatic substitution

three resonance forms. Although the arenium ion is stabilized by these resonance forms, it is destabilized by the loss of aromatic stability (~36 kcal/mol). This aromatic stability is regained in the second step of the reaction, consisting of elimination of a proton from the arenium ion, forming a substituted benzene.

To accurately design an experiment involving an electrophilic substitution reaction performed on a monosubstituted benzene, several factors must be considered. One factor is the relative rate of the reaction. The substituent group already present on the ring may cause the substitution reaction to be slower or faster than the initial reaction with benzene.

Substituent groups that increase the reaction rate relative to the reaction rate with benzene are called **activators**. Activators donate electrons, increasing the electron density of the aromatic ring and thus stabilizing the arenium ion. Activators can donate electrons to the aromatic ring in either of two ways. Most activators donate electrons by resonance. Resonance donators have a lone pair of electrons on the atom directly connected to the ring. These electrons overlap with the pi cloud of the aromatic system. Examples of resonance donating groups are $-N(CH_3)_2$ and $-OH$.

Other activators stabilize the arenium ion through hyperconjugation. **Hyperconjugation** is the overlap of a neighboring sigma bond with the aromatic pi system. Figure 2 shows the overlap with an adjacent carbocation. Alkyl substituents are common examples of activators due to hyperconjugation.

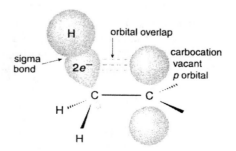

Figure 2
Hyperconjugation with a carbocation

Substituent groups that decrease the reaction rate relative to the reaction rate with benzene are called **deactivators**. Deactivators withdraw electrons and decrease the electron density of the aromatic ring, thus destabilizing the arenium ion. A substituent can withdraw electrons from the ring either by resonance or by induction.

Pi bonds that overlap a *p* orbital on the substituent with the pi system of the aromatic ring cause resonance electron-withdrawing effects. Most resonance withdrawing groups have a positive or partially positive atom directly connected to the ring. Examples of resonance withdrawing groups are $-NO_2$ and $-CN$.

Inductive effects result from electronegativity differences in bonding atoms. Electronegative atoms pull electrons away from the aromatic ring through connecting sigma bonds. Halogens are examples of deactivating groups that act through induction.

In addition to affecting the rate of substitution, the electronic nature of the substituent also directs the position of electrophilic substitution. There are three different **regioisomers** for disubstituted aromatic rings: *ortho*, or 1,2; *meta*, or 1,3; and *para*, or 1,4.

The overall directing and rate effects of a substituent can be classified into three groups: *ortho-para*-directing activators; *ortho-para*-directing deactivators; and *meta*-directing deactivators. Any substituent that activates the aromatic ring is an *ortho-para*-director. Figure 3 shows the resonance forms of the arenium ion associated with a monosubstituted aromatic system. Electrophilic attack at either the *ortho-* or *para*-position places a positive charge on the carbon that bears the substituent X, indicated by resonance forms C and E, respectively. When X is an electron-donating substituent, stabilization of the positive charge results. This stabilization is not possible when attack occurs at the *meta*-position.

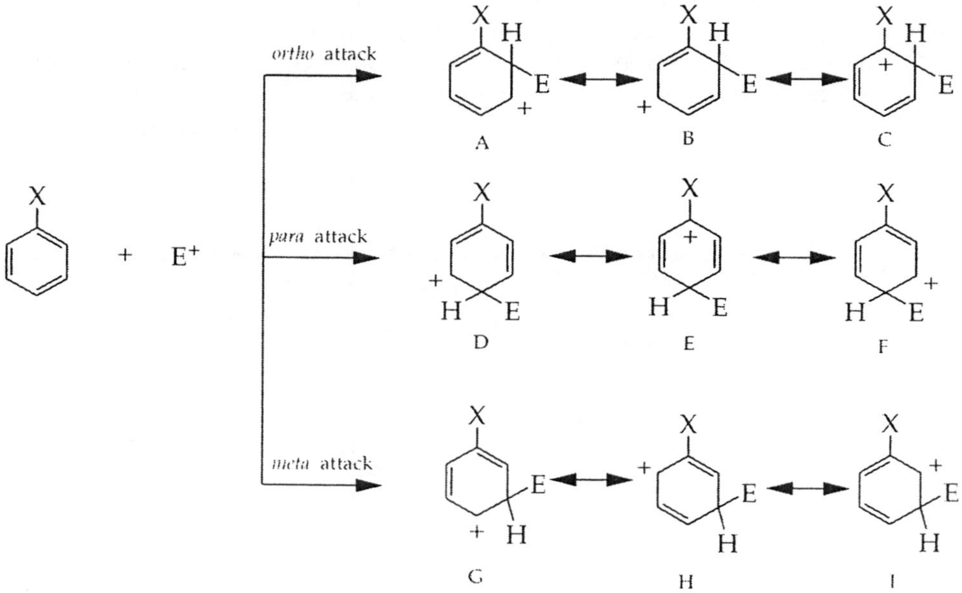

Figure 3

Resonance forms of a substituted arenium ion

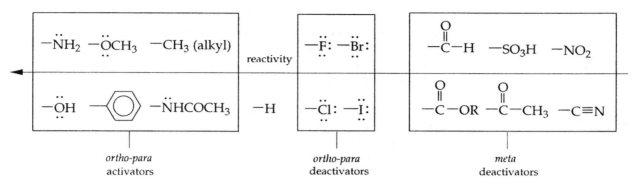

Figure 4
Classification of directing effects for substituents

Electron-withdrawing substituents are usually *meta*-directors. Orthopara attack on a deactivated ring would place a positive charge on the carbon that bears the substituent X. However, when X is an electronwithdrawing substituent, the electronic effects of the substituent destabilize the positive charge. Consequently, *meta* attack is favored because all resonance forms, G, H, and I, avoid this unfavorable electronic interaction.

The halogens are *ortho-para*-deactivators. Halogens possess both electron-withdrawing inductive effects and electron-donating resonance effects. Halogens deactivate the ring because of their high electronegativity, yet they can stabilize the arenium ion by sharing a lone electron pair. As a general rule, any atom that is directly connected to the aromatic ring and has a lone electron pair is an *ortho-para*-director. A summary of substituent directing effects is shown in Figure 4.

Nitration is one of the most important examples of electrophilic aromatic substitution. Aromatic nitro compounds are used in products ranging from explosives to pharmaceutical synthetic intermediates. The electrophile in nitration is the **nitronium ion (NO_2^+)**. The nitronium ion is generated from nitric acid by protonation and loss of water, using sulfuric acid as the dehydrating agent. The reaction is shown in Equation 1.

$$HNO_3 + 2H_2SO_4 \rightarrow NO_2^+ + H_3O^+ + 2HSO_4^- \qquad \text{(Eq. 1)}$$

In this experiment, you will nitrate either acetanilide or methyl benzoate as the substrate. You will use melting point data to determine which regioisomer is formed. The reactions, without showing regio-chemistry, are shown in Equations 2 and 3.

acetanilide $\xrightarrow{\ H_2SO_4/HNO_3\ }$ nitroacetanilide   (Eq. 2)

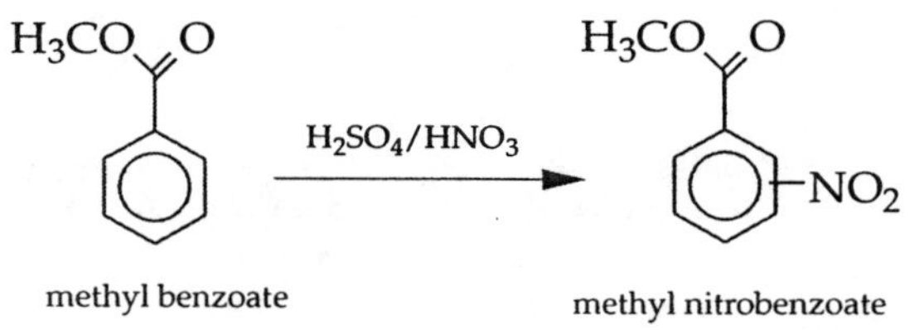

$$\text{methyl benzoate} \xrightarrow{\text{H}_2\text{SO}_4/\text{HNO}_3} \text{methyl nitrobenzoate} \qquad \text{(Eq. 3)}$$

methyl benzoate   methyl nitrobenzoate

Equipment

50-mL beaker
400-mL beaker*
Büchner funnel, with filter
    paper and adapter
25-mL Erlenmeyer flask
125-mL Erlenmeyer flask
125-mL filter flask
glass stirring rod
10-mL graduated cylinder

50-mL graduated cylinder
marking pen
microspatula
3 Pasteur pipets, with latex bulb
3 pipets, 1-mL, with rubber bulb
sand bath[†]
support stand
2 test tubes, 15 × 125-mm
tility clamp

*for ice bath
[†]or hot plate, or electric heating well with heat controller

Reagents and Properties

substance	quantity	molar mass (g/mol)	d (g/mL)	mp (°C)	bp (°C)
acetanilide	0.5 g	135.17		113–115	
ethanol, 95%	5–10 mL	46.07			78
methyl benzoate	0.55 g	136.15	1.094	−12	198
methyl nitrobenzoate*		181.13			
nitroacetanilide*		180.16			
nitric acid conc.	0.5 mL	63.01			
sulfuric acid conc.	1.6 mL	98.08			

*product

Preview

- Prepare the ice bath
- Prepare the nitration solution
- Prepare the substrate solution
- Add the nitration solution to the substrate solution and react 30–45 min
- Quench the reaction with water
- Filter the product using vacuum filtration
- Wash the product with water and air dry
- Recrystallize the product from 95% ethanol
- Weigh the product
- Measure the melting point of the product

PROCEDURE

CHEMICAL ALERT

acetanilide—*toxic and irritant*
ethanol—*flammable and irritant*
methyl benzoate—*irritant*
nitroacetanilide—*irritant*
concentrated nitric acid—*toxic and oxidizer*
concentrated sulfuric acid—*toxic and oxidizer*

CAUTION

Wear departmentally approved safety goggles at all times while in the chemistry laboratory.

1. Preparing the Ice-Water Bath and Chilled Water

Place equal volumes of ice and tap water into a 400-mL beaker, so that the beaker is 75% full. Prepare chilled water for Parts 3 and 4 by pouring approximately 30 mL of distilled or deionized water into a 125-mL Erlenmeyer flask and placing the flask into the ice-water bath.

2. Preparing the Nitrating Solution

CAUTION

Nitric acid and sulfuric acid are toxic and oxidizing. They can cause severe burns. Prevent eye, skin, clothing, and combustible material contact. Avoid inhaling vapors and ingesting these compounds. Use a *fume hood*.

Label two 15 × 125-mm test tubes "nitric acid" and "sulfuric acid", respectively. Transfer 0.5 mL of concentrated nitric acid into the "nitric acid" tube. Transfer 0.6 mL of concentrated sulfuric acid into the "sulfuric acid" tube. Chill both test tubes containing the acids in the ice-water bath for 15 min.

CAUTION

Mixing concentrated sulfuric and nitric acids is a highly exothermic reaction. Hot acid mixtures may bump and cause acid burns. Make certain the acids are *cold* before mixing.

Use a Pasteur pipet to *very slowly* add the *cold* sulfuric acid *dropwise* to the *cold* nitric acid. Swirl the reaction mixture after every 3 drops. After adding all the sulfuric acid, allow the nitrating solution to stand in the ice-water bath for 10 min.

3. Nitrating the Aromatic Compound [NOTE 1]

A. Nitrating Acetanilide

CAUTION

Acetanilide is toxic and irritating. Nitroacetanilide is irritating. Prevent eye, skin, and clothing contact. Avoid inhaling dust and ingesting these compounds.

NOTE 1: Your laboratory instructor may designate either procedure *A* or *B* for Part 3. If you do both procedures, you will need to do Part 2 for each procedure.

Place 0.5 g of acetanilide into a 25-mL Erlenmeyer flask. Add 1.0 mL of concentrated sulfuric acid. Heat the mixture *gently* to dissolve the acetanilide. Allow the mixture to cool to room temperature.

Clamp the flask containing the mixture to a support stand. Lower the flask into the ice-water bath for 5 min. Take care to prevent bath water from entering the reaction flask.

Use a Pasteur pipet to *slowly* add the nitrating solution in the test tube to the Erlenmeyer flask containing the acetanilide and sulfuric acid. [NOTE 2] After adding all the nitrating solution, allow the mixture to stand in the ice-water bath for 30–45 min, swirling the flask every 5 min.

NOTE 2: Rapid addition of the nitrating solution will cause the reaction mixture to heat up, turning the mixture dark brown. The dark product is difficult to recrystallize and has a lower melting point.

After 30–45 min, add 10 mL of chilled water to a 50-mL beaker. *Slowly and carefully* add the cold reaction mixture, with stirring, to the chilled water. Allow the chilled solution to stand 5–10 min to complete crystal formation.

B. Nitrating Methyl Benzoate

CAUTION

Methyl benzoate is irritating. Prevent eye, skin, and clothing contact. Avoid inhaling vapor and ingesting this compound.

Place 0.55 g (0.5 mL) of methyl benzoate into a 25-mL Erlenmeyer flask. Add 1.0 mL of concentrated sulfuric acid.

Clamp the flask containing the mixture to a support stand and lower the flask into the ice-water bath for 5 min. Take care to prevent bath water from entering the reaction flask.

Use a Pasteur pipet to *slowly* add the nitrating solution in the test tube to the Erlenmeyer flask containing the methyl benzoate and sulfuric acid. After adding all the nitrating solution, allow the mixture to stand in the ice-water bath for 30–45 min, swirling the flask every 5 min.

After 30–45 min, add 10 mL of chilled water to a 50-mL beaker. *Slowly and carefully* add the cold reaction mixture, with stirring, to the chilled water. Allow the chilled solution to stand 5–10 min to complete crystal formation.

4. Isolating, Purifying, and Characterizing the Product

CAUTION

Ethanol is flammable and irritating. Keep away from flames and other heat sources. Avoid inhaling vapors and ingesting this compound.

NOTE 3: Approximate recrystallization volumes of 95% ethanol are 10 mL for nitroacetanilide and 5 mL for methyl nitrobenzoate.

Filter the reaction mixture using vacuum filtration. Wash the crystals with 10 mL of chilled water to remove any residual acid. Allow your product to air dry in the filter funnel for 10 min.

Recrystallize your product from 95% ethanol. [NOTE 3] Filter the crystals using vacuum filtration. Allow your product to air dry in the filter funnel for 10 min.

Weigh your product and record its mass. Measure the melting point of your product.

5. Cleaning Up

Place your recovered materials in the appropriate labeled collection containers as directed by your laboratory instructor. Clean your glassware with soap or detergent.

CAUTION

Wash your hands thoroughly with soap or detergent before leaving the laboratory.

Name   Section   Date

Post-Laboratory Questions

1. Based on your data, answer the following questions:

   (a) What is the percent yield of your product?

   (b) What is the melting point of your product?

   (c) Using the following data table, determine the regiochemistry of your product.

compound	mol mass	ortho mp (°C)	meta mp (°C)	para mp (°C)
nitroacetanilide	180.16	94	155	214–217
methyl nitrobenzoate	181.15	−13	78–80	94–96

   (d) Draw the structure of your product.

2. Draw the resonance forms for the arenium ion formed during your reaction.

3. 2,4,6-Trinitrotoluene (TNT) is synthesized by trinitrating toluene. The first nitration proceeds much faster than the second two. Briefly explain.

Name   Section   Date

Pre-Laboratory Assignment

1. What precautions must be taken when using concentrated acids?

2. (a) At what position will electrophilic aromatic substitution occur for the following compounds?

   bromobenzene   toluene
   nitrobenzene   phenol
   benzoic acid   benzaldehyde

   (b) In the list above, which compound is the most reactive? Briefly explain.

   (c) Which compound is the least reactive? Briefly explain.

3. Using the quantities given in the Procedure, calculate the theoretical yields for the mononitration of (a) acetanilide and (b) methyl benzoate. Record your results here and in your laboratory notebook.

15.3 FRIEDEL-CRAFTS ACYLATION OF *m*-XYLENE

As described in Section 15.2 and in the Historical Highlights at the end of this chapter, Friedel and Crafts discovered that alkyl groups could be substituted onto the aromatic ring by reaction of arenes with alkyl halides in the presence of aluminum chloride, $AlCl_3$ (Eq. 15.7). The role of aluminum chloride, a strong Lewis acid, is to convert the alkyl halide into a reactive electrophilic intermediate, in the form of a carbocation or a highly polarized carbon-halogen bond. This electrophile then undergoes attack by an arene (Sec. 15.1), which functions as a Lewis base, resulting in aromatic substitution. They also explored the reaction of aluminum chloride with acid chlorides, **7**, and anhydrides, **8**, to produce **acylonium ions, 9,** which function as electrophiles, just as alkyl carbocations do. Upon reaction of **9** with an arene, an acyl group is introduced onto the ring to provide an aryl ketone, **10** (Eq. 15.12). The overall reaction is named the **Friedel-Crafts acylation.**

The resonance structures in Equation 15.12 symbolize distribution of the positive charge in acylonium ions. This charge delocalization stabilizes the cation so that acylonium ions such as **9** do *not* undergo structural rearrangements as do alkyl carbocations (Sec. 15.2). The increased stability of acylonium ions also makes them less electrophilic and thus less reactive than alkyl carbocations. Nevertheless, cation **9** is sufficiently reactive to undergo the S_E2 reaction (Sec. 15.1) with arenes, *provided* the aromatic ring does not bear strongly deactivating groups such as NO_2, R_3N^+, C(O)R, and CN.

An important difference between the Friedel-Crafts alkylation and acylation reactions is that the latter process requires use of a *stoichiometric* rather than a catalytic amount of aluminum chloride. This is because the product aryl ketones **10** undergo a Lewis acid-base reaction with aluminum chloride to form a strong 1:1 complex, **11;** the **11** aluminum chloride involved in the complex no longer fosters formation of acylonium ions and in essence is "consumed" in the reaction. Thus, although generation of acylonium ions needed for the Friedel-Crafts acylation is catalytic in aluminum chloride, complexation with the product makes aluminum chloride a stoichiometric reagent.

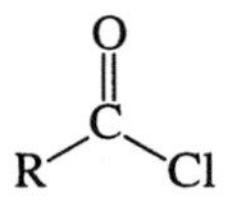

7
An acid chloride

or   (15.12)

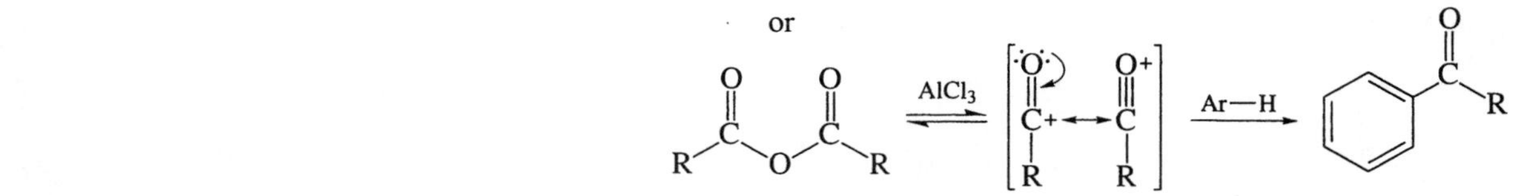

8   9   10
An acid anhydride   An acylonium ion   An aryl ketone

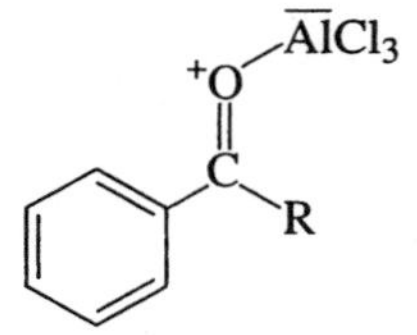

11

  The acylation performed in this section involves reaction of phthalic anhydride
(12), a cyclic anhydride, with *m*-xylene (13) in the presence of aluminum chloride
to afford 2-(2′,4′-dimethylbenzoyl)benzoic acid (15) (Scheme 15.2), a ketoacid. The
initial product of the acylation is 14, in which one mole of aluminum chloride has
reacted with the acid function to form the salt RCO_2AlCl_2, and a second mole of
aluminum chloride is complexed to the carbonyl group. Adding ice and hydrochloric acid decomposes the complex to produce 15 and water-soluble aluminum salts.

Scheme 15.2

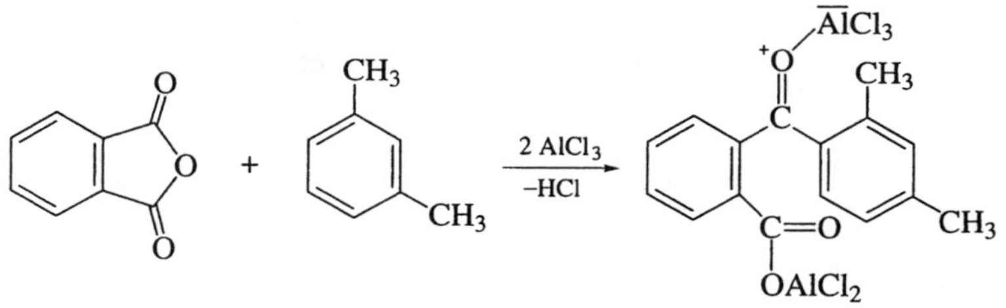

12   13
Phthalic anhydride   *m*-Xylene   14

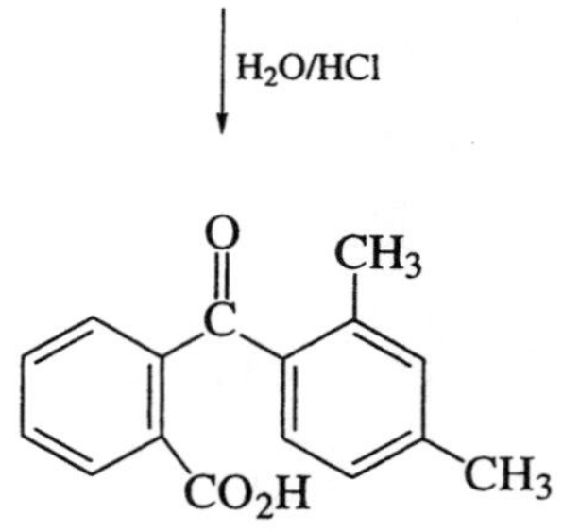

15
2-(2,4′-Dimethylbenzoyl)benzoic acid

The formation of **14** involves reaction of aluminum chloride with anhydride **12** to give the electrophile **16** (Eq. 15.13); this species then reacts with *m*-xylene (**13**). An issue in this step of the sequence is which of the three different positions of **13** undergoes attack by **16**. Because methyl groups are *o,p*-directors, reaction should occur preferentially at C2 and C4 of the ring. Steric hindrance impedes attack at C2 so *m*-xylene reacts selectively at C4 to give **14**, which provides the ketoacid **15** upon hydrolysis, as shown in Scheme 15.2.

(15.13)

EXPERIMENTAL PROCEDURES

Friedel-Crafts Acylation of m-Xylene with Phthalic Anhydride

Purpose To demonstrate acylation by electrophilic aromatic substitution.

SAFETY ALERT

1. **Anhydrous aluminum chloride is *extremely* hygroscopic and reacts rapidly with water, even the moisture on your hands, producing fumes of hydrogen chloride, which are highly corrosive. *Do not allow aluminum chloride to come in contact with your skin*. If it does, flush the affected area with copious amounts of water. *Minimize exposure of this chemical to the atmosphere!***

2. **You may be provided with a weighed amount of aluminum chloride. If not, *quickly* weigh it into a dry vial or test tube *in the hood* and then transfer it to the reaction flask. The success of this experiment is highly dependent on the quality of the aluminum chloride that is used, so obtain it from a *freshly* opened bottle. In handling this chemical, be aware that it is a powdery solid that easily becomes airborne.**

3. ***m*-Xylene is flammable. Assemble the apparatus carefully and be sure that all joints are tightly mated. Use *flameless* heating.**

Miniscale Procedures

See Pre-Lab Exercises and MSDSs

Preparation Answer the Pre-Lab Exercises on page PL. 91. Read the MSDSs for chemicals used or produced in this procedure. Review Sections 2.9, 2.10, 2.11, 2.13, 2.23, 2.25, and 2.29.

Apparatus A dry 25-mL round-bottom flask, gas trap, ice-water bath, separatory funnel, apparatus for magnetic stirring, heating under reflux, vacuum filtration, and *flameless* heating.

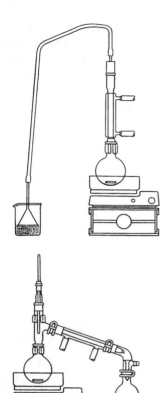

Setting Up Working at the hood, weigh 2 g of *anhydrous* aluminum chloride into a dry test tube or screw-cap vial and *immediately* close the vessel. Equip the round-bottom flask with a stirbar and a dry reflux condenser fitted with the gas trap specified by your instructor for removing fumes of hydrogen chloride. Place 1 g of phthalic anhydride and 6 mL of *m*-xylene in the flask, and cool the mixture to 0 °C in an ice-water bath.

Acylation Remove the condenser from the flask, and, in one portion, *quickly* add the anhydrous aluminum chloride. *Immediately* replace the condenser and stir the reaction mixture for a minute or two while maintaining its temperature at 0 °C and then allow it to warm to room temperature. Initiation of the reaction will be evidenced by evolution of hydrogen chloride. If this does not occur, gently warm the flask until gas evolution begins. Be prepared to immerse the flask into an ice-water bath if the reaction becomes too vigorous. Continue gently heating the mixture with stirring until the reaction is proceeding smoothly, and then heat it under reflux for about 0.5 h.

Work-Up, Isolation, and Purification Remove the flask from the apparatus and stopper it. *Working at the hood,* pour the cold reaction mixture onto 8–10 g of ice contained in a beaker, while stirring the mixture thoroughly. With continued vigorous stirring, slowly add 2 mL of *concentrated* hydrochloric acid and then 8–10 mL of ice-cold water to the beaker; if necessary, cool the mixture in an ice-water bath to keep it near room temperature during the additions. Add an additional 4 mL of ice-cold water with stirring and cool the resulting mixture to room temperature or below.★

Add 5 mL of diethyl ether to the beaker. With the aid of a stirring rod, scrape any solid from the neck and walls of the beaker and carefully break up any lumps at the bottom. Stir the mixture vigorously for several minutes to complete decomposition of the aluminum salt of the product, extraction of the organic product into diethyl ether, and dissolution of the inorganic aluminum salts.★

Transfer the two-phase mixture into a separatory funnel, rinse the beaker with a few milliliters of diethyl ether, and add the rinse to the funnel. Shake the mixture, frequently venting the funnel, and allow the layers to separate. A grayish, fluffy precipitate may appear below the organic layer. If so, dissolve the precipitate before separating the layers by adding 5 mL of 6 *M* HCl and shaking the mixture for a few minutes, occasionally venting the funnel. Should any precipitate or grayish emulsion remain with the ethereal solution, remove it by vacuum filtration through a pad of a filter-aid. After separating the layers, extract the aqueous layer sequentially with two additional 10-mL portions of diethyl ether, venting the funnel occasionally during the extraction. Combine all of the ethereal solutions in an Erlenmeyer flask and add several spatulatips full of anhydrous sodium sulfate, swirling the mixture occasionally over a period of about 15 min; if the solution appears cloudy, add additional sodium sulfate with swirling.★

Decant the ethereal solution into a 50-mL round-bottom flask and equip the flask for simple distillation. Concentrate the solution to about half its original volume. Alternatively, use rotary evaporation or other techniques to effect concentration. Transfer the concentrated solution to an Erlenmeyer flask and cool it to room temperature. Once crystallization has begun, further cool the solution in an ice-water bath and then collect **15** by vacuum filtration. Recrystallize it from 50% aqueous ethanol and air-dry the purified product.

Analysis Weigh your product and calculate the yield. Measure the melting point of **15,** which is reported to be 142.5–142.8 °C. Obtain IR and NMR spectra of your starting materials and product and compare them with those of authentic samples (Figs. 15.12–15.17).

Microscale Procedure

See Pre-Lab Exercises and MSDSs

Preparation Answer the Pre-Lab Exercises on page PL. 91. Read the MSDSs for chemicals used or produced in this procedure. Review Sections 2.9, 2.10, 2.11, 2.13, 2.23, 2.25, and 2.29.

Apparatus A dry 5-mL conical vial, gas trap, ice-water bath, 15-mL screw-cap centrifuge tube, apparatus for magnetic stirring, heating under reflux, vacuum and Craig-tube filtration, and *flameless* heating.

Setting Up Working at the hood, weigh 0.7 g of *anhydrous* aluminum chloride into a dry test tube or vial and *immediately* stopper the vessel. Equip the conical vial with a spinvane and a dry reflux condenser fitted with the gas trap specified by your instructor for removing fumes of hydrogen chloride. Add 0.3 g of phthalic anhydride and 1.8 mL of *m*-xylene to the vial and cool the mixture to 0 °C in an ice-water bath.

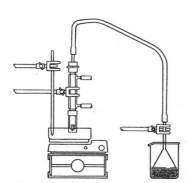

Acylation Remove the condenser from the conical vial, and, in one portion, quickly add the *anhydrous* aluminum chloride. *Immediately* replace the condenser, stir the reaction mixture for a minute or two, and then allow it to warm to room temperature. The start of the reaction will be evidenced by evolution of bubbles of hydrogen chloride. If this does not occur, gently warm the flask in a sand or oil bath until gas evolution begins. Be prepared to immerse the vial into an ice-cold water bath if the reaction becomes too vigorous. Continue heating the mixture gently with stirring until the reaction appears to be proceeding smoothly and then heat it under reflux for about 20 min. At the end of the reflux period, cool the reaction mixture to 0 °C with stirring.

Work-Up, Isolation, and Purification Remove the conical vial from the apparatus and stopper it. *Working at the hood,* pour the cold reaction mixture into a 15-mL screw-cap centrifuge tube or screw-cap vial containing 2 mL of ice-water and stir the mixture thoroughly. With continued vigorous stirring, slowly add 0.5 mL of *concentrated* hydrochloric acid and then 2 mL of ice-cold water. Cool the resulting mixture to room temperature or below.★

Add 1 mL of diethyl ether and break up any lumps of solid with the aid of a stirring rod. Cap the centrifuge tube and shake it vigorously for several minutes to complete decomposition of aluminum salts, extraction of the product into the organic phase, and dissolution of inorganic aluminum salts.★ Vent the system occasionally to relieve any pressure that may develop.

Using a Pasteur or filter-tip pipet, transfer the organic phase to a test tube or vial with a 15-mL capacity. Extract the aqueous layer sequentially with three 2-mL portions of diethyl ether, combining the organic layers with the original ethereal extract. Combine all of the ethereal solutions in an Erlenmeyer flask, and add several microspatulatips full of anhydrous sodium sulfate, swirling the mixture occasionally over a period of about 15 min; if the solution appears cloudy, add additional sodium sulfate with swirling.

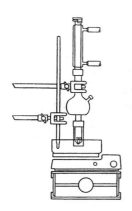

Decant about one-half of the ethereal solution into a 5-mL conical vial equipped for simple distillation and concentrate the solution to about half its original volume, removing the distillate from the Hickman stillhead as necessary. Allow the solution to cool below the boiling point, add the remainder of the dried ethereal extracts, and again concentrate the solution to about one-half its original volume. Alternatively, use rotary evaporation or other techniques to effect concentration. Cool the concentrated solution to room temperature. Once crystallization has begun, further cool the solution in an ice-water bath, and then collect the product **15** by vacuum filtration. Recrystallize it from 50% aqueous ethanol and air-dry the purified product.

Analysis Weigh the product and calculate the yield. Measure the melting point of **15,** which is reported to be 142.5–142.8 °C. Obtain IR and NMR spectra of your starting materials and product and compare them with those of authentic samples (Figs. 15.12–15.17).

WRAPPING IT UP

Discard the *grayish solid* obtained by gravity filtration in the container for nonhazardous solids. Pour the *diethyl ether* obtained by distillation in a container for non-halogenated organic liquids. Flush the *filtrate from the recrystallization* and the *aqueous layer containing aluminum salts* down the drain.

EXERCISES

1. Explain why a catalytic amount of $AlCl_3$ is insufficient to promote the Friedel-Crafts reaction of **12** and **13.**

2. Why is loss of carbon monoxide (decarbonylation) from the acylonium ion **16** an unlikely reaction?

3. Why is it important that the apparatus used for the Friedel-Crafts acylation be dry?

4. Write the products of the reaction of $AlCl_3$ and excess H_2O.

5. Write the structure of the product from reaction between phthalic anhydride and water.

6. What gas is evolved in the early stages of the reaction between *m*-xylene, phthalic anhydride, and aluminum chloride?

7. In which of the two solvents, water or ethanol, should the product first be dissolved for the mixed solvent recrystallization? Explain.

8. Why does the acylonium ion **16** react more rapidly with **13** than with **12?**

9. In the Friedel-Crafts acylation of *m*-xylene with phthalic anhydride, explain why each of the isomers shown below is *not* produced.

10. Suggest a sequence of reactions for synthesizing *m*-xylene from any substituted aromatic precursor of your choice. (*Hint:* More than one step will be necessary.)

11. Provide two reasons why intramolecular acylation involving the carboxy carbonyl group of **14** does not occur to produce the compound shown below.

12. What evidence do you have from this experiment that substitution of phthalic acid for phthalic anhydride would not provide acylonium ion **16** required for the acylation reaction? (*Hint:* Write the product of reaction of aluminum chloride with one of the carboxylic acid groups of phthalic acid and compare it to the carboxylate **14**.)

Refer to Tables 8.1–8.8 as needed for answering the following questions on spectroscopy.

See Spectra 13. Consider the spectral data for *m*-xylene (Figs. 15.12 and 15.13).

    a. In the functional group region of the IR spectrum, specify the absorption associated with the π-bonds of the aromatic ring. Indicate the bands in the fingerprint region that characterize the *meta* orientation of the methyl groups.

    b. In the ^{1}H NMR spectrum, assign the various resonances to the hydrogen nuclei responsible for them.

    c. For the ^{13}C NMR data, assign the various resonances to the carbon nuclei responsible for them.

    d. Explain how ^{13}C spectroscopy allows differentiation of the *meta* isomer from the *ortho* and *para* isomers.

See Spectra 14. Consider the spectral data for phthalic anhydride (Figs. 15.14 and 15.15).

    a. In the functional group region of the IR spectrum, specify the absorptions associated with the anhydride function and the aromatic ring.

    b. In the ^{1}H NMR spectrum, assign the various resonances to the hydrogen nuclei responsible for them.

    c. For the ^{13}C NMR data, assign the various resonances to the carbon nuclei responsible for them.

See Spectra 15. Consider the spectral data for 2-(2′,4′-dimethylbenzoyl)benzoic acid (Figs. 15.16 and 15.17).

    a. In the functional group region of the IR spectrum, specify the absorptions associated with the ketone carbonyl group, the aromatic rings, and the carboxylic acid function. Explain why the latter absorption is broad.

    b. In the ^{1}H NMR spectrum, assign the various resonances to the hydrogen nuclei responsible for them.

    c. For the ^{13}C NMR data, assign the various resonances to the carbon nuclei responsible for them.

16. What differences in the IR and NMR spectra of phthalic anhydride and 2-(2′,4′-dimethylbenzoyl)benzoic acid are consistent with the conversion of the anhydride group to ketone and carboxylic acid groups in this experiment?

17. Explain how ^{1}H NMR and ^{13}C NMR spectra could be used to differentiate between **15** and the isomer of it shown below.

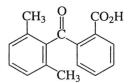

Starting Materials and Products

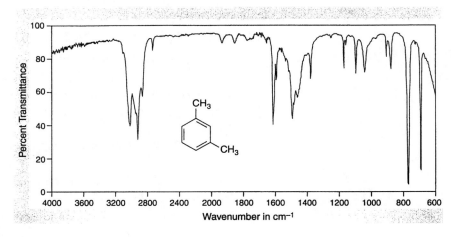

Figure 15.12
IR spectrum of m-xylene (neat).

(a) ^{1}H NMR spectrum (300 MHz).

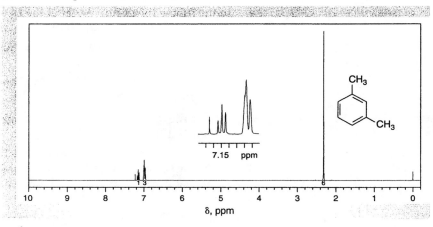

Figure 15.13
NMR data for m-xylene (CDCl$_3$).

(b) ^{13}C NMR data: δ 21.3, 126.2, 128.2, 130.0, 137.6.

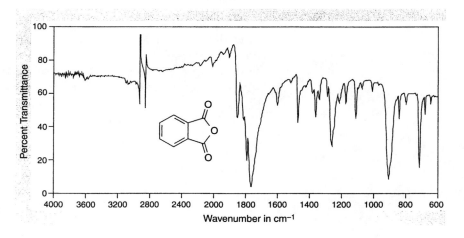

Figure 15.14
IR spectrum of phthalic anhydride (IR card).

(a) ^{1}H NMR spectrum (300 MHz).

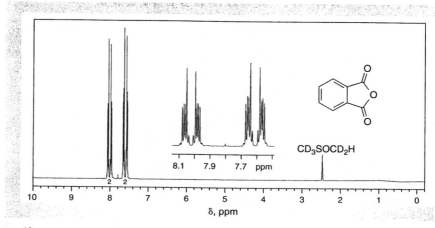

Figure 15.15
NMR data for phthalic anhydride (DMSO-d$_6$).

(b) ^{13}C NMR data: δ 125.3, 131.1, 136.1, 163.1.

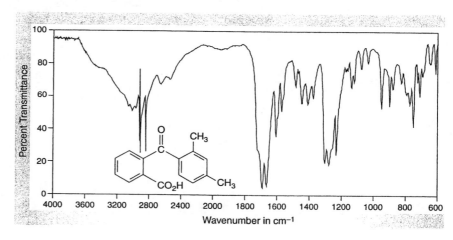

Figure 15.16
IR spectrum of 2-(2',4'-dimethyl-benzoyl)benzoic acid (IR card).

(a) ^{1}H NMR spectrum (300 MHz).

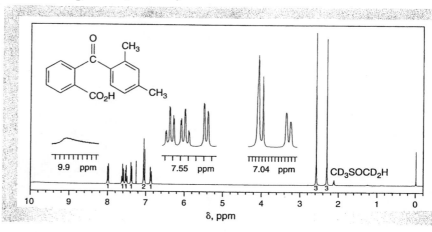

Figure 15.17
NMR data for 2-(2',4'-dimethyl-benzoyl)benzoic acid (CDCl$_3$).

(b) ^{13}C NMR data: δ 21.3, 21.4, 125.7, 128.0, 128.1, 129.4, 130.6, 131.8, 132.7, 132.8, 133.8, 140.3, 142.4, 143.9, 171.2, 198.4.

Qualitative Organic Analysis; Classification Tests

Background Reading
Relevant material in
Section 8.3 of this text

Timing
(5 h)

The classification tests that follow are a selection of the more useful tests commonly employed for the detection of aldehydes, ketones, alcohols, and phenols. It is essential that these tests be practiced on known compounds before any attempt is made to use them on unknown samples. *Although the test reagents will be available to use, methods for freshly preparing the reagents have been included.*

You will receive about 1 g (or 1 mL) of a solid or liquid unknown that is either a phenol, an alcohol, an aldehyde, or a ketone. Carry out each of the classification tests in Parts **A–G** on the suggested known samples and then on your unknown. Record the results for the unknown on the summary sheet at the end of this experiment. If two or more classification tests give conflicting results, repeat those tests carefully. Describe in your notebook the result for each test.

Purification of Liquid Samples.   It is suggested that the following simple distillation be carried out on liquid unknowns prior to running the classification tests. Place about 0.5 mL of the liquid into a small test tube with a boiling chip and bring it to a boil with a microburner or sand bath. Dip the end of a Pasteur pipet into the vapor over the boiling liquid and suck a sample of vapor into the pipet. Immediate condensation will result in several drops of distilled sample.

Use of Infrared Spectroscopy.   When you have finished running the classification tests on your unknown sample, obtain an IR spectrum and interpret as much of the spectrum as you can in terms of the presence or absence of possible functional groups. Compare the results of the classification tests and the infrared data.

Ketones and Aldehydes

A. 2,4-Dinitrophenylhydrazone (or 2,4-DNP) Test

The single most useful chemical test for distinguishing aldehydes and ketones from most other functional groups is the formation of a characteristic yellow to orange-red 2,4-dinitrophenylhydrazone precipitate when the sample is treated with an acidic, alcoholic solution of 2,4-dinitrophenylhydrazine.

$$R_2CO + O_2N-\text{⟨ring⟩}-NHNH_2 \longrightarrow O_2N-\text{⟨ring⟩}-NHN=CR_2$$

$$NO_2 \qquad\qquad\qquad NO_2$$

A 2,4-dinitrophenylhydrazone

The precipitate can be crystallized from 95% ethanol or from ethyl acetate and used as a derivative for purposes of identification. Among the functional groups other than aldehydes and ketones that form such a derivative are those that are transformed to an aldehyde or ketone with aqueous acid. Examples of such compounds include acetals, enamines, aldehyde hydrates, and imines; shown is an example of the equation for hydrolysis of an ethylene glycol acetal to the corresponding ketone.

$RCH(OR)_2$ $R_2(OR)_2$ $RCH=CR—NR_2$ $RCH(OH)_2$ $R_2C=NH$
    Acetals   An enamine   An aldehyde hydrate   An imine

$$R_2C\text{⟨dioxolane⟩} + H_2O \xrightarrow{H_3O^+} R_2CO + HOCH_2CH_2OH$$

Derivative formation has also been noted for certain very reactive esters and anhydrides, and with some benzyl alcohols (which are oxidized by the reagent to the corresponding benzaldehydes).

EXERCISES

1. What type of spectroscopic evidence would allow a distinction to be made between ketones or aldehydes and other functional groups that might give a positive 2,4-DNP test?

2. Write the structure for the pyrrolidine enamine and for the imine of cyclohexanone. Write a balanced equation for the acid-catalyzed hydrolysis of each of these compounds.

3. On the basis of the relationship between structure and color described in Section 12.4 and the observation that both yellow and red-orange 2,4-dinitrophenylhydrazones are formed, would you expect the 2,4-DNP derivative of an aldehyde or ketone conjugated with an aromatic ring or double bond to be yellow or red-orange? Explain.

2,4-Dinitrophenylhydrazine (or 2,4-DNP) Test Reagent.   Add a solution of 3 g of 2,4-dinitrophenylhydrazine in 15 mL of concentrated sulfuric acid slowly and with stirring to a mixture of 20 mL of water and 70 mL of 95% ethanol. Stir and filter.

2,4-DNP Test Procedure.   A tiny drop of the pure liquid sample or a few drops from dissolving several mg of a solid sample in a minimal amount of 95% ethanol is added to several drops of test reagent on a white spot plate (or in a small test tube). If no yellow or orange-red precipitate forms immediately, allow the solution to stand at least 15 min.

Try the 2,4-DNP test on acetone, butyraldehyde, benzaldehyde, ethyl acetate, and your unknown. Describe the results and indicate what structural features will lead to a positive test. Comment on the color of any derivative.

B. Purpald™ Test[1]

1. Aldrich trademark for 4-amino-3-hydrazine-5-mercapto-1,2,4-triazole. The procedure is adapted from H. B. Hopps, *Aldrichemica Acta*, **33**, 28 (2000) and H. D. Durst and G. W. Gokel, *J. Chem. Educ*, **55**, 206 (1978).

The reagent reacts with both aldehydes and ketones to give the heterocyclic products shown in the first reaction below. However, only in the case of aldehydes does this initial product undergo air oxidation to give a highly colored final product. Many simple aldehydes that have some water solubility give a purple color within 1 min. However, less water-soluble aldehydes require the addition of phase transfer catalyst, Aliquat 336™, to help transfer the Purpald™ anion into the aldehyde phase. Under these latter conditions, the developing color is usually deep red to rust rather than purple. Practical grade 3-pentanone gave a positive test, but 99.5% pure ketone did not. Glacial acetic acid can give a positive test because of the presence of small amounts of acetaldehyde. Vanillin and glucose give a positive test, but require at least 10 minutes.

A companion to the Purpald™ test for distinguishing aldehydes and ketones is the chromic acid test, which is discussed later as one of the tests for distinguishing primary, secondary, and tertiary alcohols.

2. The solution will not last for an entire morning or afternoon lab session before giving false positive tests.

Preparing Purpald™ Reagent. The Purpald™ reagent is a solution of 2 mg/mL of reagent in $1M$ NaOH. This air-sensitive reagent must be made very fresh[2] and checked with a known aldehyde prior to each use by a student. If the reagent solution turns pale purple (aldehyde contamination), it should be replaced.

Purpald™ Test Procedure. Place 5–6 drops of a solution of Purpald™ reagent into the depression of a white spot plate. (*Avoid bubbling air through the reagent with the dropper pipet.*) Add 1 drop of a suspected liquid aldehyde or 5–10 mg of a suspected solid aldehyde and wait for 1 min. Development of a purple color indicates a positive test. If no purple color appears and the test sample appears to be insoluble, add 1 drop of Aliquat 336 (a trademark for tridecylmethylammonium chloride) so that it makes contact with the test sample. Formation of a purple or deep-red to rust color represents a positive test.

Try the test on samples of acetaldehyde, benzaldehyde, acetone, and the unknown. Describe and explain all the results in terms of the structures of the compounds.

C. Iodoform Test

In the presence of a base, most methyl ketones are converted to an enolate ion (usually in low concentration) by removal of one of the protons adjacent to the carbonyl group.

$$RCH_2CCH_3 + OH^- \underset{slow}{\rightleftharpoons} RCH_2CCH_2^- \longleftrightarrow RCH_2C=CH_2$$

An enolate ion

Although regioisomeric enolates form, reaction of the primary enolate with halogen is favored for steric reasons.

In the presence of a halogen (iodine is commonly used), the enolate anion and halogen react to form a monohaloketone, which—because of the electronegativity of the halogen—will form an anion more readily than the original ketone. The process is rapidly repeated until the methyl group has become a trihalomethyl group. Cleavage of the trihalo compound by base as shown then produces the salt of a carboxylic acid and a haloform. If X = iodine, water-insoluble iodoform is produced, which has a characteristic medicinal odor, is yellow in color, and melts at 119–121°C.

$$RCH_2CCH_2^- + X_2 \longrightarrow RCH_2CCH_2X + X^-$$

$$RCH_2CCH_2X + OH^- \rightleftharpoons RCH_2CCHX + H_2O \longrightarrow \longrightarrow$$

$$RCH_2CCX_3 + OH^- \rightleftharpoons RCH_2C-CX_3 \longrightarrow RCH_2CO_2^- + HCX_3$$

OH

A haloform

Because of the oxidizing properties of the test solution, alkylmethylcarbinols (which are oxidized to alkyl methyl ketones) and ethanol give a positive iodoform test.

EXERCISES

4. Would any aldehyde be expected to give a positive iodoform test? Which one(s)?

5. Can you suggest a reason why 3,5-heptanedione gives a positive iodoform test?

Preparing Iodoform Test Reagent.   Dissolve 20 g of potassium iodide and 10 g of iodine in 100 mL of water.

Iodoform Test Procedure.   Add two drops or about 50 mg of sample compound to 1 mL of water in a small vial, and if necessary, the minimum amount of 1,2-dimethoxyethane to produce a homogeneous solution. After 0.5 mL of 10% (w/v) sodium hydroxide solution has been added to the solution, the test reagent is added drop-wise, with shaking, until an iodine color persists. If no yellow precipitate of iodoform appears within a few minutes, warm the mixture in a water bath at about 60°C. If the color disappears, add more of the test reagent until the color persists for at least 2 min of heating. Then add a few drops of sodium hydroxide solution to destroy the excess iodine color, dilute with water, and let stand 15 min. If yellow iodoform now precipitates, it can be recognized by its characteristic odor and the fact that it melts at 119–121°C. (A check of the mp will not be necessary unless the original sample was a pale-yellow solid.)

Try this test on cyclohexanone, acetone, isopropyl alcohol, and the unknown. Describe the results in terms of the structures of the sample compounds.

Alcohols and Phenols

D. Ferric Chloride Test

The introduction of a dilute phenol solution to a 2% solution of ferric chloride in water generally (but not always) results in the production of an intense red, orange, brown, green, blue, or violet color from the formation of a complex, the stoichiometry of which is probably as indicated.

$$3\,ArOH \; + \; [Fe(H_2O)_6]^{3+} \; \rightleftharpoons \; Fe(H_2O)_3(OAr)_3 \; + \; 3\,H_3O^+$$

Other compounds of comparable or greater acidity than phenols can also produce color changes that can interfere with the test for phenols. These include any structure, such as ethyl acetoacetate, that is capable of producing stable enols and enolate anions, and such compounds as oximes ($R_2C = NOH$) and hydroxamic acids ($RCONHOH$).

$$\underset{CH_3CCH_2CO_2Et}{\overset{O \atop \|}{}} \rightleftharpoons \underset{CH_3C = CHCO_2Et}{\overset{OH \atop |}{}} \rightleftharpoons \underset{CH_3C = CHCO_2Et \; + \; H^+}{\overset{O^- \atop |}{}}$$

Aliphatic carboxylic acids usually produce a yellow solution, whereas aromatic carboxylic acids sometimes produce tan precipitates. However, neither of these latter results is very characteristic or useful.

A modification of the test, in which chloroform is the solvent and pyridine is added as the base, frequently gives a color change for phenols.

Preparing Ferric Chloride Reagent.   Dissolve an amount of $FeCl_3$ in water to make a 2% (by weight) solution. For the modified test, use a solution prepared by dissolving 1 g of $FeCl_3$ in 100 mL of chloroform.

Ferric Chloride Test Procedures.   Add several drops of aqueous $FeCl_3$ solution to 1 mL of a dilute (0.1–0.3% by weight) solution of the sample compound in water. Compare the color with that of several drops of reagent solution in 1 mL of water. Colors produced sometimes fade and must be watched carefully.

CAUTION!

Chloroform is toxic and must be handled in a well-ventilated area or hood. Many phenols are both toxic and corrosive. They can be absorbed through the skin and should be handled with care.

As a modified procedure, add 2–3 drops of the chloroform solution of ferric chloride to approximately 20 mg of solid (1 drop of liquid) dissolved or suspended in 1 mL of chloroform. Add 1 drop of pyridine.

Try the foregoing procedures on samples of phenol, ethyl acetoacetate, benzoic acid, hydroquinone (1,4-dihydroxybenzene), and the unknown. Carefully describe the results.

E. Aqueous Bromine

The exceptional electron-donating ability of the hydroxyl group allows rapid electrophilic substitution of phenols with an aqueous solution of bromine under mild conditions. The reaction usually results in bromine substitution at each available *ortho* and *para* position, with simultaneous formation of HBr, which is readily detected by the increased acidity (lower pH) of the solution. Other compounds that can give a positive test with aqueous bromine are various substituted anilines.

EXERCISE

6. Phenols and alkenes will both decolorize a solution of bromine in carbon tetrachloride, yet there are simple observations that can be made during the test that will allow you to distinguish between them. Can you suggest what these observations might be?

Preparing Aqueous Bromine Reagent. Dissolve bromine in water until a saturated solution is obtained.

Aqueous Bromine Test Procedure. Add the aqueous solution of bromine drop by drop to a solution of approximately 20 mg (or 1 drop) of the sample in 1 mL of water. Stop when the bromine color is no longer discharged. A positive test is obtained if a sparingly soluble derivative precipitates and the solution becomes strongly acidic (as indicated by pH paper).

Try this test on phenol and the unknown. Write equations to describe the results in each case.

CAUTION!

Bromine or its solutions can cause serious burns on the skin and should always be handled with great care.

EXERCISE

7. Aqueous bromine converts aniline to 2,4,6-tribromoaniline and HBr. Explain why the brominated aniline does not dissolve in the acid solution as a soluble anilinium bromide salt.

F. Lucas Test (ZnCl$_2$ + HCl)

This test relies on the fact that the ease of formation of carbocations from the corresponding alcohols is highly dependent on structural features in the molecule. When other data, such as spectra, solubility properties, and negative results with other classification tests, suggest the possible presence of an alcohol, treatment with a solution of zinc chloride in hydrochloric acid can serve as a means of distinguishing between those alcohols that are quickly and easily converted to the corresponding alkyl chlorides (via the carbocation) and those that are not.

Coordination of the zinc chloride with the hydroxyl function results in the production of a sufficiently good leaving group that carbon–oxygen cleavage can now occur if a reasonably stable carbocation can form.

$$R\overset{+}{O}\overset{-}{Z}nCl_2 \longrightarrow R^+ + Zn(OH)Cl_2^-$$
$$|$$
$$H$$

$$R^+ + Cl^- \longrightarrow RCl$$

If R is tertiary, benzylic, or allylic, the reaction takes place almost immediately, whereas secondary alcohols require several minutes to undergo reaction and simple primary alcohols do not react over a period of 10–15 min. The test depends on observing the formation of an insoluble liquid, alkyl chloride, as a cloudy suspension that later separates into a distinct upper layer. This requires that the alcohol be soluble in the test reagent and thus restricts the test to simple alcohols below hexyl and other alcohols that have additional functional groups that enhance the solubility in the reagent. See Table E54.1 for a summary of Lucas test results.

Use this test in conjunction with the chromic acid test described in the next section.

Preparing Lucas Reagent. Dissolve 16 g of anhydrous zinc chloride in 10 mL of concentrated hydrochloric acid with cooling.

Lucas Test Procedure. Add about 50 mg (2–3 drops) of the sample to 1 mL of the reagent in a small vial, cap, shake vigorously for a few seconds, and allow to stand at room temperature. Consult the summary table above.

If there is still doubt in distinguishing secondary from tertiary, treat the alcohol with concentrated hydrochloric acid. Only a tertiary, benzylic, or allylic alcohol will react rapidly to form the cloudy suspension of alkyl chloride.

Try this test on samples of *tert*-butyl alcohol, isoamyl alcohol (3-methyl-1-butanol), benzyl alcohol, *sec*-butyl alcohol, and the unknown.

Table E54.1 Summary of Lucas Test Results

Type of Alcohol	Time for Alkyl Halide Formation
Tertiary, allylic, benzylic	<1 min
Secondary	2–3 min
Primary	No reaction in 15 min

Type of Compound	Approx. Oxidation Time
Primary alcohols	2 sec
Secondary alcohols	2 sec
Tertiary alcohols	No reaction
Aliphatic aldehydes	15 sec
Aromatic aldehydes	30–45 sec

Table E54.2   Summary of Chromic Acid Test Results[a]

[a] Times will vary with temperature as well as structure variation.

G. Chromic Acid Test (Jones Oxidation)

Primary and secondary alcohols are rapidly oxidized by chromium trioxide in acidic, aqueous acetone, whereas tertiary alcohols are stable to oxidation. Oxidation is readily detected by the appearance of the green Cr^{3+} ion. The test can also be used as a companion to the Purpald™ test for aldehydes, because it allows a distinction to be made between aliphatic and aromatic aldehydes that differ in the time required for oxidation. Ketones are not oxidized by these conditions. Although Table E54.2 summarizes the anticipated results, it is useful to check some authentic samples before any decisions are made based on the time required for oxidation.

EXERCISE

8. Write balanced equations for the oxidation of a primary alcohol to a carboxylic acid and a secondary alcohol to a ketone by chromic acid, H_2CrO_4.

Preparing Chromic Acid Reagent.   Add 5 g of CrO_3 in 5 mL of concentrated sulfuric acid to 15 mL of water. Allow the solution to cool.

Chromic Acid Test Procedure.   Dissolve 1 drop of liquid or 20 mg of solid sample in 1 mL of acetone in a small vial. Add 1 drop of chromic acid reagent, cap the vial, and shake it briefly.

Try this test on butyl alcohol, *sec*-butyl alcohol, *tert*-butyl alcohol, benzaldehyde, butyraldehyde, and the unknown.

Summary Form for Classification Tests

Name: _____

Unknown # _____ (aldehyde, alcohol, ketone, phenol)
2,4-DNP Test Description:

Conclusion _____
Purpald™ Test Description:

Conclusion _____
Iodoform Test Description:

Conclusion _____
Ferric Chloride Test Description:

Conclusion _____
Aqueous Bromine Test Description:

Conclusion _____
Lucas Test Description:

Conclusion _____
Chromic Acid Test Description:

Conclusion _____
Infrared data on aldehyde, alcohol, ketone, or phenol unknown (spectrum attached): Indicate all important peak assignments on the spectrum.

Conclusion _____

Synthesis of trans-9-(2-Phenylethenyl)-anthracene: A Wittig Reaction

Prepared by William M. Loffredo, East Stroudsburg University

PURPOSE OF THE EXPERIMENT

Synthesize *trans*-9-(2-phenylethenyl)anthracene using a Wittig reaction. Characterize the product by melting point, thin-layer chromatography, infrared spectroscopy, and nuclear magnetic resonance spectroscopy.

EXPERIMENTAL OPTIONS

Semi-Microscale Wittig Synthesis
Microscale Wittig Synthesis
Characterizing the Product

BACKGROUND REQUIRED

You should be familiar with techniques for drying organic solvents and measuring melting points. You should be familiar with the techniques for extraction, distillation, recrystallization, and vacuum filtration. You should know how to speed the evaporation of microscale quantities of solvent using air or nitrogen. You should be familiar with thin-layer chromatography (TLC), infrared spectroscopy (IR), and nuclear magnetic resonance spectroscopy (NMR).

BACKGROUND INFORMATION

Chemical reactions involving organic molecules can be classified into three very broad categories: molecular rearrangement, elimination, and addition. Although alkenes are commonly formed from *elimination* reactions, such as dehydration of alcohols and dehydrohalogenation of alkyl halides, these reactions usually result in a mixture of structural isomers. The Wittig reaction is often preferred as a method of synthesizing alkenes because of its high level of **regioselectivity**, which is the tendency of a reaction to form predominantly one isomer from a single reactant. The Wittig reaction allows the chemist to choose the precise location of the newly formed bond.

The Wittig reaction is an *addition* reaction. It generates an alkene from the reaction of a carbonyl compound with a carbon-containing phosphorus reagent known as an ylide, which is made from a phosphonium halide. The phosphonium halide is generated from the nucleophilic substitution reaction of a primary or secondary alkyl halide and triphenylphosphine, Ph_3P. Ph_3P is a good nucleophile and a relatively weak base. Therefore, the potentially competing elimination reaction does not occur. The substitution products are phosphonium salts, as shown in Equations 1 and 2.

$$RCH_2X \quad + \quad Ph_3P \longrightarrow RCH_2\overset{+}{P}Ph_3 \quad X^- \qquad \text{(Eq. 1)}$$
1° alkyl halide

$$R_2CHX \quad + \quad Ph_3P \longrightarrow R_2CH\overset{+}{P}Ph_3 \quad X^- \qquad \text{(Eq. 2)}$$
2° alkyl halide

The phosphonium salt must have phosphorus attached to a carbon containing at least one hydrogen atom. This hydrogen atom is moderately acidic and can be extracted in the presence of a strong base. Typically, alkyl lithium compounds or metal hydrides are used as the strong base. In this experiment, however, a concentrated solution of aqueous sodium hydroxide will be used.

The product resulting from the reaction of the phosphonium halide with a strong base is called an **ylide**. An ylide is a neutral molecule, which, among its atoms, has two adjacent atoms that have opposite charges. The two charged atoms are the phosphorus from the phosphine and the carbon from the alkyl halide, as shown in Equation 3.

$$RCH_2\overset{+}{P}Ph_3 \quad X^- \xrightarrow{\text{base}} R\overset{-}{C}H\overset{+}{P}Ph_3 \qquad \text{(Eq. 3)}$$
ylide

This carbon group attached to the phosphorus has carbanionic character and acts as a nucleophile toward carbonyl groups. The general mechanism of the reaction is shown in Equation 4.

carbonyl compound   triphenylphosphonium ylide   betaine   oxaphosphetane

alkene   triphenylphosphine oxide   (Eq. 4)

The mechanism is still under investigation. The controversy lies in whether the oxaphosphetane intermediate is formed by a one-step concerted process or by a two-step process. Formation of the oxaphosphetane through a two-step process involves the initial formation of a dipolar intermediate known as a betaine. The betaine then reacts to form the oxaphosphetane. The oxaphosphetane is stable at −78 °C, but at room temperature, it decomposes to yield the alkene and triphenyl-phosphine oxide. The driving force for the decomposition of the oxaphosphetane is thought to be the formation of the strong phosphorus–oxygen bond of the phosphine oxide, a bond strength estimated to be at least 540 kJ/mol.

The Wittig reaction forms the carbon–carbon double bond between the carbonyl carbon and the carbon adjacent to the phosphorus atom in the ylide. For example, consider the formation of methylenecyclohexane. The Wittig reaction could be conducted with formaldehyde and bromocyclohexane or with bromomethane and cyclohexanone, as shown in Equation 5.

$$H_2CO \quad + \qquad \text{bromocyclohexane} \xrightarrow[\text{2. base}]{\text{1. Ph}_3\text{P}}$$

$$CH_3Br \quad + \qquad \text{cyclohexanone} \xrightarrow[\text{2. base}]{\text{1. Ph}_3\text{P}} \text{methylene cyclohexane} \quad + \quad Ph_3PO \qquad (Eq. 5)$$

The synthetic route chosen will depend on the availability of the possible starting materials.

In this experiment, the alkene *trans*-9-(2-phenylethenyl)anthracene will be synthesized from 9-anthraldehyde and the ylide derived from triphenylbenzylphosphonium chloride. The ylide formation and the subsequent reaction are shown in Equation 6.

$$(C_6H_5)_3\overset{+}{P}\overset{Cl^-}{-}CH_2C_6H_5 \xrightarrow{\text{50\% NaOH}} (C_6H_5)_3\overset{+}{P}-\overset{-}{C}HC_6H_5 \quad + \quad \text{9-anthraldehyde}$$

benzyltriphenylphosphonium chloride   benzyltriphenylphosphonium ylide

betaine intermediate   oxaphosphetane intermediate

(Eq. 6)

trans-9-(2-phenylethenyl)anthracene

SEMI-MICROSCALE WITTIG SYNTHESIS

Equipment

50-mL beaker	hot plate
2 beakers, 100-mL	magnetic stir bar
250-mL beaker*	magnetic stirrer
boiling chip	medicine dropper
Büchner funnel, with adapter	microspatula
condenser, with tubing	product vial
distilling head	25-mL round-bottom flask
25-mL Erlenmeyer flask	125-mL separatory funnel
250-mL filter flask,	2 support stands
with vacuum tubing	2 utility clamps
filter paper	watch glass
10-mL graduated cylinder	

*for ice bath and for hot-water bath

Reagents and Properties

substance	quantity	molar mass (g/mol)	bp (°C)	mp (°C)	d (g/mL)
9-anthraldehyde	0.520 g	206.24		104–105	
benzyltriphenyl-phosphonium chloride	0.980 g	388.88			
calcium chloride, anhydrous	1 g	110.99			
dichloromethane	18 mL	84.93	40		1.325
trans-9-(2-phenyl-ethenyl)anthracene*		280.4		130–132	
2-propanol	20 mL	60.10	82		0.785
50% sodium hydroxide	1.3 mL				

* product

Preview

- Dissolve benzyltriphenylphosphonium chloride and 9- anthraldehyde in dichloromethane
- Add 50% aqueous sodium hydroxide
- Stir the reaction mixture vigorously for 30 min
- Use a separatory funnel to separate the dichloromethane layer from the aqueous layer
- Extract the aqueous layer with additional dichloromethane
- Dry the combined dichloromethane layers over anhydrous calcium chloride
- Remove the solvent from the crude product
- Recrystallize the crude product from 2-propanol
- Dry and weigh the product

PROCEDURE

CHEMICAL ALERT

9-anthraldehyde—*irritant*
benzyltriphenylphosphonium chloride—*irritant and hygroscopic*
anhydrous calcium chloride—*irritant and hygroscopic*
dichloromethane—*toxic and irritant*
2-propanol—*flammable and irritant*
50% sodium hydroxide—*corrosive and toxic*

CAUTION

Wear departmentally approved safety goggles at all times while in the chemistry laboratory.

1. Using a Wittig Reagent to Synthesize *trans*-9-(2-Phenylethenyl)anthracene

CAUTION

Benzyltriphenylphosphonium chloride and 9-anthraldehyde are irritating. Dichloromethane is toxic and irritating. Use a *fume hood*.

50% Sodium hydroxide (NaOH) is corrosive and toxic. Wear gloves when using this solution. Prevent eye, skin, and clothing contact. Avoid inhaling and ingesting these compounds.

Weigh 0.980 g of benzyltriphenylphosphonium chloride and 0.520 g of 9-anthraldehyde. Place them into a 25-mL Erlenmeyer flask. Add 3 mL of dichloromethane. Place the flask on top of a magnetic stirrer and add a stir bar.

While the mixture is vigorously stirring, add 1.3 mL of 50% aqueous sodium hydroxide at a rate of 1 drop every 7 s. Vigorously stir the reaction mixture for an additional 30 min.

II. Isolating *trans*-9-(2-Phenylethenyl)anthracene

CAUTION

2-Propanol is flammable and irritating. Keep away from flames or other heat sources. Anhydrous calcium chloride ($CaCl_2$) is irritating and hygroscopic. Prevent eye, skin, and clothing contact. Avoid inhaling and ingesting these compounds.

Transfer the reaction mixture from the Erlenmeyer flask to a 125-mL separatory funnel. Rinse the reaction flask with 10 mL of dichloromethane and transfer the rinse to the separatory funnel. Then rinse the reaction flask with 10 mL of distilled or deionized water and transfer the rinse to the separatory funnel.

Shake and vent the contents in the funnel. Allow the layers to separate. Drain the organic layer from the funnel into a 100-mL beaker labeled, "Organic Layer".

Add an additional 5 mL of dichloromethane to the aqueous layer in the funnel. Shake and vent the contents in the funnel. Drain the organic layer into the beaker containing the initial organic layer.

Dry the combined organic layers by adding up to 1 g of anhydrous $CaCl_2$ to the beaker. Cover the beaker with a watch glass and allow the solution to dry for 10 min. Decant the organic layer from the drying agent into a dry 25-mL round-bottom flask.

3. Removing the Dichloromethane [NOTE 1]

NOTE 1: Use the separation method designated by your laboratory instructor.

Using a Rotary Evaporator

Use a rotary evaporator to collect the dichloromethane from the product, as directed by your laboratory instructor.

Using Distillation

Set up a simple distillation apparatus in the *fume hood.* Use the 25-mL round-bottom flask containing your product as the distilling flask. Add a boiling chip. Use a hot-water bath to distill the dichloromethane from the product. Collect the dichloromethane in a 50-mL beaker.

4. Purifying trans-9-(2-Phenylethenyl)-anthracene

Add 20 mL of 2-propanol to a 100-mL beaker. Heat the 2-propanol to boiling using a hot plate or electric flask heater. Recrystallize the crude product from 2-propanol. Allow the flask to cool to room temperature. Then place the solution in an ice-water bath for 5–10 min.

Collect the product by vacuum filtration using a Büchner funnel. Continue the suction for 5 min to dry the product. Weigh the product and place it into a labeled product vial.

Proceed to the Characterizing the Product Section later in this experiment. Use the procedures designated by your laboratory instructor.

5. Cleaning Up

Use the labeled collection containers as directed by your laboratory instructor. Clean your glassware with soap or detergent.

CAUTION   ⚠

Wash your hands with soap or detergent before leaving the laboratory.

MICROSCALE WITTIG SYNTHESIS

Equipment

2 beakers, 10-mL	hot plate
250-mL beaker*	magnetic stir bar
10-mL centrifuge tube, with screw cap	magnetic stirrer
	medicine dropper
5-mL conical vial	microspatula
25-mL Erlenmeyer flask	2 Pasteur pipets, with latex bulb
25-mL filter flask, with vacuum tubing	1-mL pipet[†]
filter paper	product vial
10-mL graduated cylinder	support stand
Hirsch funnel, with adapter	utility clamp
	watch glass

*for ice bath and for hot-water bath
†or adjustable micropipet

Reagents and Properties

substance	quantity	molar mass (g/mol)	bp (°C)	mp (°C)	d (g/mL)
9-anthraldehyde	0.110 g	206.24		104–105	
benzyltriphenyl-phosphonium chloride	0.210 g	388.88			
calcium chloride, anhydrous	0.3 g	110.99			
dichloromethane	3.1 mL	84.93	40		1.325
trans-9-(2-phenyl-ethenyl)anthracene*		280.4		130–132	
2-propanol	5 mL	60.10	82		0.785
50% sodium hydroxide	0.26 mL				

* product

Preview

- Dissolve benzyltriphenylphosphonium chloride and 9-anthraldehyde in dichloromethane
- Add 50% aqueous sodium hydroxide
- Stir the reaction mixture vigorously for 30 min
- Separate the dichloromethane layer from the aqueous layer in a centrifuge tube
- Extract the aqueous layer with additional dichloromethane
- Dry the combined dicloromethane layers over anhydrous calcium chloride
- Remove the solvent from the crude product
- Recrystallize the crude product from 2-propanol
- Dry and weigh the product

PROCEDURE

CHEMICAL ALERT

9-anthraldehyde—*irritant*
benzyltriphenylphosphonium chloride—*irritant and hygroscopic*
anhydrous calcium chloride—*irritant and hygroscopic*
dichloromethane—*toxic and irritant*
2-propanol—*flammable and irritant*
50% sodium hydroxide—*corrosive and toxic*

Wear departmentally approved safety goggles at all times while in the chemistry laboratory.

1. Using a Wittig Reagent to Synthesize *trans*-9-(2-Phenylethenyl)anthracene

CAUTION

Benzyltriphenylphosphonium chloride and 9-anthraldehyde are irritating. Dichloromethane is toxic and irritating. Use a *fume hood*. Prevent eye, skin, and clothing contact. Avoid inhaling and ingesting these compounds.

50% Sodium hydroxide (NaOH) is corrosive and toxic. Wear gloves when using this solution. Prevent eye, skin, and clothing contact. Avoid inhaling and ingesting this compound.

Weigh 0.210 g of benzyltriphenylphosphonium chloride and 0.110 g of 9-anthraldehyde. Place them into a 5-mL conical vial. Add 0.6 mL of dichloromethane. Place the vial on top of a magnetic stirrer and add a stir bar. Clamp the vial in place for added stability.

While the mixture is vigorously stirring, add 0.26 mL of 50% aqueous sodium hydroxide at a rate of 1 drop every 7 s. Vigorously stir the reaction mixture for an additional 30 min.

2. Isolation and Purification of *trans*-9-(2-Phenylethenyl)anthracene

Transfer the reaction mixture from the vial to a 10-mL centrifuge tube. Rinse the reaction vial with 1.5 mL of dichloromethane and transfer the rinse to the centrifuge tube. Then rinse the reaction vial with 1.5 mL of distilled or deionized water and add the rinse to the centrifuge tube.

Screw the cap onto the centrifuge tube and shake it vigorously, venting the tube periodically. Allow the layers to separate. Using a Pasteur pipet, transfer the organic layer from the centrifuge tube to a 10-mL beaker labeled, "Organic Layer".

Add an additional 1 mL of dichloromethane to the aqueous layer in the centrifuge tube. Shake and vent the contents in the tube. Transfer the organic layer to the beaker containing the initial organic layer.

Dry the combined organic layers by adding up to 0.3 g of anhydrous $CaCl_2$ to the beaker. Cover the beaker with a watch glass and allow the solution to dry for 10 min.

Decant the organic layer from the drying agent into a dry 10-mL beaker. Use a steam bath or a hot-water bath in a *fume hood* to carefully evaporate the dichloromethane from the crude product. Do not overheat the beaker and melt the crude product. Use a *gentle* stream of air or nitrogen to speed the evaporation process.

Add 5 mL of 2-propanol to a 25-mL Erlenmeyer flask. Heat the 2-propanol to boiling, using a hot plate or electric flask heater. Recrystallize the crude product from hot 2-propanol. Allow the flask to cool to room temperature. Then place the solution in an ice-water bath for 5–10 min.

Collect the product by vacuum filtration using a Hirsch funnel. Continue the suction for 5 min to dry the product. Weigh the product and place it into a labeled product vial.

Proceed to the Characterizing the Product Section. Use the procedures designated by your laboratory instructor.

3. Cleaning Up

Use the labeled collection containers as directed by your laboratory instructor. Clean your glassware with soap or detergent.

CAUTION

Wash your hands with soap or detergent before leaving the laboratory.

CHARACTERIZING THE PRODUCT

Equipment

Melting Point

melting point capillary tubes

Thin-Layer Chromatography

1.0-mL conical vial	pencil
12-cm filter paper,	0.1-mL transfer pipet
cut to fit the developing chamber	ruler
10-mL graduated cylinder	2 screw-cap jars, 4-oz*
microburner	2 × 9-cm silica gel TLC plate,
open-ended capillary tubes	with fluorescent indicator

*or 400-mL beakers, with aluminum foil covers

Infrared Analysis

KBr pellet press*
NaCl or AgCl plates, with sample holder†
*for KBr pellets
†for mull

NMR Analysis

3.0-mL conical vial   NMR sample tube
Pasteur pipet, with latex bulb

Reagents and Properties

substance	quantity	molar mass (g/mol)	bp (°C)	mp (°C)
9-anthraldehyde		206.24		104–105
deutero-chloroform	1 mL	120.39	60.9	
potassium bromide	100 mg			
toluene	10 mL	92.14	110.6	

Preview

- Measure the melting point of the product
- Prepare a thin-layer chromatogram and measure the product R_f
- Analyze the product using infrared spectroscopy
- Analyze the product using nuclear magnetic resonance spectroscopy

PROCEDURE

CHEMICAL ALERT

9-anthraldehyde—*irritant*
deutero*-chloroform—*toxic and suspected carcinogen
toluene—*flammable and toxic*

CAUTION

Wear departmentally approved safety goggles at all times while in the chemistry laboratory.

1. Measuring Melting Point

Take a melting point of the product. Heat the melting point tube quickly to 110 °C, then slow the heating rate to 2 °C per min. Observe and record the temperature range over which the solid melts.

2. Using Thin-Layer Chromatography

CAUTION

Toluene is flammable and toxic. Do not use toluene near flames or other heat sources. *Use toluene only when all students have prepared their micropipets and all flames have been extinguished.* Use a *fume hood*. Prevent eye, skin, and clothing contact. Avoid inhaling vapors and ingesting toluene.

Prepare micropipets for spotting the TLC plate by drawing out open-ended capillary tubes.

Prepare a developing chamber using approximately 10 mL of toluene as the eluent.

Place 0.1-mL of toluene in a 1.0-mL conical vial. Add 1–2 mg of your product and mix to dissolve.

Using a *pencil*, lightly draw a line across the bottom of a TLC plate, 1 cm above the bottom. Carefully make two light hash marks on the line and label them as "starting material" and "product".

CAUTION

9-Anthraldehyde is irritating. Prevent eye, skin, and clothing contact.

Spot 9-anthraldehyde, using the solution provided by your laboratory instructor, and the product, using the solution you prepared, on the plate. Place the plate into the developing chamber.

Develop the plate until the eluent front is approximately 1 cm from the top. Then remove the chromatogram from the chamber and *immediately* mark the eluent front with a pencil.

CAUTION

Ultraviolet radiation can cause severe damage to the eyes. Wear goggles. Do not look directly into the lamp.

Allow the eluent to evaporate under the *fume hood.* Examine the chromatogram under the UV lamp and lightly circle the spots using a pencil.

Using a ruler, measure the distance to the eluent front and to the center of each spot. Record the values.

3. Using Infrared Spectroscopy

CAUTION

Potassium bromide (KBr) is irritating. Prevent eye, skin, and clothing contact. Avoid inhaling dust.

Prepare the sample for IR analysis following the instructions of your laboratory instructor. Obtain an IR spectrum of your sample.

4. Using Nuclear Magnetic Resonance Spectroscopy

CAUTION

***deutero*-Chloroform (*d*-chloroform) is toxic and a suspected carcinogen. Use gloves. Use a *fume hood.* Prevent eye, skin, and clothing contact. Avoid inhaling vapors and ingesting the compound.**

Obtain an NMR sample tube from your laboratory instructor. In a dry vial, place approximately 10 mg of product and 1 mL of *d*-chloroform. Swirl the vial until all of the solid has dissolved. Use a Pasteur pipet to transfer at least 0.600 mL of the solution to the NMR tube and cap the tube.

Follow the instructions of your laboratory instructor to obtain an NMR spectrum of your sample.

5. Cleaning Up

Use the labeled collection containers as directed by your laboratory instructor. Clean your glassware with soap or detergent.

CAUTION

Wash your hands with soap or detergent before leaving the laboratory.

POST-LABORATORY QUESTIONS

1. Calculate the percent yield of product you obtained from this reaction.
2. Calculate R_fs for each spot on your chromatogram.
3. Using your melting point data and thin-layer chromatogram, what evidence allows you to conclude that your product is *trans*-9-(2-phenylethenyl)anthracene?
4. Compare the IR spectra for 9-anthraldehyde and that of your product. What evidence allows you to conclude that your product is *trans*-9-(2-phenylethenyl)anthracene?
5. Using your IR and NMR spectra, what evidence supports the synthesis of the *trans* isomer rather than the *cis* isomer?

Name   Section   Date

Pre-Laboratory Assignment

1. What safety precautions must be observed when using

   (a) dichloromethane?

   (b) 50% aqueous sodium hydroxide?

   (c) toluene?

2. Briefly explain the advantage of a Wittig synthesis over the more common dehydrohalogenation reaction.

3. Using the data in the Reagents and Properties table,

   (a) identify which reactant is the limiting reagent in the reaction;

   (b) calculate the theoretical yield, in grams, of *trans*-9-(2-phenylethenyl)anthracene. Show your calculation here and in your laboratory notebook.

4. What combination of carbonyl compound and phosphorus ylide could you use to prepare the following alkenes?

   (a) $CH_3CH_2CH(CH_3)CH=CHCH_3$

   (b) $(CH_3)_2C=CHC_6H_5$

m-Aminoacetophenone; Selective Reduction of Nitro[1]

Background Reading
Material on the reduction of nitro groups to amines in any modern organic textbook

Timing
(Parts **A** and **B**: 2 h without a 1-h recrystallization)

The success or failure of many organic syntheses depends on the ability of the chemist to choose appropriate reagents and conditions for the selective reaction of certain functional groups while others remain untouched. As an example of such a selective process, only the nitro group of *m*-nitroacetophenone is reduced by tin metal in acidic solution. The following experiment illustrates this process.

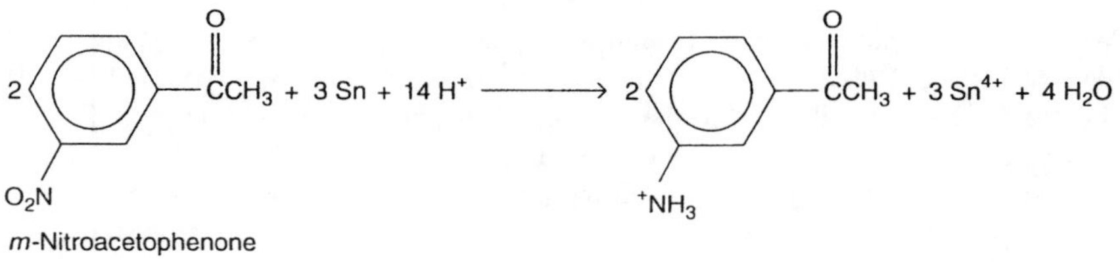

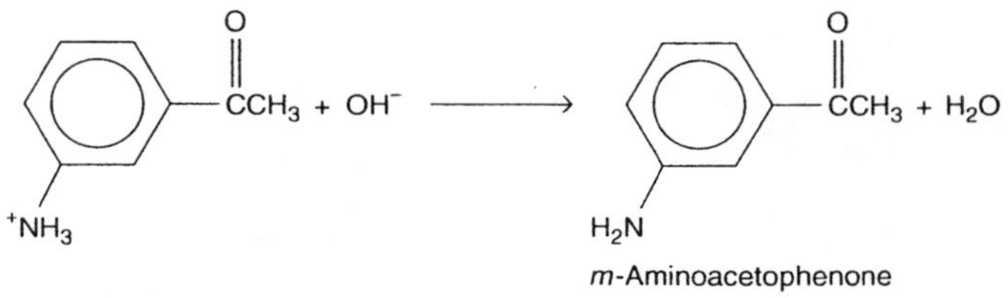

m-Nitroacetophenone

m-Aminoacetophenone

In contrast, the use of sodium borohydride in ethanol reduces the carbonyl group without affecting the nitro group.

EXERCISES

1. Write a balanced equation for the reduction of nitrobenzene to aniline by iron in aqueous acid.

2. From information in your lecture textbook, suggest a single reducing agent capable of reducing both the nitro and carbonyl groups of *m*-nitroacetophenone.

CAUTION!

Concentrated hydrochloric acid is corrosive. Even small amounts should be handled with care.

---

1. The following experiment is adapted from A. G. Jones. *J. Chem. Educ.*, **52**, 668 (1975).

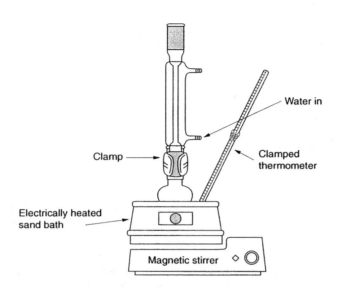

Figure E33.1 Apparatus for preparation of *m*-aminoacetophenone

A. Preparation of *m*-Aminoacetophenone

Weigh 100 mg (0.605 mmol) of *m*-nitroacetophenone into a 10-mL pear-shaped flask. Weigh 200 mg (1.69 mmol) of granulated tin (20 mesh) on an ordinary top loader (to the nearest 10 mg) and add it to the flask through a small funnel. Set up the flask for stirring and heating as shown in Figure E33.1. Prepare some dilute hydrochloric acid in a 10-mL graduated cylinder by adding about 0.5 mL of *concentrated* HCl with a Pasteur pipet to1.5 mL of water. Pour the dilute acid into the flask through the condenser, and stir and heat the mixture until it begins to reflux (about 5 min) and then long enough to dissolve all the tin (usually 30 min or less); a small amount of undissolved tin will do no harm.

B. Product Isolation

Add about 0.5 g of sodium hydroxide to 1.2 mL of water in a small test tube (12 mm × 100 mm) and set it aside to cool. Weigh the sodium hydroxide pellets quickly because of their extremely hygroscopic nature.

Cool the reaction solution and the sodium hydroxide solution in ice for a few minutes. Add all of the aqueous base to the reaction solution to precipitate the product and convert the Sn(IV) to soluble stannate. Stir the pale yellow slurry magnetically to ensure thorough mixing and cool the pale yellow suspension in ice. Filter the pale yellow precipitate by suction on the Hirsch funnel, rinse the last bit of solid from the flask with a small amount of ice water, and wash the filtered solid with a few drops of ice water. Allow the crude product to suck dry for about 10 min. Transfer it into a weighed vial and warm it in the vacuum oven (Figure E33.2). The yield of unrecrystallized solid should be greater than 80% with mp 94–97°C. Recrystallization is optional.

If you recrystallize the product, skip the vacuum drying step above and weigh the slightly moist material from the Hirsch funnel into the recrystallization tube (Pasteur pipet method) or a small test tube (Craig tube method). Recrystallize the

NOTE

If you obtain a gray precipitate (tin compounds), you have failed to add enough sodium hydroxide. Check the pH with pH paper to be certain that the solution is distinctly basic. Add more sodium hydroxide if necessary, and heat the mixture with stirring until the tin salts dissolve. A yellow precipitate should remain.

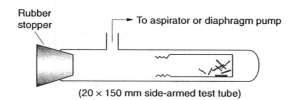

Figure E33.2   Microscale vacuum oven

Rubber stopper

→ To aspirator or diaphragm pump

(20 × 150 mm side-armed test tube)

sample from water near the boiling point (about 0.2 mL for each 10 mg of crude nearly dry solid). Dry the fine pale yellow plate crystals thoroughly with a warm vacuum oven (Figure E33.2). This will require 1 h. The final yield of product should be at least 65% with a mp of 96–98°C. An IR spectrum can be taken as a solid dispersed on Teflon tape.

EXERCISES

3. **(Optional; Spectroscopic)** The IR spectrum of *m*-aminoacetophenone exhibits a doublet at about 3500 cm^{-1} that is not present in the spectrum of *m*-nitroacetophenone. Explain.

4. **(Optional; Spectroscopic)** How could a ^{1}H NMR spectrum be used to distinguish between *m*-nitroacetophenone and *m*-aminoacetophenone?

Preparing Isopentyl Acetate by the Fischer Esterification

Prepared by Ronald J. Wikholm, University of Connecticut

PURPOSE OF THE EXPERIMENT

Prepare isopentyl acetate from isopentyl alcohol and acetic acid by the Fischer esterification.

EXPERIMENTAL OPTIONS

Semi-Microscale Fischer Esterification
Microscale Fischer Esterification
    Using Glassware with Elastomeric Connectors
    Using Glassware with a Hickman Still

BACKGROUND REQUIRED

You should be familiar with the techniques for extraction and distillation. You should be familiar with gas chromatography, infrared spectroscopy, and/or nuclear magnetic resonance spectroscopy for characterizing the product and assessing its purity.

BACKGROUND INFORMATION

Esters are derivatives of carboxylic acids in which the acyl carbon bears an alkoxy substituent (–OR) rather than the hydroxyl substituent (–OH) of the acid. Simple esters tend to have pleasant, fruity odors and are widely used as flavors and fragrances. Table 1 on the next page shows the flavors or fragrances associated with some esters.

The volatile compounds in natural fruits and flowers are usually complex mixtures of compounds, where esters frequently predominate. Many artificial flavorings contain esters or mixtures of esters. For example, the volatile oil of ripe pineapple contains several esters, as shown in Table 2 on page 3 later in this experiment.

Table 1 *Fragrances of esters*

ester	formula	fragrance
isopentyl acetate	$CH_3COCH_2CH_2CHCH_3$ (with O double bond on first C, CH_3 branch on CH)	banana
isobutyl formate	$HCOCH_2CHCH_3$ (with O double bond, CH_3 branch)	raspberry
isopentenyl acetate	$CH_3COCH_2CH{=}CCH_3$ (with O double bond, CH_3 branch)	juicy fruit
isobutyl propionate	$CH_3CH_2COCH_2CHCH_3$ (with O double bond, CH_3 branch)	rum
n-propyl acetate	$CH_3COCH_2CH_2CH_3$ (with O double bond)	pear
methyl butyrate	$CH_3CH_2CH_2COCH_3$ (with O double bond)	apple
methyl anthranilate	benzene ring with $COCH_3$ (O double bond) and NH_2	grape
methyl salicylate	benzene ring with $COCH_3$ (O double bond) and OH	wintergreen
ethyl butyrate	$CH_3CH_2CH_2COCH_2CH_3$ (with O double bond)	pineapple
ethyl phenyl acetate	benzene ring—$CH_2COCH_2CH_3$ (with O double bond)	honey
benzyl acetate	CH_3COCH_2—benzene ring (with O double bond)	peach
benzyl butyrate	$CH_3CH_2CH_2COCH_2$—benzene ring (with O double bond)	cherry
octyl acetate	$CH_3COCH_2(CH_2)_6CH_3$ (with O double bond)	orange

Table 2 *Composition of the volatile oil of ripe pineapple*

constituent	percent, %
total volatile oil	0.1900
ethyl acetate	0.1196
ethyl alcohol	0.0605
acetaldehyde	0.0014
ethyl acrylate	0.0008
ethyl *i*-valerate	0.0004
ethyl *n*-caproate	0.0008

Isopentyl acetate is known as banana oil because of its characteristic odor. This ester has also been shown to be one of the active substances in the alarm pheromone of the honeybee. When a honeybee worker stings an intruder, an alarm pheromone is secreted along with the venom. The pheromone causes other bees to become aggressive and attack the intruder.

Esterification generally refers to the formation of esters from alcohols and carboxylic acids, as shown in Equation 1.

$$RCOOH \; + \; R'OH \; \rightleftharpoons \; RCOOR' \; + \; H_2O \quad (Eq. 1)$$

carboxylic   alcohol   ester
acid

The reaction proceeds by way of a nucleophilic substitution at the acyl carbon of the carboxylic acid. When catalyzed by a strong acid, usually sulfuric acid or *p*-toluenesulfonic acid, the reaction is called the **Fischer esterification.**

The reaction mechanism is shown in Equations 2–6. Equation 2 shows the protonation of the acyl oxygen of the carboxylic acid. The protonation activates the acyl carbon toward nucleophilic attack. Equation 3 shows the nucleophilic attack at the acyl carbon by the alcohol oxygen atom to form a tetrahedral intermediate. Equation 4 shows a proton transfer to the hydroxyl oxygen of the carboxyl group. This protonation converts the hydroxyl group into the good leaving group, water. Equation 5 shows the loss of water forming the protonated ester. Finally, Equation 6 shows the proton transfer to a base, resulting in the formation of the ester.

Protonation

(Eq. 2)

Nucleophilic Attack

$$
\underset{\text{alcohol}}{
\overset{\displaystyle \overset{+}{\ddot{O}}H}{\underset{\displaystyle R'\ddot{O}H}{\underset{R}{\overset{\|}{C}}}\!\!-\!OH}}
\quad\rightleftharpoons\quad
\underset{\text{tetrahedral intermediate}}{
R-\overset{\displaystyle :\ddot{O}H}{\underset{\displaystyle \overset{+}{\underset{R'}{O}}\diagdown H}{C}}-OH}
\qquad \text{(Eq. 3)}
$$

Proton Transfer

$$
R-\overset{\displaystyle :\ddot{O}H}{\underset{\displaystyle \overset{+}{\underset{R'}{O}}\diagdown H}{C}}-\ddot{O}H
\quad\rightleftharpoons\quad
R-\overset{\displaystyle :\ddot{O}H}{\underset{\displaystyle \underset{R'}{\ddot{O}}}{C}}-\overset{\displaystyle H}{\underset{\displaystyle \overset{+}{}}{O}}-H
\qquad \text{(Eq. 4)}
$$

Dehydration

$$
R-\overset{\displaystyle :\ddot{O}H}{\underset{\displaystyle \underset{R'}{\ddot{O}}}{C}}-\overset{\displaystyle H}{\underset{\displaystyle \overset{+}{}}{O}}-H
\quad\xrightarrow{-H_2O}\quad
\underset{\text{protonated ester}}{
\underset{R}{\overset{\displaystyle \overset{+}{\ddot{O}}H}{\overset{\|}{C}}}\diagdown \ddot{O}R'}
\qquad \text{(Eq. 5)}
$$

Dehydrogenation

$$
\underset{R}{\overset{\displaystyle \overset{+}{\ddot{O}}H}{\overset{\|}{C}}}\diagdown OR
\quad\xrightarrow{H^+}\quad
\underset{\text{ester}}{
\underset{R}{\overset{\displaystyle \ddot{O}:}{\overset{\|}{C}}}\diagdown \ddot{O}R}
\qquad \text{(Eq. 6)}
$$

Each step of the reaction mechanism is reversible and, therefore, the reaction reaches an equilibrium. **Le Chatelier's principle** suggests that the amount of ester produced in an equilibrium reaction might be increased either by using an excess of one of the reactants or by removing one of the products. In practice, an excess of carboxylic acid or alcohol, whichever is more readily available, is added, and/or water is removed as the reaction proceeds. A water-absorbing substance such as molecular sieves might be included in the reaction mixture, or the water might be removed as part of an azeotrope with benzene or toluene.

The mechanism suggests that steric effects might be important in Equation 3, the step involving the attack by the alcohol at the acyl carbon of the carboxylic acid. Indeed, alkyl-group branching at the α or β carbon of the acid slows the rate of esterification. For example, the relative rates of esterification with methanol, CH_3OH, follow the order

$$CH_3CO_2H > CH_3CH_2CO_2H > (CH_3)_2CHCO_2H > (CH_3)_3CCO_2H$$

Sterically hindered alcohols also react more slowly in the esterification reaction. The relative rates for esterification of alcohols with acetic acid, CH_3CO_2H, follow the order

$$CH_3OH > CH_3CH_2OH > (CH_3)_3CCH_2OH$$

Fischer esterification is an example of an acyl transfer reaction. The acyl group from the acid is transferred to the alcohol. Acid chlorides and anhydrides also serve as acylating agents. Because acid chlorides and anhydrides contain good leaving groups, these compounds are very reactive toward nucleophilic substitution by an alcohol, as shown in Equations 7 and 8.

$$R-\overset{O}{\underset{||}{C}}-Cl \quad + \quad R'-OH \quad \longrightarrow \quad R-\overset{O}{\underset{||}{C}}-OR' \quad + \quad HCl \qquad \text{(Eq. 7)}$$

$$R-\overset{O}{\underset{||}{C}}-O-\overset{O}{\underset{||}{C}}-R'' \quad + \quad R'-OH \quad \longrightarrow \quad R-\overset{O}{\underset{||}{C}}-OR' \quad + \quad R''-\overset{O}{\underset{||}{C}}-OH \qquad \text{(Eq. 8)}$$

The Fischer esterification reaction is conducted at reflux. The purpose of **reflux** is to heat a reaction mixture at its boiling temperature to form products, without losing any of the compounds in the reaction flask.

In practice, a condenser is set vertically into the top of the reaction flask. Any compound that vaporizes will condense when it enters the cool environment of the reflux condenser and will then drain back into the reaction flask. Reflux apparatus using glassware for semi-microscale and microscale techniques are shown in their appropriate sections of the Procedure.

In this experiment, you will prepare isopentyl acetate by reacting an excess of acetic acid with isopentyl alcohol. After the reaction is complete, you will remove the excess acetic acid from the reaction mixture by extraction with sodium hydrogen carbonate ($NaHCO_3$).

You will use either sulfuric acid or Dowex® 50 ion exchange resin to catalyze the reaction. **Dowex® 50** is a polystyrene resin containing sulfonic acid groups on some of the styrene units that compose the polymer. A representative section of Dowex® 50 is shown in Figure 1.

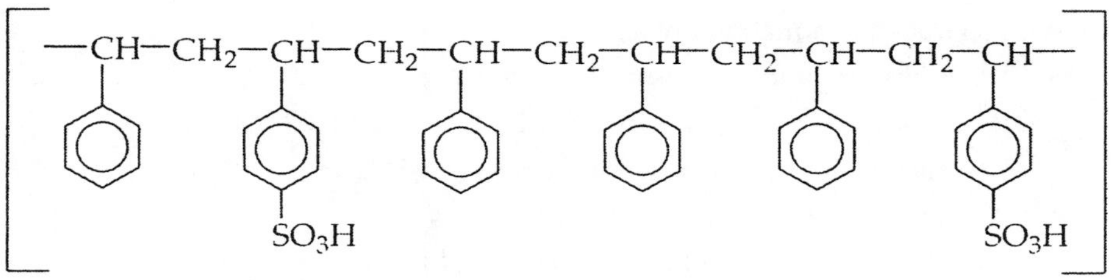

Figure 1
A representative section of Dowex® 50

SEMI-MICROSCALE FISCHER ESTERIFICATION

Equipment

aluminum foil
150-mL beaker
400-mL beaker*
boiling chips, acid resistant
electric flask heater, with
    heat controller
50-mL Erlenmeyer flask
50-mL graduated cylinder
microspatula
standard taper glassware:
    condenser, with adapter and
      tubing
*for ice-water bath

distilling head
2 round-bottom flasks, 25-mL
thermometer, −10 to 260 °C,
    with adapter
125-mL separatory funnel
Pasteur pipet, with latex bulb
10-mL graduated pipet, with bulb
10-mL product vial
support ring
2 support stands
25 × 150-mm test tube
2 utility clamps

Reagents and Properties

substance	quantity	molar mass (g/mol)	bp (°C)	d (g/mL)
glacial acetic acid	8.5 mL	60.05		1.049
isopentyl acetate*		130.19	142	0.876
isopentyl alcohol	4.37 g	88.15	130	0.809
sodium chloride, saturated solution	25 mL			
sodium hydrogen carbonate, 5%	50 mL			
sodium sulfate, anhydrous	1.5 g	142.04		
sulfuric acid, concentrated	1.0 mL	98.08		

*product

Preview

- Assemble the reflux apparatus for semi-microscale glassware
- Add the isopentyl alcohol, acetic acid, and H_2SO_4 to the flask and reflux the mixture for 1–1.5 hr
- Cool the reaction mixture
- Place cold water into the separatory funnel and add the reaction mixture
- Separate the aqueous layer
- Wash the organic layer with two 25-mL portions of 5% $NaHCO_3$
- Wash the organic layer with 25 mL saturated NaCl solution
- Dry the organic layer over anhydrous Na_2SO_4
- Assemble a simple distillation apparatus
- Distill the product, collecting the 134–143 °C fraction
- Weigh the product
- Characterize the product for purity using GC, IR, and/or NMR

PROCEDURE

CHEMICAL ALERT

glacial acetic acid—*corrosive*
isopentyl acetate—*flammable and irritant*
isopentyl alcohol—*irritant*
sodium sulfate—*irritant and hygroscopic*
sulfuric acid—*corrosive and oxidant*

CAUTION

Wear departmentally approved safety goggles at all times while in the chemistry laboratory.

1. Refluxing the Reaction Mixture

CAUTION

Isopentyl alcohol (3-methyl-1-butanol) is irritating. Glacial acetic acid is corrosive. Concentrated sulfuric acid (H_2SO_4) is corrosive and oxidizing. Prevent eye, skin, clothing, and combustible material contact. Avoid inhaling vapors and ingesting these compounds. Use a *fume hood.*

Assemble the reflux apparatus shown in Figure 2.

Place 4.37 g (5.4 mL) of isopentyl alcohol into the 25-mL round-bottom flask. Add 8.5 mL of glacial acetic acid and 1 mL of concentrated H_2SO_4. Add two *acid-resistant* boiling chips. Attach the round-bottom flask to the reflux apparatus.

NOTE 1: A slightly higher yield is obtained with the longer reaction time.

Start the flow of water through the reflux condenser. Heat the reaction mixture to boiling and reflux the mixture gently for 1–1.5 hr. [NOTE 1]

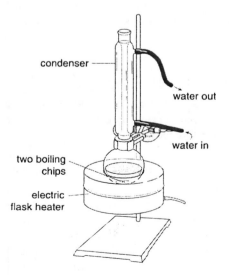

Figure 2
Reflux apparatus for semi-microscale glassware

Turn off the flask heater and lower the heater away from the flask. Allow the flask to cool to room temperature. Turn off the water to the condenser.

Prepare an ice-water bath in a 400-mL beaker. Remove the flask from the reflux apparatus.

Cool the flask in the ice-water bath. Place 30 mL of distilled or deionized water in a 25×150-mm test tube. Cool the test tube in the ice-water bath.

2. Separating and Washing the Product Layer

NOTE 2: Vigorous shaking may result in an emulsion.

NOTE 3: It is a good practice to keep all extraction layers in a labeled container until the conclusion of the experiment.

Pour 20 mL of the cold water into a 125-mL separatory funnel. Carefully pour the reaction mixture from the round-bottom flask into the funnel containing the water. Rinse the reaction flask with the remaining 10 mL of cold water and pour the rinse water into the separatory funnel. Swirl the mixture gently, stopper the separatory funnel, and shake once. [NOTE 2] Vent the funnel carefully.

Label a 150-mL beaker "Aqueous Layers". Drain the lower aqueous layer from the funnel into the beaker. [NOTE 3].

CAUTION ⚠️

Neutralizing acids with sodium hydrogen carbonate ($NaHCO_3$) generates CO_2 gas. Vent the funnel frequently so that pressure does not build up in the stoppered separatory funnel.

Carefully add 25 mL of 5% $NaHCO_3$ to the separatory funnel. Swirl the funnel gently until bubbles no longer appear. Stopper the funnel and shake it cautiously. Vent the funnel. Shake the funnel vigorously and vent it immediately.

Allow the layers to separate. Remove the stopper and drain the lower aqueous layer into the same labeled beaker.

Wash the organic layer in the funnel with a second 25-mL portion of 5% $NaHCO_3$. Again, drain the lower aqueous layer into the labeled beaker.

Finally, wash the organic layer with 25 mL of saturated NaCl solution. Drain the lower aqueous layer into the labeled beaker.

NOTE 4: Your laboratory instructor may instruct you to add the anhydrous Na_2SO_4 gradually until the solution is no longer cloudy or until the Na_2SO_4 no longer clumps.

Weigh 1.5 g of anhydrous sodium sulfate (Na_2SO_4) and place it into a 50-mL Erlenmeyer flask [NOTE 4]. Pour the organic layer into the Erlenmeyer flask. Dry the organic layer over anhydrous Na_2SO_4 for 15 min.

3. Distilling the Product

CAUTION ⚠️

Isopentyl acetate is flammable and irritating. Keep away from flames or other heat sources. Prevent eye, skin, and clothing contact. Avoid inhaling vapors and ingesting this compound.

Assemble a simple distillation apparatus. Tare a clean 10-mL product vial for a receiver.

Decant the crude ester from the flask containing the Na_2SO_4 into a clean 25-mL round-bottom flask. Add a boiling chip to the flask. Attach the round-bottom flask to the distillation apparatus. Wrap the distilling head with aluminum foil to minimize temperature fluctuations during distillation. Start the flow of water through the condenser. Heat the flask.

Collect the compound that distills from 134–143 °C in the tared receiver. Measure and record the mass of the product.

4. Characterizing the Product [NOTE 5]

NOTE 5: Use the product characterization techniques designated by your laboratory instructor.

Analyze the purity of your product by gas chromatography. Compare the retention time of your product with that of pure isopentyl acetate under identical conditions.

Obtain an infrared spectrum of your product. Compare your spectrum to that of pure isopentyl acetate, provided by your laboratory instructor. Analyze your spectrum for absorption bands consistent with the structure of isopentyl acetate.

Obtain a nuclear magnetic resonance spectrum of your product. Compare your spectrum to that of pure isopentyl acetate, provided by your laboratory instructor.

5. Cleaning Up

Place your recovered materials in the appropriate labeled collection containers as directed by your laboratory instructor. Clean your glassware with soap or detergent.

> **CAUTION**
>
> **Wash your hands thoroughly with soap or detergent before leaving the laboratory.**

MICROSCALE FISCHER ESTERIFICATION

Using Glassware with Elastomeric Connectors

Equipment

100-mL beaker	5-mL round-bottom flask
boiling chip, acid-resistant	sand bath*
condenser, with tubing	stirring rod
distilling head–air condenser	support ring
elastomeric connectors	support stand
microspatula	13 × 100-mm test tube
3 Pasteur pipets, with latex bulb	thermometer, −10 to 260 °C, or
2-mL pipet	equivalent, with adapter
5-mL product vial	utility clamp
2 reaction tubes, with stoppers	

*sand in crystallizing dish on electric hot plate or sand in electric heating well with heat controller

Reagents and Properties

substance	quantity	molar mass (g/mol)	bp (°C)	d (g/mL)
Dowex® 50W 2–100*	50 mg			
glacial acetic acid	2 mL	60.05		1.049
isopentyl acetate[†]		130.19	142	0.876
isopentyl alcohol	0.809 g	88.15	130	0.809
sodium hydrogen carbonate, 5%	3 mL			
sodium sulfate, anhydrous	0.3 g	142.04		

* or 3 drops (0.15 mL) concentrated sulfuric acid
[†] product

Preview

- Assemble the reflux apparatus using glassware with elastomeric connectors
- Add the reagents to the flask and reflux the mixture for 1 hr
- Cool the reaction mixture
- Separate the mixture from the ion-exchange resin
- Add 5% $NaHCO_3$
- Separate the aqueous layer
- Wash the organic layer with two additional portions of 5% $NaHCO_3$
- Wash the organic layer with water
- Dry the organic layer over anhydrous Na_2SO_4
- Transfer the product to a 5-mL round-bottom flask
- Assemble a simple distillation apparatus
- Distill the product, collecting the 134-143 °C fraction
- Weigh the product
- Characterize the product for purity using GC, IR, and/or NMR

PROCEDURE

CHEMICAL ALERT

glacial acetic acid—*corrosive*
isopentyl acetate—*flammable and irritant*
isopentyl alcohol—*irritant*
sodium sulfate—*irritant and hygroscopic*

CAUTION

Wear departmentally approved safety goggles at all times while in the chemistry laboratory.

1. Refluxing the Reaction Mixture

CAUTION

Isopentyl alcohol (3-methyl-1-butanol) is irritating. Glacial acetic acid is corrosive. Prevent eye, skin, and clothing contact. Avoid inhaling vapors and ingesting these compounds. Use a *fume hood*.

Weigh a 5-mL round-bottom flask supported in a small beaker and record the tare mass. Place 0.809 g (1.0 mL) of isopentyl alcohol in the flask. Reweigh the container to obtain the precise mass of the alcohol.

Add 2 mL of glacial acetic acid. Add 50 mg of Dowex® 50W 2–100 ion-exchange resin. Finally, add an *acid-resistant* boiling chip.

Use the round-bottom flask containing the alcohol to assemble the reflux apparatus shown in Figure 3.

Use a sand bath to heat the mixture to boiling. Reflux the mixture for 1 hr. Turn off the heat and lower the sand bath away from the flask. Allow the flask to cool to room temperature. Turn off the water to the condenser.

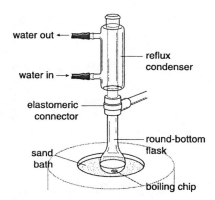

water out ←
water in →

reflux
condenser

elastomeric
connector

round-bottom
flask

sand
bath

boiling chip

Figure 3
Reflux apparatus for glassware using elastomeric connectors

Use a Pasteur pipet to separate the product mixture from the ion-exchange resin. Place the mixture into a clean reaction tube.

2. Separating and Washing the Product Layer

NOTE 1: It is a good practice to keep all extraction layers in labeled containers until the conclusion of the experiment.

Slowly add 1 mL of 5% sodium hydrogen carbonate (NaHCO$_3$) to the reaction tube. Carefully stir the mixture until bubble evolution is no longer vigorous. Stopper the reaction tube and shake it gently. Vent the reaction tube repeatedly until no more bubbles appear.

Label a test tube "Aqueous Layers". Use a Pasteur pipet to remove the lower aqueous layer. Place the layer into the labeled test tube. [NOTE 1]

Repeat the extraction of the upper organic layer two more times with new 1-mL portions of 5% NaHCO$_3$. Each time place the lower aqueous layer into the labeled test tube.

NOTE 2: Your laboratory instructor may direct you to add the anhydrous Na$_2$SO$_4$ gradually until the solution is no longer cloudy or until the Na$_2$SO$_4$ no longer clumps.

Finally, wash the organic layer with 1 mL of distilled or deionized water. Again, remove the lower aqueous layer.

Add 0.3 g of anhydrous sodium sulfate (Na$_2$SO$_4$) to the organic layer to dry the product [NOTE 2]. Stopper the reaction tube and allow it to stand for 15 min.

3. Distilling the Product

⚠ **CAUTION**

Isopentyl acetate is flammable and irritating. Keep away from flames or other heat sources. Prevent eye, skin, and clothing contact. Avoid inhaling vapors and ingesting this compound.

Use a Pasteur pipet to transfer the dried ester into a 5-mL round-bottom flask. Add a boiling chip. Assemble a simple distillation apparatus. Tare a product vial for a receiver.

Heat the flask. Collect the compound that distills from 134–143 °C in the tared receiver. Measure and record the mass of the product.

4. Characterizing the Product [NOTE 3]

NOTE 3: Use the product characterization techniques designated by your laboratory instructor.

Analyze the purity of your product by gas chromatography. Compare the retention time of your product with that of pure isopentyl acetate under identical conditions.

Obtain an infrared spectrum of your product. Compare your spectrum to that of pure isopentyl acetate, provided by your laboratory instructor.

Analyze your spectrum for absorption bands consistent with the structure of isopentyl acetate.

Obtain a nuclear magnetic resonance spectrum of your product. Compare your spectrum to that of pure isopentyl acetate, provided by your laboratory instructor.

5. Cleaning Up

Place your recovered materials in the appropriate labeled collection containers as directed by your laboratory instructor. Clean your glassware with soap or detergent.

> **CAUTION**
>
> **Wash your hands thoroughly with soap or detergent before leaving the laboratory.**

MICROSCALE FISCHER ESTERIFICATION

Using Glassware with a Hickman Still

Equipment

aluminum foil
3-mL conical vial
5-mL conical vial, with cap
forceps
Hickman still
magnetic spin vane
microspatula
4 Pasteur pipets, with latex bulb
2-mL pipet
5-mL product vial

sand bath*
13 × 100-mm test tube
thermometer, −10 to 150 °C,
    small size to fit Hickman still
thermometer, −10 to 260 °C,
    or equivalent
3 utility clamps
water-cooled condenser,
    with tubing

*stirring hot plate with crystallizing dish filled with sand or magnetic stirrer and electric flask heater filled with sand

Reagents and Properties

substance	quantity	molar mass (g/mol)	bp (°C)	d (g/mL)
glacial acetic acid	2 mL	60.05		1.049
isopentyl acetate*		130.19	142	0.876
isopentyl alcohol	0.809 g	88.15	130	0.809
sodium hydrogen carbonate, 5%	3 mL			
sodium sulfate, anhydrous	0.3 g	142.04		
sulfuric acid, concentrated	0.15 mL	98.08		

* product

Preview

- Weigh a 5-mL conical vial
- Add isopentyl alcohol and reweigh the vial

- Add glacial acetic acid and sulfuric acid to the vial and reflux the mixture for 1 hr
- Cool the reaction mixture
- Add 5% $NaHCO_3$
- Separate the aqueous layer
- Wash the organic layer with two additional portions of 5% $NaHCO_3$
- Wash the organic layer with water
- Dry the organic layer over anhydrous Na_2SO_4
- Transfer the product to a clean conical vial
- Assemble a distillation apparatus
- Distill the product
- Weigh the product
- Characterize the product for purity using GC, IR, and/or NMR

PROCEDURE

CHEMICAL ALERT

glacial acetic acid—*corrosive*
isopentyl acetate—*flammable and irritant*
isopentyl alcohol—*irritant*
sodium sulfate—*irritant and hygroscopic*
sulfuric acid—*corrosive and oxidant*

CAUTION

Wear departmentally approved safety goggles at all times while in the chemistry laboratory.

1. Refluxing the Reaction Mixture

CAUTION

Isopentyl alcohol (3-methyl-1-butanol) is irritating. Glacial acetic acid is corrosive. Concentrated sulfuric acid (H_2SO_4) is corrosive and oxidizing. Prevent eye, skin, clothing, and combustible material contact. Avoid inhaling vapors and ingesting these compounds. Use a *fume hood*.

Weigh a 5-mL conical vial and record the tare mass. Place 0.809 g (1.0 mL) of isopentyl alcohol in the vial. Reweigh the vial to obtain the precise mass of the alcohol.

Add 2 mL of glacial acetic acid to the vial. Finally, use a Pasteur pipet to add 3 drops of concentrated H_2SO_4 to the vial.

Add a magnetic spin vane. Attach a water-cooled condenser, as shown in Figure 4 on the next page.

Turn on the magnetic stirrer. Start the flow of water through the condenser. Heat the sand bath to 150–160 °C. Reflux the mixture for 1 hr.

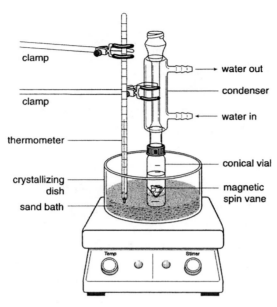

Figure 4
Reflux apparatus for glassware using a conical vial

Turn off the heat and the magnetic stirrer. Raise the reflux apparatus out of the sand bath. Allow the reaction mixture to cool to room temperature. Turn off the water to the condenser.

2. Separating and Washing the Product Layer

Use forceps to remove the spin vane from the vial. *Slowly* add 1 mL of 5% sodium hydrogen carbonate ($NaHCO_3$) to the reaction mixture in the conical vial. Swirl the vial gently, then cap the vial. Shake the vial gently, with venting, until bubbles are no longer produced.

Label a test tube "Aqueous Layers". Use a Pasteur pipet to remove the lower aqueous layer from the conical vial. Place the aqueous layer into the labeled test tube. [NOTE 1]

NOTE 1: It is a good practice to keep all extraction layers in labeled containers until the conclusion of the experiment.

Repeat the extraction of the upper organic layer two more times with new 1-mL portions of 5% $NaHCO_3$. Each time, place the lower aqueous layer into the labeled test tube.

Finally, wash the organic layer with 1 mL of distilled or deionized water. Again, remove the lower aqueous layer.

NOTE 2: Your laboratory instructor may instruct you to add the anhydrous Na_2SO_4 gradually until the solution is no longer cloudy or until the Na_2SO_4 no longer clumps.

Add 0.3 g of anhydrous sodium sulfate (Na_2SO_4) to the vial to dry the product [NOTE 2]. Allow the mixture to stand for 15 min.

3. Distilling the Product

⚠️ **CAUTION**

Isopentyl acetate is flammable and irritating. Keep away from flames or other heat sources. Prevent eye, skin, and clothing contact. Avoid inhaling vapors and ingesting this compound.

Use a Pasteur pipet to transfer the dried product to a 3-mL conical vial. Add a magnetic spin vane to the vial. Attach a Hickman still and a water-cooled condenser, as shown in Figure 5.

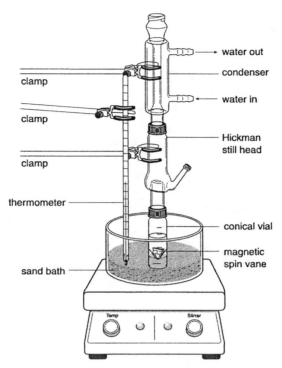

water out
condenser
clamp
water in
clamp
Hickman
still head
clamp
thermometer
conical vial
magnetic
spin vane
sand bath

Figure 5
Distillation apparatus using Hickman still

Tare a product vial. Turn on the magnetic stirrer. Start the flow of water through the condenser. Distill the product by heating the sand bath to 150–160 °C. Cover the top of the sand bath with aluminum foil.

As distillate collects in the Hickman still, use a Pasteur pipet to transfer the distillate to the tared product vial. Weigh the product.

4. Characterizing the Product [NOTE 3]

NOTE 3: Use the product characterization techniques designated by your laboratory instructor.

Analyze the purity of your product by gas chromatography. Compare the retention time of your product with that of pure isopentyl acetate under identical conditions.

Obtain an infrared spectrum of your product. Compare your spectrum to that of pure isopentyl acetate, provided by your laboratory instructor. Analyze your spectrum for absorption bands consistent with the structure of isopentyl acetate.

Obtain a nuclear magnetic resonance spectrum of your product. Compare your spectrum to that of pure isopentyl acetate, provided by your laboratory instructor.

5. Cleaning Up

Place your recovered materials in the appropriate labeled collection containers as directed by your laboratory instructor. Clean your glassware with soap or detergent.

CAUTION

Wash your hands thoroughly with soap or detergent before leaving the laboratory.

POST LABORATORY QUESTIONS

1. Calculate your percent yield of isopentyl acetate.

2. List the distinctive features of the IR spectra of isopentyl acetate, isopentyl alcohol, and acetic acid and assign the absorption bands to the appropriate functional groups.

3. Check your gas chromatogram for the presence of compounds other than isopentyl acetate. Explain the presence of any additional compounds.

4. Compare the NMR spectrum for your product with pure isopentyl acetate. Explain any differences.

5. Write the equation for the reaction of 5% $NaHCO_3$ with acetic acid.

6. What is the IUPAC name for isopentyl acetate?

© 1998 Cengage Learning

Name   _Section_   _Date_

Pre-Laboratory Assignment

1. What are the hazards you should be aware of when you work with the following reagents?

   (a) concentrated H_2SO_4

   (b) glacial acetic acid

2. **(a)** Write a detailed mechanism for the formation of ethyl acetate from ethanol and acetic acid with H_2SO_4 as catalyst.

   (b) How does concentrated H_2SO_4 catalyze the esterification reaction? Briefly explain.

3. Give two methods by which the Fischer esterification equilibrium of the reaction described in Assignment 2 can be shifted to produce more of the ester.

4. Calculate the theoretical yield of isopentyl acetate for the esterification reaction described in the Procedure.

A Multistep Synthesis Sequence: An Aldol Condensation, a Michael Addition, and Ethylene Ketal Formation

Prepared by A. T. Rowland, Gettysburg College

PURPOSE OF THE EXPERIMENT

Use an aldol condensation to produce dianisalacetone from *p*-anisaldehyde and acetone. React dianisalacetone with dimethylmalonate under catalysis by methoxide ion to accomplish a Michael addition. React the Michael addition product with ethylene glycol and an acid catalyst to prepare an ethylene ketal product. Use melting point determination and NMR spectroscopy to characterize products at each sequence step.

EXPERIMENTAL OPTIONS

Semi-Microscale

Synthesis 1: Aldol Condensation
Synthesis 2: Michael Addition
Synthesis 3: Ethylene Ketal Preparation

Microscale

Synthesis 1: Aldol Condensation
Synthesis 2: Michael Addition
Synthesis 3: Ethylene Ketal Preparation

BACKGROUND REQUIRED

You should be familiar with vacuum filtration, extraction, distillation, recrystallization, melting point measurement, and NMR spectroscopy.

BACKGROUND INFORMATION

The first step of the sequence you will perform is the aldol condensation of acetone and *p*-anisaldehyde. A **condensation reaction** is a reaction that combines two molecules while removing a small molecule such as water or an alcohol. An aldol condensation is shown in Equation 1.

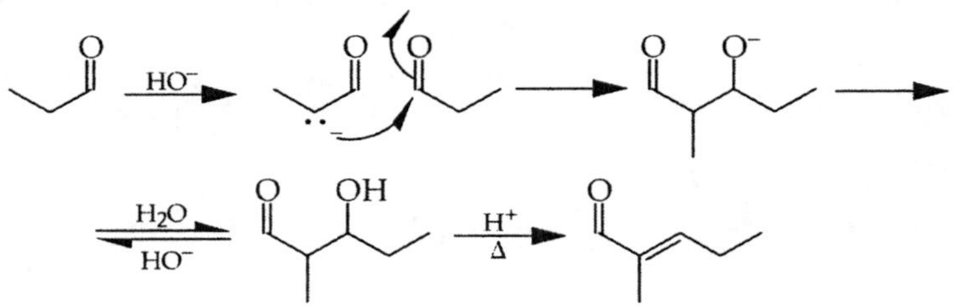

(Eq. 1)

In the first part of this reaction, the removal of a proton from the α-carbon of one carbonyl compound molecule creates a nucleophile. This nucleophile attacks the electrophilic carbonyl carbon of a second molecule. The negatively charged oxygen that results is protonated by the solvent.

The second part of the aldol condensation reaction is dehydration, which is usually accomplished by heating the aldol with acid or base. However, dehydration can also occur without heating under the conditions performed in this sequence, as shown in Equation 2. The product, dianisalacetone, is very stable and relatively easy to produce because the double bonds formed by dehydration are conjugated with the carbonyl group and with the benzene rings.

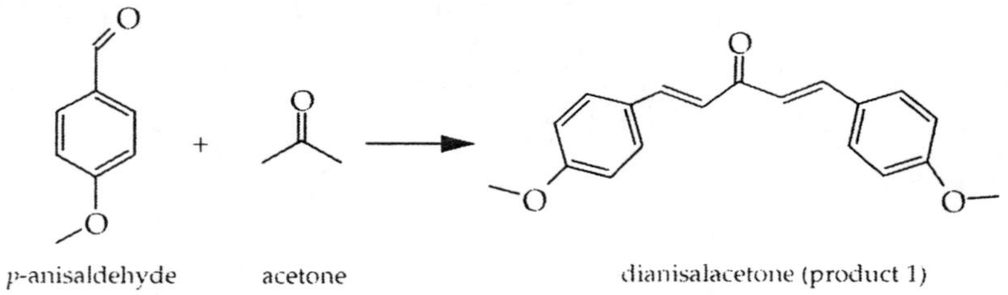

(Eq. 2)

p-anisaldehyde   acetone   dianisalacetone (product 1)

The second step in the sequence is called a Michael addition. This reaction involves the base-catalyzed addition of a compound containing an active α-hydrogen to the β-carbon of an α, β-unsaturated carbonyl compound. The mechanism of the reaction, as shown in Equation 3, involves the abstraction of the acidic α-hydrogen to create a carbanion. The carbanion subsequently bonds to the β-carbon of the acceptor carbonyl compound. The result is protonated to give an enol, which converts (tautomerizes) into a ketone.

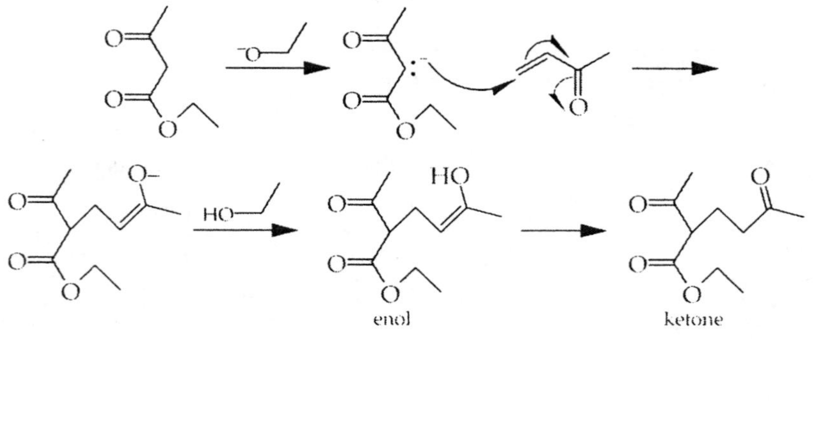

(Eq. 3)

enol   ketone

When the acceptor molecule contains two α, β-unsaturated carbon–carbon linkages that flank the carbonyl group, the initial intermolecular reaction may be followed by an intramolecular reaction, producing a cyclic ketone. An example is shown in Equation 4.

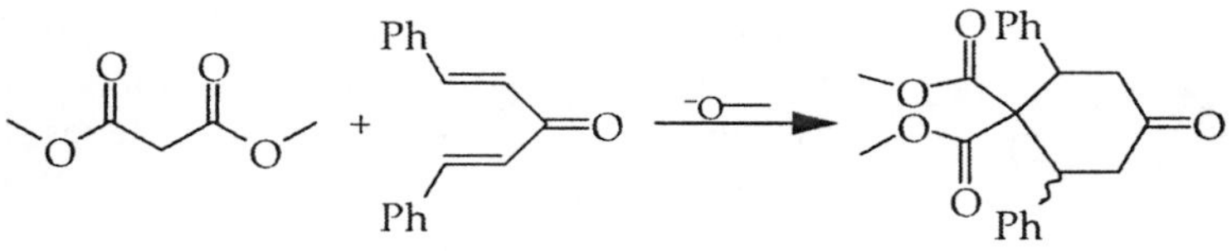

(Eq. 4)

The reaction mechanism of the cyclization step parallels the mechanism described in Equation 3 and is detailed in Equation 5.

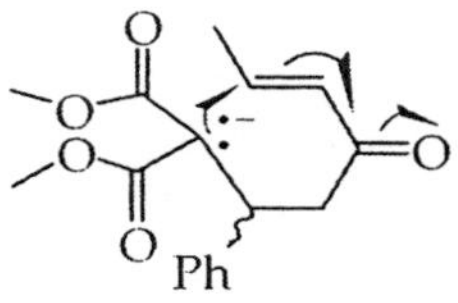

(Eq. 5)

The Michael addition performed in this synthesis, shown in Equation 6, involves the reaction of dianisalacetone (product 1) with dimethylmalonate under catalysis by methoxide ion to form the Michael addition product, dimethyl-2,6-bis(p-methoxyphenyl)-4-oxo-cyclohexane-1,1-dicarboxylate.

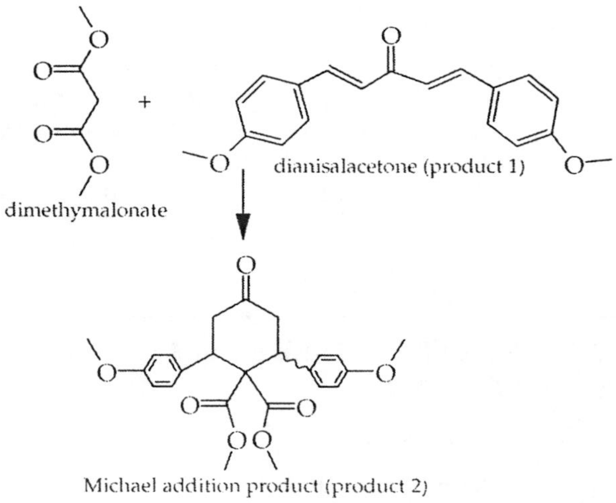

dimethymalonate

dianisalacetone (product 1)

(Eq. 6)

Michael addition product (product 2)

The third step of this sequence is the preparation of the ethylene ketal of dimethyl-2,6-bis(p-methoxyphenyl)-4-oxocyclohexane-1,1-dicarboxylate (the Michael addition product). The general mechanism for this reaction is shown in Equation 7.

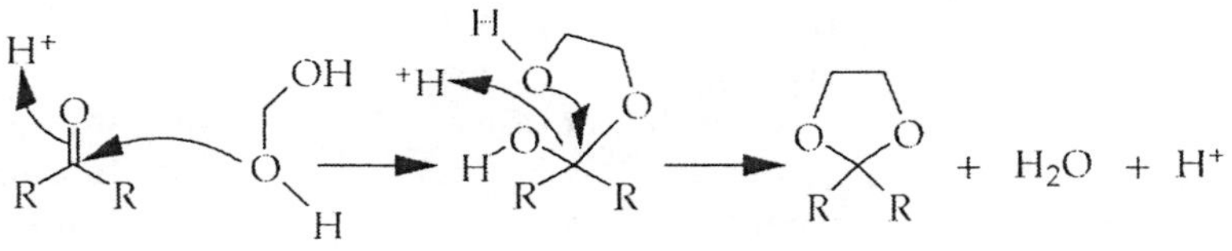

$+ \; H_2O \; + \; H^+$ (Eq. 7)

An acid catalyst is required to protonate the carbonyl oxygen, making it susceptible to attack by one of the oxygens in ethylene glycol. Following the loss of water, the tetrahedral carbon is susceptible to nucleophilic attack by the second oxygen. Deprotonation results in the ethylene ketal plus water and hydrogen ion by-products.

The reaction performed in this sequence, shown in Equation 8, is conducted by slow distillation of a mixture of Michael addition product, ethylene glycol, toluene, and *p*-toluenesulfonic acid catalyst to form the ethylene ketal product, dimethyl-2,6-bis(*p*-methoxyphenyl)-4, 4-ethylenedioxocyclohexane-1,1-dicarboxylate. During distillation, water formed in the condensation is removed gradually as an azeotrope with toluene.

$$\text{Michael addition product (product 2)} \quad \xrightarrow[\substack{HO \qquad OH}]{H^+} \quad \text{ethylene ketal product (product 3)} \quad + \quad H_2O \qquad \text{(Eq. 8)}$$

Ethylene ketal formation may also be used to temporarily block a carbonyl group while a reaction is conducted at another site on a molecule. After the second site reaction is complete, the ethylene ketal-blocking group is removed by reaction with acid and water. While the ketal removal is not a part of this experiment, care must be taken to avoid the presence of acid and water with the ketal or the ketal group will be removed.

SEMI-MICROSCALE SYNTHESIS 1: ALDOL CONDENSATION

Equipment

400-mL beaker*
Büchner funnel, with adapter
2 Erlenmeyer flasks, 50-mL, with
   stoppers
125-mL filter flask, with vacuum
   tubing
filter paper
10-mL graduated cylinder
heating well with heat
   controller, or other heat
   source
magnetic stir bar
magnetic stirrer
*for ice-water bath

melting point capillary tube
micropipet, 100–1000 µL
microspatula
Pasteur pipets, with latex bulb
standard taper distillation apparatus
   condenser
   distilling head
   25-ml round-bottom
     flask, with stopper
support stand
15 × 150-mm test tube
2 utility clamps
wide-bore plastic funnel

Reagents and Properties

substance	quantity	molar mass (g/mol)	mp (°C)	bp (°C)	density (g/mL)
acetic acid, 10%	6.5 mL				
acetone	10–11 mL	58.1		56	0.791
p-anisaldehyde	1.00 g	136.2		248	1.119
ethanol, 95%	6.5 mL	46.07		78	
methanol	7 mL	32.04		64.6	
sodium hydroxide, 10%	6.5 mL				

Preview

- Place 10% sodium hydroxide in a flask
- Place p-anisaldehyde, acetone, and ethanol into another flask
- Combine the two solutions and stir for 45 min
- Use vacuum filtration to collect the precipitate
- Recrystallize the crude product from acetone and methanol
- Dry and weigh the purified product
- Characterize the product using melting point and NMR spectroscopy

PROCEDURE

1. Conducting the Aldol Condensation

To a 50-mL Erlenmeyer flask, add a magnetic stir bar and 6.5 mL of 10% NaOH. To a second 50-mL Erlenmeyer flask, add 0.894 mL (1.000 g) of p-anisaldehyde and 0.278 mL (0.220 g) of acetone.

Add 6.5 mL of ethanol to the acetone/aldehyde mixture. Mix these reagents and pour the solution into the flask containing the NaOH. Stir for a minimum of 45 min. [NOTE 1]

Using the 400-mL beaker, prepare an ice-water bath. After stirring is complete, cool the solution in the ice-water bath for 5 min.

NOTE 1: The mixture becomes bright transparent yellow in less than 1 min and becomes increasingly opaque with time.

© 2004 Cengage Learning

2. Isolating the Product

Collect the precipitate by vacuum filtration. Rinse the flask and crystals with 7 mL of distilled or deionized water. Release the vacuum and repeat the rinse with 7 mL of distilled water. Allow the water to stand in the funnel for 1 min. Reattach the vacuum to remove the water.

Repeat the rinse, including the 1-min stand time, substituting 6.5 mL of 10% acetic acid for the distilled water. Similarly, use a final rinse of 7 mL of distilled water. Continue the vacuum for 1–2 min more. Refilter the filtrate to increase the yield of crude product.

3. Recrystallizing the Product

Place 2 mL of methanol in a test tube. Cool the methanol in the ice-water bath for later use.

Transfer the product through a wide-bore plastic funnel into a 25-mL round-bottom flask. Rinse the filter paper and funnel with 10 mL of acetone. Swirl the flask to dissolve the crystals.

Set up a simple distillation apparatus, using the reaction round-bottom flask. Warm the solution to completely dissolve the crystals. Concentrate the yellow solution to about 5 mL by distillation. [NOTE 2]. *Alternatively, reduce the volume to 5 mL using a rotary evaporator, as directed by your laboratory instructor.*

NOTE 2: Compare your volume with the demonstration 25-mL round-bottom flask containing 5 mL of water, provided by your laboratory instructor.

Add 5 mL of methanol, stopper the flask, and leave it undisturbed. Note that the product begins to crystallize as gold-colored plates.

After approximately 10 min, when the precipitation appears complete, cool the flask in the ice-water bath for 5 min. Break up the crystals with a microspatula.

Collect the crystals by vacuum filtration. Wash the crystals with 2 mL of cold methanol. Allow the crystals to air dry.

Measure the mass and the melting point. Characterize the product using NMR spectroscopy, as directed by your laboratory instructor.

4. Cleaning Up

Use the labeled collection containers as directed by your laboratory instructor. Clean your glassware with soap or detergent.

CAUTION   ⚠

Wash your hands with soap or detergent before leaving the laboratory.

SEMI-MICROSCALE SYNTHESIS 2: MICHAEL ADDITION

Equipment

400-mL beaker*
boiling chip
25-mL filter flask, with
   vacuum tubing
filter paper
forceps
gloves
25-mL graduated cylinder
heating well with heat
   controller, or other
   heat source
*for ice-water bath

Hirsh funnel, with adapter
melting point capillary tube
micropipet, 100–1000 μL
microspatula
reflux apparatus
   condenser
   25-mL round-bottom flask
support stand
2 utility clamps

Reagents and Properties

substance	quantity	molar mass (g/mol)	mp (°C)	bp (°C)	density (g/mL)
dianisalacetone (aldol condensation product)	0.800 g	294.4	130		
dimethylmalonate	0.800 mL	132.1		180–181	1.156
methanol	12 mL	32.04		64.6	
Michael addition product*		426.5	194		
sodium methoxide, 25% in methanol	0.200 mL				

* dimethyl-2,6-bis(p-methoxyphenyl)-4-oxocyclohexane-1,1-dicarboxylate

Preview

- Prepare a solution of dianisalacetone in methanol
- Add dimethylmalonate and 25% sodium methoxide in methanol to the solution
- Reflux the solution for 5–6 min
- Cool the reaction mixture and collect the product by vacuum filtration
- Dry and weigh the product
- Characterize the product using melting point and NMR spectroscopy

PROCEDURE

> **CAUTION**
>
> **Wear departmentally approved safety goggles at all times while in the chemistry laboratory. Always use caution in the laboratory. Many chemicals are potentially harmful. Prevent contact with your eyes, skin, and clothing. Avoid ingesting any of the reagents.**

1. Conducting the Michael Addition

> **CAUTION**
>
> **Methanol is flammable and toxic. Sodium methoxide in methanol is flammable, toxic, and corrosive. Keep them away from flames or other heat sources. *Wear gloves.***

NOTE 3: Or use the total product amount from the aldol synthesis.

NOTE 4: Dianisalacetone will dissolve and the product will begin to separate as tiny, white crystals moments after the solution begins to boil.

© 2004 Cengage Learning

Weigh 0.800 g of dianisalacetone from the previous synthesis [NOTE 3] into a 25-mL round-bottom flask. Add 12 mL of reagent grade methanol.

Wearing gloves, use a micropipet to add 0.800 mL (0.692 g) of dimethylmalonate and 0.200 mL of 25% sodium methoxide in methanol to the flask.

Assemble a reflux apparatus using the reaction round-bottom flask. Add a boiling chip. *Gently* heat to boiling and boil the solution for 5–6 min. Watch for bumping of the solution. [NOTE 4]

After boiling the solution for 5–6 min, remove the heat. Separate the flask, remove the boiling chip, and allow the solution to cool to room temperature.

Prepare an ice-water bath using a 400-mL beaker. After the reaction reaches room temperature, cool the flask in the ice-water bath for 5 min.

Collect the product by vacuum filtration. Allow the white crystals to air dry.

Measure the product mass and the melting point. Characterize the product using NMR spectroscopy.

2. Cleaning Up

Use the labeled collection containers as directed by your laboratory instructor. Clean your glassware with soap or detergent.

> **CAUTION**
>
> **Wash your hands with soap or detergent before leaving the laboratory.**

SEMI-MICROSCALE SYNTHESIS 3: ETHYLENE KETAL PREPARATION

Equipment

400-mL beaker*
boiling chip
50-mL Erlenmeyer flask
25-mL filter flask, with
    vacuum tubing
filter paper
glass stirring rod
10-mL graduated cylinder
25-mL graduated cylinder
heating well with heat
    controller, or other heat source
Hirsh funnel, with adapter

hot plate
melting point capillary tube
microspatula
Pasteur pipets, with latex bulb
standard taper distillation apparatus
    condenser
    distilling head
    50-mL round-bottom flask
support stand
2 test tubes, 20 × 150-mm
2 utility clamps
wide-bore plastic funnel

* for warm-water bath and ice-water bath

Reagents and Properties

substance	quantity	molar mass (g/mol)	mp (°C)	bp (°C)
acetone	*	58.08		56
ethylene glycol	1.169 g	62.1		196
ethyl ether	12.5 mL	74.12		34.6
methanol	7.0 mL	32.04		65
Michael addition product[†]	0.700 g	426.5	194	
ethylene ketal product[‡]		470.5	147[§] and 171	
sodium hydroxide, 0.25M	3.0 mL			
toluene**	13 mL	92.14		111
p-toluenesulfonic acid monohydrate	0.07 g	190.22	103–106	

* you decide what amount is needed
[†] dimethyl-2,6-bis(p-methoxyphenyl)-4-oxocyclohexane-1,1-dicarboxylate
[‡] dimethyl-2,6-bis(p-methoxyphenyl)-4,4-ethylenedioxocyclohexane-1,1-dicarboxylate
[§] freshly prepared product may melt at 147 °C; older product melts at 171 °C
** dried over molecular sieves

Preview

- Place all reactants into a round-bottom flask
- Add dry toluene
- Distill the reaction mixture for 12–15 min and collect about 8 mL of distillate containing toluene–water azeotrope
- Extract the product from the reaction mixture using ethyl ether
- Concentrate the organic phase and cool to induce crystallization of the product
- Collect the product by vacuum filtration
- Dry and weigh the purified product
- Characterize the product using melting point and NMR spectroscopy

PROCEDURE

CAUTION

Wear departmentally approved safety goggles at all times while in the chemistry laboratory. Always use caution in the laboratory. Many chemicals are potentially harmful. Prevent contact with your eyes, skin, and clothing. Avoid ingesting any of the reagents.

1. Producing the Ketal

CAUTION

Ethylene glycol is toxic and irritating. *p*-Toluenesulfonic acid monohydrate is corrosive and toxic. Toluene is flammable and toxic. Keep them away from flames or other heat sources.

To a 50-mL round-bottom flask, add 0.700 g of Michael addition product, imethyl 2,6-bis(*p*-methoxyphenyl)-4-oxocyclohexane-1,1-dicarboxylate [NOTE 5], through a wide-bore plastic funnel.

NOTE 5: Or use the total product amount from the Michael addition.

Add 1.169 g ethylene glycol, 0.70 g of *p*-toluenesulfonic acid monohydrate, and 13 mL of *dry* toluene. Add a boiling chip.

Using the round-bottom flask, assemble a simple distillation apparatus. Use a 10-mL graduated cylinder as a receiving vessel.

NOTE 6: Toluene forms an azeotrope with water to remove water from the reaction mixture.

Distill the mixture at a rate of 1 drop per second. Collect about 8 mL of distillate over a period of 12–15 min. [NOTE 6]. Discard the distillate in the container provided by your laboratory instructor.

2. Extracting the Product

CAUTION

Ethyl ether is *very flammable* and toxic. Keep it away from flames or other heat sources. 0.25*M* Sodium hydroxide (NaOH) is corrosive. Use a *fume hood*.

© 2004 Cengage Learning

Allow the solution to cool. Remove the round-bottom flask. Add 3 mL of 0.25*M* NaOH to the flask and mix well. Then add 4.5 mL of distilled or deionized water. Swirl the mixture and wait for 2 min.

Pour the contents of the flask, minus the boiling chip, into a test tube. Rinse the flask with 9 mL of ethyl ether. Pour the rinse into the test tube. Mix the layers well.

Using a Pasteur pipet, draw off the lower aqueous layer. Note that the product may start to precipitate from the organic layer.

Add 3.5 mL of ethyl ether and 3.5 mL of distilled water to the test tube. Mix well. Draw off the aqueous layer.

3. Crystallizing the Product

CAUTION

Acetone is flammable and irritating. Methanol is flammable and toxic. Keep them away from flames or other heat sources.

Use a 400-mL beaker to make a 50 °C water bath. Add acetone to a test tube and place the tube into the bath to heat the acetone.

Pour the organic phase from Part 2 into a 50-mL round-bottom flask. Use hot acetone to rinse any product that sticks to the test tube.

Set up a simple distillation apparatus, using a 10-mL graduated cylinder as a receiver. Concentrate the organic solution by distillation to about 2–3 mL. *Alternatively, reduce the volume to 2–3 mL using a rotary evaporator, as directed by your laboratory instructor.*

Using a Pasteur pipet, transfer the concentrated solution from the round-bottom flask to a 50-mL Erlenmeyer flask. Add 5 mL of methanol to the warm solution.

Allow the mixture to stand at room temperature until the precipitation is complete. If necessary, scratch the bottom of the flask with a glass stirring rod to induce crystallization.

Use the 400-mL beaker to prepare an ice-water bath. Cool the reaction flask in the ice-water bath for 5 min. At the same time, put 2 mL of methanol in a test tube. Chill the methanol in the ice-water bath.

Collect the product by vacuum filtration. Rinse the product with a small amount of cold methanol. Allow the white crystals to air dry.

Measure the mass and the melting point. Characterize the product using NMR spectroscopy.

4. Cleaning Up

Use the labeled collection containers as directed by your laboratory instructor. Clean your glassware with soap or detergent.

CAUTION

Wash your hands with soap or detergent before leaving the laboratory.

MICROSCALE SYNTHESIS 1: ALDOL CONDENSATION

Equipment

100-mL beaker*

2 Erlenmeyer flasks, 10-mL,
 with stopper

25-mL filter flask,
 with vacuum tubing

filter paper

Hirsh funnel, with adapter

magnetic stir bar

melting point capillary tube

micropipet, 10–100 μL

micropipet, 100–1000 μL

microspatula

Pasteur pipets, with latex bulb

5.0-mL pipet, with pump or bulb

sand bath†

stirring hot plate‡

15 × 150-mm test tube

*for ice-water bath
† crystallizing dish on hot plate or electric flask heater filled with sand
‡ or electric flask heater and magnetic stirrer

Reagents and Properties

substance	quantity	molar mass (g/mol)	mp (°C)	bp (°C)	density (g/mL)
acetic acid, 10%	2.0 mL				
acetone	5–6 mL	58.1		56	0.791
p-anisaldehyde	0.300 g	136.2		248	1.119
ethanol, 95%	1.95 mL	46.07		78	
methanol	4–5 mL	32.04		64.6	
sodium hydroxide, 10%	1.95 mL				

Preview

- Place 10% sodium hydroxide in a flask
- Place p-anisaldehyde, acetone, and ethanol into another flask
- Combine the two solutions and stir for 45 min
- Use vacuum filtration to collect the precipitate
- Recrystallize the crude product from acetone and methanol
- Dry and weigh the purified product
- Characterize the product using melting point and NMR spectroscopy

PROCEDURE

CAUTION

⚠

**Wear departmentally approved safety goggles at all times while in the
chemistry laboratory. Always use caution in the laboratory. Many chemicals are
potentially harmful. Prevent contact with your eyes, skin, and clothing. Avoid
ingesting any of the reagents.**

1. Conducting the Aldol Condensation

CAUTION

10% Sodium hydroxide (NaOH) is corrosive. ***p*-Anisaldehyde is irritating. Acetone and ethanol are flammable and irritating. Keep them away from flames or other heat sources.**

To a 10-mL Erlenmeyer flask, add a magnetic stir bar and 1.95 mL of 10% NaOH. To a second 10-mL Erlenmeyer flask, add 0.268 mL (0.300 g) of *p*-anisaldehyde and 0.083 mL (0.066 g) of acetone.

Add 1.95 mL of ethanol to the acetone/aldehyde mixture. Mix these reagents and pipet the solution into the flask containing the NaOH. Stir for a minimum of 45 min. [NOTE 1]

NOTE 1: The mixture becomes bright transparent yellow in less than 1 min and becomes increasingly opaque with time.

Prepare an ice-water bath using the 100-mL beaker. After stirring is complete, cool the solution in the ice-water bath for 5 min.

2. Isolating the Product

CAUTION

10% Acetic acid is irritating.

Collect the precipitate by vacuum filtration. Rinse the flask and crystals with 2 mL of distilled or deionized water. Release the vacuum and repeat the rinse with 2 mL of distilled water. Allow the water to stand in the funnel for 1 min. Reattach the vacuum to remove the water.

Repeat the rinse, including the 1-min stand time, substituting 2 mL of 10% acetic acid for the distilled water. Similarly, use a final rinse of 2 mL of water. Continue the vacuum for 1–2 min more. Refilter the filtrate to increase the yield of crude product.

3. Recrystallizing the Product

Place 1 mL of methanol in a test tube. Cool the methanol in the ice-water bath for later use.

Transfer the product from both filtrations into a 10-mL Erlenmeyer flask. Rinse the filter papers and funnel with ~5 mL of acetone. Swirl the flask to dissolve the crystals.

Set up a sand bath in a *fume hood*. *Gently* warm the solution to completely dissolve the crystals. [NOTE 2]

NOTE 2: The solution foams if heated too rapidly.

Using air or nitrogen, reduce the volume of the yellow solution to 2–3 mL. Take care not to splatter the solution when drying. Cool the solution at room temperature for 5 min.

Add an equal volume of methanol, stopper the flask, and leave it undisturbed. Note that the product begins to crystallize as gold-colored plates.

After approximately 10 min, when the precipitation appears complete, cool the flask in the ice-water bath for 5 min. Break up the crystals with a microspatula.

Collect the crystals by vacuum filtration. Wash the crystals with 1 mL of cold methanol. Allow the crystals to air dry.

Measure the mass and the melting point. Characterize the product by NMR spectroscopy, as directed by your laboratory instructor.

4. Cleaning Up

Use the labeled collection containers as directed by your laboratory instructor. Clean your glassware with soap or detergent.

> **CAUTION**
>
> **Wash your hands with soap or detergent before leaving the laboratory.**

MICROSCALE SYNTHESIS 2: MICHAEL ADDITION

Equipment

100-mL beaker*

boiling chip

25-mL filter flask,
  with vacuum tubing

filter paper

forceps

gloves

Hirsh funnel, with adapter

melting point capillary tube

micropipet, 10–100 μL

micropipet, 100–1000 μL

microspatula

5.0-mL pipet, with pump or bulb

plastic funnel

reflux apparatus
  condenser
  5-mL round-bottom flask
    or 5-mL conical vial

sand bath†

support stand

15 × 150-mm test tube

2 utility clamps

* for ice-water bath
† crystallizing dish on hot plate or electric flask heater filled with sand

Reagents and Properties

substance	quantity	molar mass (g/mol)	mp (°C)	bp (°C)	density (g/mL)
dianisalacetone (aldol condensation product)	0.240 g*	294.4	130		
dimethylmalonate	0.240 mL	132.1		180–181	1.156
methanol	6–7 mL	32.04		64.6	
Michael addition product *		426.5	194		
sodium methoxide, 25% in methanol	0.060 mL				

* dimethyl-2,6-bis(p-methoxyphenyl)-4-oxocyclohexane-1,1-dicarboxylate

Preview

- Prepare a solution of dianisalacetone in methanol
- Add dimethylmalonate and 25% sodium methoxide to the solution
- Reflux the solution for 5–6 min
- Cool the reaction mixture and collect the product by vacuum filtration
- Dry and weigh the product
- Characterize the product using melting point and NMR spectroscopy

PROCEDURE

1. Conducting the Michael Addition

NOTE 3: Or use the total product amount from the aldol synthesis.

Weigh 0.240 g of dianisalacetone from the previous synthesis. [NOTE 3]. Use a small plastic funnel to transfer the dianisalacetone into a 5-mL round-bottom flask or 5-mL conical vial. Add 3.6 mL of reagent-grade methanol.

Wearing gloves, use micropipets to add 0.240 mL (0.210 g) of dimethylmalonate and 0.060 mL of 25% sodium methoxide in methanol to the flask.

Assemble a reflux apparatus using the reaction round-bottom flask or conical vial. Add a boiling chip.

Adjust the clamps to hold the reaction vessel well above the surface of the sand bath. Heat up the sand bath. *Carefully and gradually* lower the vessel to the sand bath until it just begins to boil.

Gently boil the solution for 5–6 min. Watch for bumping of the solution. [NOTE 4]

NOTE 4: Dianisalacetone will dissolve and the product will begin to separate as tiny, white crystals moments after the solution begins to boil.

After boiling the solution for 5–6 min, remove the heat. Separate the flask and remove the boiling chip. Allow the solution to cool to room temperature.

Prepare an ice-water bath using a 100-mL beaker. After the reaction reaches room temperature, cool the flask in the ice-water bath for 5 min. At the same time, place 2–3 mL of methanol in a test tube. Chill the methanol in the ice-water bath.

Collect the product by vacuum filtration. Rinse the flask with cold methanol. Allow the white crystals to air dry.

Measure the product mass and the melting point. Characterize the product using NMR spectroscopy.

2. Cleaning Up

Use the labeled collection containers as directed by your laboratory instructor. Clean your glassware with soap or detergent.

MICROSCALE SYNTHESIS 3: ETHYLENE KETAL PREPARATION

Equipment

100-mL beaker*
boiling chip
15-mL conical
  centrifuge tube
distillation glassware,
  conical vial assembly[†]
  Hickman still
  5.0-mL conical vial
distillation glassware,
  elastomeric connectors
  assembly[†]
  5.0-mL conical vial,
    graduated
  distilling head/
    air condenser
  elastomeric connector
  5-mL round-bottom flask

10-mL Erlenmeyer flask
25-mL filter flask,
  with vacuum tubing
filter paper
glass stirring rod
Hirsh funnel, with adapter
hot plate
melting point capillary tube
micropipet, 100–1000 μL
microspatula
Pasteur pipets, with latex bulb
plastic funnel
sand bath[‡]
support stand
2 test tubes, 20 × 150-mm
2 utility clamps

*for 50 °C warm-water bath and ice-water bath
[†] use glassware provided by your laboratory instructor
[‡] crystallizing dish on hot plate or electric flask heater filled with sand

Reagents and Properties

substance	quantity	molar mass (g/mol)	mp (°C)	bp (°C)
acetone	*	58.08		56
ethylene glycol	0.350 g	62.1		196
ethyl ether	3.7 mL	74.12		34.6
methanol	2.5 mL	32.04		65
Michael addition product[†]	0.210 g	426.5	194	
ethylene ketal product[‡]		470.5	147[§] and 171	
sodium hydroxide, 0.25M	0.9 mL			
toluene[**]	3.9 mL	92.14		111
p-toluenesulfonic acid monohydrate	0.020 g	190.22	103–106	

* you decide what amount is needed
[†] dimethyl-2,6-bis(p-methoxyphenyl)-4-oxocyclohexane-1,1-dicarboxylate
[‡] dimethyl-2,6-bis(p-methoxyphenyl)-4,4-ethylenedioxocyclohexane-1,1-dicarboxylate
[§] freshly prepared product may melt at 147 °C; older product melts at 171 °C
[**] dried over molecular sieves

Preview

- Place all reactants into a round-bottom flask or conical vial
- Add dry toluene
- Distill the reaction mixture for 12–15 min and collect about 2.4 mL of distillate containing toluene–water azeotrope

- Extract the product from the reaction mixture using ethyl ether
- Concentrate the organic phase and cool to induce crystallization of the product
- Dry and weigh the purified product
- Characterize the product using melting point and NMR spectroscopy

PROCEDURE

> **CAUTION** ⚠
> **Wear departmentally approved safety goggles at all times while in the chemistry laboratory. Always use caution in the laboratory. Many chemicals are potentially harmful. Prevent contact with your eyes, skin, and clothing. Avoid ingesting any of the reagents.**

1. Producing the Ketal

> **CAUTION** ⚠
> **Ethylene glycol is toxic and irritating. *p*-Toluenesulfonic acid monohydrate is corrosive and toxic. Toluene is flammable and toxic. Keep them away from flames or other heat sources.**

NOTE 5: Or use the total product amount from the Michael addition. Use glassware indicated by your laboratory instructor.

To a 5-mL round-bottom flask or a 5-mL conical vial, add 0.210 g of Michael addition product, dimethyl-2,6-bis(*p*-methoxyphenyl)-4-oxocyclohexane-1,1-dicarboxylate, through a plastic funnel. [NOTE 5]

Add 0.350 g ethylene glycol, 0.020 g of *p*-toluenesulfonic acid monohydrate, and 3.9 mL of *dry* toluene. Add a boiling chip.

Using the round-bottom flask or conical vial, assemble a simple distillation apparatus. For glassware requiring a separate receiver, use a 5-mL graduated vial as a receiving vessel.

NOTE 6: Toluene forms an azeotrope with water to remove water from the reaction mixture.

Distill the mixture at a rate of 1 drop per second. Collect about 2.4 mL of distillate over a period of 12–15 min. [NOTE 6]. Discard the distillate in the container provided by your laboratory instructor.

2. Extracting the Product

> **CAUTION** ⚠
> **Ethyl ether is *very flammable* and toxic. Keep it away from flames or other heat sources. 0.25*M* Sodium hydroxide (NaOH) is corrosive. Use a *fume hood*.**

Allow the solution to cool. Remove the round-bottom flask. Transfer the solution to a 15-mL conical centrifuge tube.

Add 0.900 mL of 0.25*M* NaOH to the flask and mix well. Then add 1.35 mL of distilled or deionized water. Swirl the mixture and wait for 2 min.

Add 2.70 mL of ethyl ether. Mix the layers well.

Using a Pasteur pipet, draw off the lower aqueous layer. Note that the product may start to precipitate from the organic layer.

Add 1.0 mL of ethyl ether and 1.0 mL of distilled water to the tube. Mix well. Draw off the aqueous layer.

3. Crystallizing the Product

CAUTION

Acetone is flammable and irritating. Methanol is flammable and toxic. Keep them away from flames or other heat sources.

Use a 100-mL beaker to make a 50 °C water bath. Add acetone to a test tube and place the tube into the bath to heat the acetone.

Pour the organic phase from Part 2 from the centrifuge tube into a 10-mL Erlenmeyer flask. Use hot acetone to rinse any product that sticks to the centrifuge tube or pipet.

Set up a sand bath in a *fume hood*. Use air or nitrogen to reduce the volume of the organic solution to 0.6–0.9 mL.

Add 1.5 mL of methanol to the warm solution. Allow the mixture to stand at room temperature until the precipitation is complete. If necessary, scratch the bottom of the flask with a glass stirring rod to induce crystallization.

Use the 100-mL beaker to prepare an ice-water bath. Cool the reaction flask in the ice-water bath for 5 min. At the same time, put 1 mL of methanol in a test tube. Chill the methanol in the ice-water bath.

Collect the product by vacuum filtration. Rinse the product with a small amount of cold methanol. Allow the white crystals to air dry.

Measure the mass and the melting point. Characterize the product using NMR spectroscopy.

4. Cleaning Up

Use the labeled collection containers as directed by your laboratory instructor. Clean your glassware with soap or detergent.

CAUTION

Wash your hands with soap or detergent before leaving the laboratory.

POST-LABORATORY QUESTIONS

1. Calculate the yield of aldol condensation product, dianisalacetone, from Synthesis 1. [*Note:* Recheck limiting reagent and theoretical yield calculations based on actual amounts of reagents used.]

2. Calculate the yield of Michael addition product, dimethyl-2,6-bis (*p*-methoxyphenyl)-4-oxocyclohexane-1,1-dicarboxylate, from Synthesis 2. [*Note:* Adjust your theoretical yield calculation to reflect the starting amount of dianisalacetone.]

3. Calculate the yield of ethylene ketal product, dimethyl-2,6-bis (*p*-methoxyphenyl)-4,4-ethylenedioxocyclohexane-1,1-dicarboxylate, from Synthesis 3. [*Note:* Adjust your theoretical yield calculation to reflect the starting amount of dimethyl-2,6-bis(*p*-methoxyphenyl)-4-oxocyclohexane-1,1-dicarboxylate.]

4. Calculate the overall yield of ethylene ketal (product 3) from *p*-anisaldehyde, if you used all of each product from synthesis to synthesis.

5. Compare the NMR spectra for each stage of the synthesis sequence. Explain how the spectra support the identity of the product in each case.

6. Why is sodium hydroxide added *before* water in the work-up of the ethylene ketal product? Briefly explain.

Name	Section	Date

Pre-Laboratory Assignment

1. What precautions should you take when working with:

   (a) ethyl ether?

   (b) 25% sodium methoxide in methanol?

2. What is the purpose of the toluene in the reaction for forming the ethylene ketal in Synthesis 3?

3. Calculate the theoretical yield for each of the three syntheses. Use the amount of starting material listed in the *Reagents and Properties* table for each synthesis; that is, aldol condensation product from *p*-anisaldehyde, Michael addition product from aldol condensation product, and ethylene ketal product from Michael addition product. [*Note:* Determine the limiting reagent in Synthesis 1.]

4. Calculate the overall theoretical yield for the sequence, *p*-anisaldehyde to the ethylene ketal.

Properties of Amines

Amines have an unshared pair of electrons on nitrogen and, therefore, act as bases, nucleophiles, and compounds that may be oxidized. As Lewis bases, they form salts with acids and form coordination complexes with metal cations. As nucleophiles, they displace halogen from alkyl halides and acid chlorides to give more highly alkylated amines and amides, respectively. They may be oxidized by a variety of oxidizing agents including oxygen, permanganate ion, hydrogen peroxide, and nitrous acid.

The basicity of an amine is influenced by the number and type of groups attached to the nitrogen atom. Aliphatic amines are stronger bases than ammonia because the alkyl groups are electron donors relative to hydrogen. Aromatic amines are weaker bases than ammonia because delocalization of the unshared electron pair on nitrogen into the ring lowers the electron density on nitrogen.

Amines up to approximately five carbon atoms are soluble in water. Higher molecular weight amines that are water insoluble dissolve in aqueous acid through the formation of salts. This provides a convenient method for separating such amines from water insoluble neutral and acidic compounds (see Chapter 4, Experiment B).

Many amines, as well as other nitrogen compounds, are physiologically active and should be handled with caution. Amines that occur naturally in plants are called alkaloids; the potency of many of these such as morphine, cocaine, and nicotine is widely known.

EXPERIMENTS

SAFETY NOTE

Many amines are toxic substances; inhalation of their vapors or contact with the skin should be avoided. If any should contact the skin, wash with water, then with 5% acetic acid solution, and again with water. Benzenesulfonyl chloride is corrosive and gives off irritating vapors. 2-naphthol is a toxic irritant.

A. SOLUBILITY IN WATER

Place 1 mL of water in a 13 × 100-mm test tube, add 1 drop of cyclohexylamine, and shake the tube to mix the two materials. Note whether the amine is soluble; if it is, determine the solubility of a second and third drop. Save the mixture for use in Experiment B.

Repeat this solubility test with aniline, pyridine, and triethylamine. Also save the mixtures for Experiment B.

B.   BASICITY

1.   Determine the pH of each of the mixtures from Experiment A by placing a drop of the aqueous phase on a piece of universal pH paper.
2.   To those mixtures from Experiment A in which the amine is insoluble, add 10% HCl dropwise with stirring. Does the amine dissolve?

C.   HINSBERG TEST

Amines react as nucleophiles toward acid chlorides and acid anhydrides to yield amides. Many of these amides, such as those of acetic, benzoic, and benzenesulfonic acid, are crystalline solids that may be used as derivatives to identify the amine.

The reaction of an amine with benzenesulfonyl chloride can be useful in determining whether the amine is primary, secondary, or tertiary. The sulfonamide from a primary amine is acidic and dissolves in sodium hydroxide solution, but the sulfonamide of a secondary amine lacks the amide hydrogen and is insoluble. Tertiary amines do not form amides. This overall process is known as the **Hinsberg test.**

$$\text{C}_6\text{H}_5\text{—SO}_2\text{Cl} + \text{RNH}_2 \xrightarrow{\text{NaOH}} \text{C}_6\text{H}_5\text{—SO}_2\text{—NHR} + \text{NaCl} + \text{H}_2\text{O}$$

$$\text{HCl} \uparrow \downarrow \text{NaOH}$$

$$\text{C}_6\text{H}_5\text{—SO}_2\text{—}\overset{-}{\text{N}}\text{R Na}^+$$

Place two drops of amine, 4 drops of benzenesulfonyl chloride, and 4 mL of 10% sodium hydroxide in a 13×100-mm test tube. Stopper the tube and shake it for approximately 5 minutes. If a clear or nearly clear solution is obtained, a primary amine is indicated; acidification with hydrochloric acid should precipitate the sulfonamide. The presence of a solid or liquid residue in the original reaction mixture indicates a secondary or tertiary amine. Separate the residue and determine its solubility in 10% HCl. A tertiary amine will dissolve; if the residue does not dissolve, then it is a sulfonamide of a secondary amine. Perform the Hinsberg test on aniline, *N*-methylaniline, and triethylamine, and then determine whether an unknown is a primary, secondary, or tertiary amine.

D.   REACTIONS OF DIAZONIUM SALTS

(Microscale)

Amines undergo a variety of reactions with nitrous acid depending on whether the amine is a primary, secondary, or tertiary amine and whether it is aliphatic or aromatic. The reaction of primary aromatic amines with nitrous acid is unique and provides a very versatile synthetic intermediate. The process is called **diazotization,** and the intermediates formed are called diazonium salts. Aqueous solutions of diazonium salts are stable at 0 to 5°C for several hours; however, they lose nitrogen on warming and form phenols. Solid diazonium salts sometimes crystallize from solution but should *never* be separated by filtration as they can decompose explosively.

$$\text{C}_6\text{H}_5-\text{NH}_2 \xrightarrow[\text{HCl}]{\substack{\text{HONO}\\ 0-5°C}} \text{C}_6\text{H}_5-\overset{+}{\text{N}}\equiv\text{N Cl}^-$$

Diazonium salts react with nucleophiles to liberate N_2 and form phenols, aryl halides, and nitriles with such nucleophiles as water, halide ion, and cyanide ion, respectively. They react with phenols and tertiary aromatic amines (aromatic compounds particularly reactive towards electrophilic aromatic substitution) to give azo compounds by a reaction known as **azo coupling.** In the following experiment, *p*-nitroaniline will be reacted with nitrous acid to form the diazonium salt, *p*-nitrobenzenediazonium chloride, which will then be used to prepare *p*-iodonitrobenzene and/or the dye Para Red.

1.   Preparation of the Diazonium Salt

$$\text{O}_2\text{N}-\text{C}_6\text{H}_4-\text{NH}_2 \xrightarrow[\text{HCl}]{\substack{\text{HONO}\\ 0-5°C}} \text{O}_2\text{N}-\text{C}_6\text{H}_4-\text{N}_2^+\text{Cl}^-$$

In a 50-mL Erlenmeyer flask, place 16 mL of water, 2 mL of 6M hydrochloric acid, and 0.552 g (0.004 mole) of *p*-nitroaniline. Warm the mixture, stir until the amine has dissolved, and then cool the solution to 0 to 5 °C. Add approximately 2 g of chipped ice and keep the mixture at 0 to 5°C in an ice bath.

   Next prepare a solution of 0.276 g (0.004 mole) of sodium nitrite in 2 mL of cold water. Add the sodium nitrite solution to the solution of amine hydrochloride while swirling the latter vigorously. Continue swirling for 3 to 5 minutes, and then keep the solution at ice temperature until ready for use in Part 2 and Part 3 below. If appreciable solid remains, filter the cold solution through a small cotton plug.

   The diazonium solution may be tested for nitrous acid with potassium iodide–starch paper (a purple to black coloration indicates HNO_2; the test paper must darken immediately) and for the actual formation of a diazonium salt (streak a solution of 2-naphthol in aqueous NaOH across a piece of filter paper, and then cross it with a streak of the reaction solution; an orange to red coloration at the junction indicates the presence of a diazonium salt).

2.   Preparation of *p*-Iodonitrobenzene

$$\text{O}_2\text{N}-\text{C}_6\text{H}_4-\text{N}_2^+ + \text{I}^- \longrightarrow \text{O}_2\text{N}-\text{C}_6\text{H}_4-\text{I} + \text{N}_2 \uparrow$$

Dissolve 0.6 g of potassium iodide in 2 mL of water and cool the solution to 0 to 5°C. Add it, with swirling, to three-fourths of the diazonium salt solution at such a rate that the temperature of the latter is maintained below 5°C. When the addition is complete, allow the mixture to stand in an ice bath for 3 to 5 minutes with occasional swirling. Collect the product by vacuum filtration, dry it, and recrystallize it from ethanol. Determine the weight, melting point, and percent yield.

3.   Preparation of Para Red

In a 50-mL Erlenmeyer flask, dissolve 0.288 g of 2-naphthol (0.002 mole) in a mixture of 3 mL of 10% sodium hydroxide and 20 mL of water. Chill this solution in an ice bath until the temperature is below 5°C (a few chips of ice may be added to lower the temperature). Pour the remaining diazonium solution all at once into the cold solution of 2-naphthol, and swirl the mixture for 5 to 10 minutes. Add 1 mL of concentrated hydrochloric acid, heat the mixture with stirring for 20 to 30 minutes on a steam bath, and filter the product. Allow the dye to dry and weigh the crude material. Do not determine a melting point or percent yield since the product contains inorganic salts.

QUESTIONS

1. Write an equation for the reaction of butylamine with one mole of HCl.
2. Write equations for the reaction of aniline with
    a.   acetyl chloride
    b.   benzoyl chloride
    c.   acetic anhydride
3. How might one distinguish between the following pairs of substances using reactions described in this chapter?
    a.   butylamine and dibutylamine
    b.   cyclohexylamine and aniline
4. Write equations to illustrate the diazotization of aniline and subsequent reaction with phenol; with dimethylaniline.

PRELABORATORY QUESTIONS

1. Write an equation for the reaction of butylamine with hydrochloric acid.
2. Is the benzenesulfonamide of aniline soluble in aqueous NaOH? Explain your answer.
3. Write the structure of the product of the reaction between benzenediazonium chloride and potassium iodide.
4. Write an equation for the redox reaction between nitrous acid and potassium iodide. Why does the KI/starch paper turn black?
5. Which is a stronger base. aniline or butylamine?

index

2-Methylcyclohexanol, 187-190

?Concerted? step, 176

A

Acid(s)

safety note of. 171

Acylation.

See Friedel-Crafts reaction.

Alcohol(s)

dehydration of. 186

Alcohol(s)

dehydration of

safety note on, 186

Alkaloids, 351

Alkanes, 171

Alkenes

formation from alcohol dehydration. 185-190

Alkyl halides

substitution of. 175

Alkyl halides

substitution of

unimolecular (SN1), 175

Alkylation.

See Friedel-Crafts reaction.

Alkynes, 171

Amines

solubility in water. 351-353

Aromatic hydrocarbons, 171

Azo coupling, 353

B

Benzene, 171

Benzenesulfonyl chloride, 352

Bromine, addition of hydrocarbons to, 172

Bronsted acids, dehydration of alcohols using, 185-190

C

Chemical literature.

See Literature of organic chemistry.

Chromatography.

See also Column chromatography; Gas chromatography (GC); High performance liquid chromatography (HPLC); Thin layer chromatography (TLC).

Cycloalkanes, 171

Cyclohexene, preparation of, 186-188

D

Diazonium salts reactions, 352-355

Diazotization, 352

Displacement reactions.

See Substitution.

F

Flammability of hydrocarbons, 172

H

Hinsberg test, 352

Hydrocarbons

unsaturated. 171

L

Leaving group, 175

Liquid chromatography.

See High performance liquid chromatography (HPLC).

N

Nuclear magnetic resonance (NMR).

See 1H NMR; 13C NMR.

P

Potassium permanganate, 172

Proton spectrum.

See 1H NMR.

Purification by recrystallization.

See Recrystallization.

R

Relative density of hydrocarbons, 172

S

Safety notes

on amines. 351

Saturated hydrocarbons, 171

SN1 reaction, 175

SN1 reactivity